HIGHWAY HYPODERMICS:

TRAVEL NURSING 2015

By

Epstein LaRue, RN, CGM
(CertifiedGrad-level Management)

With contributing author,
Joseph Smith, RRT, EA, MS Tax

Highway Hypodermics:
Travel Nursing 2015

Trade Paperback
ISBN: 978-1-935188-69-8

Edited by Star Publish
Interior Design by T.C. McMullen
Cover Design by Epstein LaRue
Authors Picture on Back Cover by Sherry Atwell

Published in 2014 by Star Publish, LLC

Printed in the United States of America

A Star Publish Book
www.starpublishllc.com
Pennsylvania, U.S.A.

Dedicated to:

All my wonderful friends back in Grace, Idaho.
Without you guys coming home wouldn't be so much fun!

INTERIOR CONTENTS:

Chapter One

An Introduction To Travel Nursing

In 2003 I entered the exciting world of travel nursing. Since that time, I have crisscrossed the United States three different times, experienced the Grand Canyon, whirled my way through Hurricane Wilma, and made several trips to visit our neighbors in Canada. During the last 10 years, not only have I changed as a nurse and traveler, but I have seen plenty travel nursing companies exceed in the business while many have succumbed to their injuries.

At the time of writing this, the five largest travel companies were AMN Healthcare (American Mobile, Medical Express, Nurse Choice), Cross Country Healthcare (Cross Country TravCorp, Nova Pro, CRU48), Medical Solutions, CHG Healthcare Services, and Medical Staffing Network. The top five smaller companies include: Premier Healthcare Professionals, PRCS Healthcare, Flexcare Medical Staffing, IPI Travel, and Trinity Healthcare.

Upon doing some research I found that greatest demand is in the fields of medical/surgical/telemetry (MST), intensive care units (ICU), and the emergency room (ER). On the date of this investigation (January 27th, 2013), there were 3852 MST jobs, 2583 ICU jobs, and 1764 ER jobs (Job Conglomerant, 2013). These three specialties encompass 64% of all the traveling nursing jobs out there. Finishing at a 9% tie was the operating room and labor/delivery. Under 5% of the jobs included pediatric intensive care (PICU), progressive care unit (PCU), neonatal intensive care (NICU), cardiovascular intensive care (CVICU), and the post anesthesia care unit (PACU). (Travel Nursing Jobs, 2013).

One of the biggest staffing questions is the use of agency and/or travel staff. In a recent healthcare staffing study presented by KMPG, it was reported that once you look at the total cost of training a new nurse (orientation, benefits, and continuing education) it is cost effective to hire agency or travel nurses to fill those spots. The great thing about travel nurses is that we are experienced nurses that are trained to hit the floor running (Institute, 2011).

The big world of travel nursing and allied health is exciting, but it can also be very stressful. You need to educate yourself in the way of the travel healthcare world so that you can navigate the high seas with open eyes. That has been my purpose for the last 10 years, to educate nurses and therapist on the field of travel nursing and healthcare through my books, website, and blogs

My Travel Nursing Career

My life as a traveling nurse started out in 2003. I was having problems at work and my son had become a victim to bullying; therefore, the timing just seemed right! I always thought that I couldn't go on the road and travel related to the fact that I needed to give my son a "stable" environment. Well, that's a bunch of BS! He learned a lot more on the road, and remembers it!

At this time, I had written the novels, "*Love At First Type*" about how two people had come together online, and "*Crazy Thoughts of Passion*," my attempt to bring my writing romance world into my nursing world.

When I started investigating the life of a traveling nurse, I wrote everything down and began to make notes about how to find an assignment, and where to go. I was frustrated in having to go to multiple website to look up this information and there was only one book out there on traveling nursing, "*Hitting The Road*" by ShalonWeddington.

There ought to be a better way to do things! Soon I had compiled all the information that I had collected into a book called, "*Highway Hypodermics: Your Road Map To Travel Nursing*." The 2005 version did okay in sales, but things would look brighter!

In January 2007, Star Publish and I put out the second edition, *Highway Hypodermics: Travel Nursing 2007*. In that edition there was a lot of information added about the PBDS test, JCAHO, homeschooling and traveling with family. It went to number one on Amazon three times in the nursing trends, issues, and roles category.

In 2009 the third edition of *Highway Hypodermics*, which had the subtitle of "*On The Road Again*" was published, which added the aspects of traveling as an LPN/LVN, Allied Health traveling, and travel nursing when you are coming from other countries. By this time three other books had been written on the travel nursing subject. Two of the three along with my book was all turned into the 2009 USA Book News' annual contest. *Highway Hypodermics: On the Road Again* was a winner that year!

The fourth edition: *Highway Hypodermics: Travel Nursing 2012* saw even more changes to include: "Traveling With Pets," "the BKAT," "General Testing That is Required," and "The National Association of Travel Healthcare Organizations (NATHO)." All of the nursing stories were new and the travel company profiles have been updated, including several new companies.

In this fifth edition, a lot of the chapters have been completely rewritten and the format has changed just a skosh. Although not all the chapters have been changed, the book has had a total facelift from 10 years ago with chapters reorganized for a better flow. Added to this year's information includes a chapter dedicated to contracts, one solely dedicated to finding the right recruiter.

In this book we also concentrate on the traits of a quality travel nurse and how you need to behave once you are on assignment. Travel nurses are one of the biggest stereotyped groups out there. One nurse can ruin your assignment before you even enter the hospital doors.

Why Nursing to Begin With?

Why would someone want to go into a profession where you are begged to work overtime so you can hear from the families a confirmation of the fact that nurses don't have time to take care of patients the way they should. Families are, however, somewhat more tolerant of it because they know that "all hospitals are short-staffed."

Why would you want to run around "like a chicken with its head cut off" for eight hours before you get time to stop long enough to get a drink, go to the restroom, and grab a sandwich on your way back because we can't waste time for lunch? That abscess has to be drained!

Why would someone want to get into a profession where your feet are abused by all the long hours spent traipsing down the corridors of illness? If you are not one of the lucky ones to marry a foot masseur, you'd better learn self-message techniques and get some comfortable shoes.

Why would anyone want to spend time wiping butts, giving enemas, taking blood, then giving some back, cleaning up vomit, and my personal favorite—cleaning up that stringy sputum!

I am expected to work long hours, contend with ridiculous staffing circumstances, be treated like a dog by the administration, be yelled at by the physicians while dodging the clipboard, and be ridiculed by my nursing colleagues because I am definitely not working as hard as they are and I am not as good as they are.

I never could understand the old saying, "Nurses always eat their young," but that is exactly what we do. The new graduates are inexperienced and "stupid" because they haven't been around the block like we have, but I drag myself out of bed at 4:00 AM every morning because I care about the patients I take care of. I don't know why anybody wouldn't want to live the dream of being a nurse!

Career nurses are nurses because we are dedicated to our profession—because we really are concerned about patient care and the health of others. It is just hard to convey to someone else that this profession really does have its high points. If only they could see the patient's son who gives us a hug because we took care of his mother so well as she slipped from this life to the next. If only they could visit with the patient who went into ventricular fibrillation before my eyes and told me "thank you" ten minutes after I had defibrillated her. Making a difference in someone else's life—*that,* my friend is what nursing is all about.

Another concern for professional nurses is the issue of mandatory overtime. My colleague Melissa James stated, "After working a twelve-hour day shift at the nursing home, the night shift nurse called in. I was then informed by the director of nursing that I would stay or be turned into the state for patient abandonment."

Once being coerced into working those extra shifts, the nurses recognize in their hearts that they should not be touching syringes, handing out medications, or providing medical treatment, but they carry on as instructed because they have a family to feed at home and a nursing license to protect.

Investigative reports show that insomnia has some bearing on more than just a few aspects of nursing implementation, leading to sluggish responses, delayed reaction times, failure to make a start when appropriate, erroneous functions, decelerated thoughts, and a diminished recollection of nursing actions already performed.

Another factor influencing the nursing shortage is the increase of government interventions. With the rules and regulations of Medicare, medical treatment is ruled by money, not by patient need. This also is a factor with insurance entities, including HMOs, PPOs, and private insurance.

The patient's length of stay is governed by the patient's DRG (Diagnostic Related Group). If you have a hernia surgery, the government, not the physicians, tells you when your time is up. As a nurse, this bothers me terribly, because I see repeat patients that should have been taken care of longer the first time, who have been discharged only to return two weeks later with a severe infection and wound dehiscence. Now we have the new government mandated insurance "Obamacare" that brings a whole new degree of difficulty to the government involvement in healthcare.

Who wants to work with people who have new diseases like vancomycin resistance enterococci (VRE), methicillin resistance staphylococcus aureus (MRSA), AIDS, HIV, tuberculosis, hepatitis, and other life-threatening contagious diseases?

Travel Nursing Basics

Travel nursing is for those nurses who are competent, can hit the floor running, and who have at least two years of experience. The job description also includes working 13 weeks at a hospital, long-term care facility, or home health setting to help out when there are nursing shortages.

You will have many housing options including a fully furnished one-bedroom apartment, corporate housing, an extended stay, or just a plain ole motel room. More and more nurses are finding that it is much easier to take to the road in an RV!

In most situations you will take your own vehicle, but there are some assignments, like Hawaii or Alaska, that the company will provide a rental car or a rental car stipend. You can take your car to Alaska, but it is a long trip! Upon submission to Ketchikan, Alaska, my husband and I also explored taking the ferry from Washington State to Ketchikan. With Hawaii your most sensible option is to fly, although I guess you could take a boat. Some people have their car shipped over there, but more tend to get a rental car or take public transportation. (It's reported that one hospital in Honolulu charges $20 a day just for parking!)

The three major players in the travel nursing field are the hospital, the agency, and the nurse. Hospitals all around the country are having trouble filling all their full time spots with nurses in their general area. When the shortage gets extreme, they put in an "order" for a nurse.

These orders specify exactly what they are looking for. For example they would want a nurse who has BLS, ACLS, PALS, and TNCC to work in the ER. They will want BLS and ACLS for the ICU. If you are critical care certified (CCRN), your profile will jump up the manager large pile of profiles on their desk. Usually a hospital will add what they need to a job database, also known as a vendor management system, which we will talk about more later!

Who are looking at the job databases? Travel nursing companies! These companies are compromised usually of a President/CEO, Nursing Manager, Recruiting Manager, and recruiters. If large enough, they will also have a housing and credentialing department. The one that you will have the most contact with is the recruiter! It is his or her job to look at the database to see if there is a hospital that needs you! They look at their list of needs to see if there is a job that fits your experience and certifications.

You, the traveling nurse or therapist, have the biggest job in weeding through all the travel companies to find the perfect assignment at the perfect time. The Internet has made this process easier. I couldn't imagine doing this before the Internet was available, but I know that some did it! Now your job is even easier considering that several websites, including *www.highwayhypodermics.com* have travel companies reviews. Highway Hypodermics is also the only website that lists the benefits that each company provides. After finding an assignment that you like with a company that fits your needs, the travel nurse's profile will be sent to the hospital and hopefully an interview is soon to follow.

After the travel assignment is accepted, the finer details of housing and travel are then worked out. It is your job as a travel nurse to be adaptable and flexible, but on the other hand, don't let them break you! Number one when you get your contract - READ IT CAREFULLY! It's like nursing documentation, if it isn't documented it isn't done! When you get to your assignment, remember that you are representing all traveling nurses. If you look bad, it has a direct reflection on the travel nursing field. Your job is to go to the hospital, do what they do, and provide quality nursing care.

Educational Factors

There are travel nursing jobs for all levels of nursing, Certified Nursing Assistants (CNAs), Licensed Practical Nurses (LPN), associate level Registered Nurses (RNs), along with Bachelor prepared RNs, and Masters prepared RNs.

CNAs and LPNs have a harder time finding assignments, but they are out there. I found it easier for these two categories to go with a larger company who has more job openings for these levels. RNs are the most widely sought after nurses. Associate level RNs have absolutely no problems finding jobs in a lot of hospitals, but the larger teaching hospitals and those hospitals with "Magnet" status are starting to require that all RNs have a Bachelor's Degree in Nursing.

The one job level that is becoming more prevalent is traveling nursing managers and supervisors. For this level, it helps to have a Masters in Nursing or at least some Grad-Level classes. Since my bachelor is in Secondary Science Education, I found a program through Excelsior College in which they are now awarding a Certificate in Graduate-level nursing Management (CGM). This requires you to take the 4 graduate-level classes and prepares you to take the test to become a Certified Nursing Manager and Leader (CNM-L), which was developed in partnership with the American Association of Critical Care Nurses (AACN).

Certificates are also a great way to get your resume to the top of the resume pile. Other AACN certification programs include Critical Care, Progressive Care, Cardiac Medicine, and Acute Care Nurse Practitioners. Again, the advanced degrees are not required, but can help you get to the top of the resume pile.

Why Travel Nursing?

The number one reason nurses travel is to stay out of the politics. One of my colleagues was fed up with being a unit manager. Being in middle management was stressing her out to the max. She left her management position for the open road, and hasn't ever looked back. Another friend of mine states that she was tired of all the "riff-raff" that the hospital required. She just wants to go to work, take care of her patients, and then come home.

What really happens is that we trade hospital politics for company politics. This is most especially true if you change companies every 13 to 26 weeks. There are all kinds of credentialing that we have to go through before we can even be considered for an assignment.

Some people travel related to the higher wages. The wage differences between staff and travel used to be a wide margin, but recently this margin has become less and less although staff nurses still think that we are out there making quite a bit more. When you consider the fact that we have a permanent home also with double the expenses, the traveler is making some more, but not as much as staff members think we are making. This margin is bigger, though, if you are from a southern state and traveling to the coastal states.

Another great aspect of travel nursing is exploring the country. On our days off you can find us hiking or biking in the great outdoors, shopping at quaint little local shops, or just exploring our new territory.

My husband and I like to take a few days off and go each way exploring our environment. In California, we started out going west to Monterey, then south to Los Angeles on weekends, and the next month we went north to San Francisco taking in all the sights along the southern part of the Pacific Coast Highway. During my assignments in Puyallup, Washington, and Tillamook, Oregon, we made the northern loop of the Pacific Coast Highway.

Professional growth is another great reason to start travel nursing. There are new technologies entering the medical field all the time. In a smaller hospital you may not see some of the bigger technologies, but you will obtain the knowledge about many different technologies. In a bigger hospital, you can learn all about the higher level of technology. For instance, I have done a lot of smaller critical access facilities; therefore, I know a little bit about everything from fetal monitoring, to cardiac monitoring, to emergency nursing, and rehabilitation. I'm now traveling at a larger hospital, and I was totally amazed the other day when in the middle of a code we got out the ultrasound machine and we knew exactly what was going on with that patient's heart, because we could see it!

The one consistent thing I find with travel nursing is that you either love it or hate it. There aren't very many people who are stuck in the middle. For many of us travelers the top question is, "Why didn't I become a traveler sooner?"

Travel Nursing Goals

The diversity of goals is just as broad as the reasons we decided to become nurses to begin with! Many have the goal of traveling through or working in all 50 states and seeing all the National Parks and Monuments.

One of my first goals was to travel the entire distance of the Pacific Coast Highway all the way from San Diego to the Washington state peninsula. We did this in many trips. I was on assignment in the Monterey, California, area, and one weekend we took off and went south from Monterey to Los Angeles. Another time we set the GPS on "shortest route" and went to Big Sir, over the mountain. During another outing, we took the I-5 freeway down to San Diego. On two other trips we made the journey to San Francisco and up to as far as Garberville, CA. During this time, we got to see plenty of lighthouses and enjoyed many state and national parks. While on assignment in Tillamook, Oregon, we made the rest of the journey, from Tillamook down to Garberville, CA, and then another weekend we went up to the Washington Peninsula and Port Angeles.

I put this out on a Facebook Forum and these are some of the other great responses that I got!

- See all the Major League Baseball parks. Currently there are 29 parks that are being played on with 3 formerly used ones standing (Metrodome in Minneapolis, the Astrodome in Houston, and Olympic Stadium in Montreal, Canada) (Major League Baseball Parks, 2014)
- See all the National Football League stadiums. Currently there are 31 stadiums that are being played on. You would think that Lambeau Field in Green Bay would be the oldest stadium (built in 1957), but actually Soldier Field in Chicago has been around since 1924. (National Football League Stadiums, 2014)
- National Parks: currently there are 59 National Parks. Yellowstone was the first park to receive NPS status in 1872 (National Park Service, 2014). In the middle of 1986, the National Park Passport Stamp book was published. Travelers take this book to every national park that they go to and get a Park, City, and Date stamp. (National Park Passport Stamp, 2014)
- Two other big hits are wineries and microbreweries! According to Wines and Vines, there are more than 8,000 wineries in the United States. While most of them are in California, Washington, Oregon, New York, and Virginia round out the top 5 states (Klingensmith & Gordon, 2013). The microbreweries have not taken off that fast. The number of Brewpubs in June 2013 was 1165, and the number of Microbreweries was at 1221,

with the number of local craft beers totaling 97. This makes for a total of 2483 U.S. Craft Breweries in the United States (Craft Brewing Statistics, 2013).

- Lighthouses: There are hundreds of lighthouses all around the United States with Michigan having the most at 150. Most of these were built by the United States Coast Guard, and are now protected by the National Lighthouse Preservation Act of 2000. (Lighthouses In the U.S., 2014)
- Covered Bridges: According to sources there are about 1600 covered bridges in the world. Some of the most famous ones can be found right in the Heartland of America: the bridges of Madison County, Iowa. These were made famous by the book and movie of the same name, *Bridges of Madison County.* Bridges for world travelers can be found in China, Canada, Switzerland, Germany, and the United States (Covered Bridges, 2014).
- Other interesting goals I found was to be able to ride a motorcycle year around, play golf year round, hike the mountains, bike the mountains, ski the mountains, working in all the major trauma centers in the United States, and collect the flat "memory" coins from each state.
- Professionally, I have had many nurses and therapists that are in search of "the perfect" place to live. Having a great job in a great community seems to elude most of us. As another nurse states, "To find a hospital and staff that are actually supportive, good teamwork, provides care that makes sense and where I can be proud to work. Physicians, respiratory and other nurses work collaboratively. I have been doing this for 15 years and haven't found it yet." I personally have been traveling for 13 years, and I have yet to find a hospital that I love in a community that I couldn't live without.

Conclusion

It takes a special type of person to be a nurse, and now travel nursing brings a whole new different aspect to nursing. On top of that, travel nursing is a different animal all itself. I'm all for better patient care and easing the nursing shortage, and that is why I take my turn helping out those hospitals in need. I don't get bored in the same old routine because I change hospitals, and even floors, every three to six months.

No, travel nursing is not for everyone, but after reading this book you can make a more informed decision on whether or not travel nursing is right for you.

References

Covered Bridges. (2014). Retrieved from Wikipedia: http://en.wikipedia.org/wiki/Covered_bridge

Craft Brewing Statistics. (2013, June). Retrieved from The Brewer Association: http://www.brewersassociation.org/pages/business-tools/craft-brewing-statistics/number-of-breweries

Institute, K. H. (2011). *KPMG's 2011 U.S. Hospital Nursing Labor Costs Study.* USA: KPMG.

Job Conglomerant. (2013). *Different companies may include the same job as another company.*

Klingensmith, C., & Gordon, J. (2013, 02 14). *North American Winery Total Passes 8,000.* Retrieved from Wines and Vines: http://www.winesandvines.com/template.cfm?section=news&content=111242

Lighthouses In the U.S. (2014). Retrieved from Wikipedia: http://en.wikipedia.org/wiki/List_of_lighthouses_in_the_United_States

Major League Baseball Parks. (2014). Retrieved from Wikipedia: http://en.wikipedia.org/wiki/List_of_Major_League_Baseball_stadiums

National Football League Stadiums. (2014). Retrieved from Wikipedia: http://en.wikipedia.org/wiki/National_Football_League_Stadiums

National Park Passport Stamp. (2014). Retrieved from Wikipedia: http://en.wikipedia.org/wiki/National_Park_Passport_Stamps

National Park Service. (2014). Retrieved from Wikipedia: http://en.wikipedia.org/wiki/National_parks

Travel Nursing Jobs. (2013, January 27). Aureus Medical Group, Cross Country TravCorp, Freedom Healthcare Staffing, Healthcare Providers Choice, Trinity Healthcare Staffing Group, The Right Solutions, Tailored Healthcare Staffing, Trustaff, Talemed, and RN Network.

Chapter Two

Traits Of A Quality Travel Nurse

Any nurse can be a traveling nurse, right? Just like anyone can be a nurse, any nurse can be a traveling nurse. In my 10 years of travel nursing, I have found one definite about travel nursing…either you love it or you hate it. I have not found very many people who are stuck in between.

Travel nurses aren't just nurses who cruise around the United States being nurses. They have special qualities about them that make them the best in their field. For some nurses these traits come automatically, some nurses have to work at them, but one thing is for sure, if you are a great traveling nurse, you have to obtain these quality traits!

I recently posted this question to The Gypsy Nurse Caravan group on Facebook and here are the top nine traits: flexibility, confidence, professionalism, integrity, adaptability, dependability, independence, wanderlust, and adventure. Other traits that were mentioned include: sense of humor, courage, relatability, personality, curiosity, fortitude, self-respect, diligence, honor, patience, tolerance, resourcefulness, maturity, and humility.

Flexibility

"The capability of being bent without breaking," is how Webster's defines flexibility. The truth of the matter is, if you can't be flexible in floating, shifts, schedule, and housing, don't even think about travel nursing. It's the point of breakability that is so individualized!

In many hospitals, the traveler is the first to float. The floor that you are floated to is the point that can break you. To protect yourself, always in the interview ask how much floating you will do? And to what floors? When I was in Tennessee, I floated from telemetry to ICU overflow and

ER only about 10% of the time; when I was in Florida, I floated from telemetry to the ER 50% of the time; as a supervisor here in California, I float the ICU travelers to telemetry floor about 90% of the time.

I don't mind floating 10% of the time. I'm the travel nurse. I'm supposed to be willing to float. I really didn't even mind floating 50/50 telemetry/ER. The people I worked with on both floors were great and I enjoyed the change. In fact, my husband and I made a game of it "betting" on if I was going to work that night on the telemetry floor or in the emergency room.

Floating 90% of the time, now that would be my breaking point. Why did they hire for ICU if I'm going to be floating almost every day to telemetry? I've asked the travel nurses and all were told that they would be floating to step-down or telemetry, but only a few of them knew that they would be floating almost every day. This would be a problem to me. As an ICU nurse, I wouldn't want to lose my ICU skills by working telemetry floor. Not that working telemetry floor is "bad," but you don't have all the higher level of critical thinking for all the drips, ventilator settings, and arterial line experience.

It is also important in floating that you only float to units of competency. My previous experience (before traveling) was in medical, surgical, rehab, psych, and then emergency room. My first travel assignment was in the ER, and I found that I didn't like traveling as an ER nurse. At my little hospital in California, we had standing orders and therefore, autonomy. We could use our professional judgment and start the chest pain protocol while the physician was on his way (from a sleep room in the hospital). When I went to "the big city" of Phoenix, we had to ask the doctor for everything. I couldn't even do an EKG on a chest pain patient until the physician saw the patient. So, I took a telemetry job and absolutely loved it. So floating from telemetry to lower level ICU and ER was not a big deal for me, but being floated to the dialysis floor or cancer floor was my breaking point.

It is important that you discuss with the house supervisors the floors that you absolutely cannot be floated to. Always start the conversation with, "I don't mind being floated, to MICU, SICU, or CCU, but I am not comfortable working telemetry or med/surg." It is important to put into your contract your areas of competency. I have yet to have a travel company refuse to put into my contract the floors that I can and cannot float to.

You must start this process in the interview with the hospital. Not only is it important to discuss the percentage of time that you will be floated, but also what floors you will float to. Then in your contract you put in a paragraph that reads, "As discussed with the manager, I am willing to float to other floors of competency. I will not be required to float to dialysis, renal, OB, or OR." If the list is shorter, you can put down the floors that you are competent to float to. "As discussed with the manager, I am willing to float to medical, psychiatric, telemetry, rehab, ER, step-down, and PACU."

What shift do you usually work? I have worked night shift primarily for the last 20 years. Will I work day shift? Yes, but I want to know ahead of time that is the shift I'm agreeing to. One of the things that I'm seeing more and more in job listings is the day/night rotation. This is my breaking point. Maybe working 8 hours and floating between evenings and nights or even floating between days and evenings wouldn't be bad, but working 12 hours and floating between days/nights is really hard.

Make sure that you put in your contract that you are contracted for the exact time that you will be working. If you can do the day/night rotation, more power to you, but I would definitely ask for a few more dollars an hour to do this! Remember, anything is negotiable!

What is your schedule going to be like and does it matter to you? I don't mind working every weekend or 2 days here and there, but don't schedule me for every other day. That just drives me nuts!!! I have found a trend in that the younger travelers want all their day in a row. In fact, I've heard of some travelers doing 7 days on and 7 days off. When I was in Phoenix, I still had my home in Lake Havasu City, and I loved my 3 on, 1 off, 3 on, then I spent a week at home, but when I'm not close to home, I would just my 3 days in a row, or at least 2 days in the middle of the week and 2 days on the weekend. Some of the older nurses I have found also like 2 days then a random day then 2 days and another random day. What every nurse needs to think of is what you can be flexible with, and what you cannot safely handle and put this in your contract!

Housing is another area that you might have to be flexible with. My perfect housing picture is my 3 bedroom 2 bath house on a hill on the Oregon coast. Do you travel with pets or a family? Is it just you and hubby or just you? When my husband and son traveled with me, we had a two-bedroom apartment with utilities, including cable for television and Internet until we decided to get a recreational vehicle (RV).

If you are single, do you want private housing or do you want to save money and live with a roommate? Does the hospital have its own housing? One hospital system that I know of owns its own apartment complex to house the travelers. Another hospital that I have traveled to housed the travelers on a floor that wasn't currently being used. Do you prefer the company handling the housing or do you want to do things by yourself with the housing stipend? The housing coordinator, which may be your recruiter, needs to know exactly what type of housing you are looking for.

Unfortunately, travel nurses are not immune to housing disasters. From gunshots on the street to cockroaches in the living room, I've heard nightmare stories! I'm okay with non-luxury housing, but filth is my breaking point! If you get to your assignment housing and things are bad, you have every right to call your recruiter and tell them about it! Be flexible, but don't put yourself in danger.

Housing and commutes is another deal breaker. I don't mind housing that is 20 to 30 minutes away, but I'm not driving and hour or two from my housing to the assignment location. This is especially important if you take an assignment in a larger city. After you arrive and get settled into the apartment, always make a maiden voyage to the hospital. How long does it take? Are you traveling on a freeway that is congested in the morning traffic? Talk to your recruiter as soon as possible to resolve this issue.

You can also put specifics into your contract. "I understand that I will be housed at 12345 Rockford Lane, which is a 20 minute drive to the hospital." If your company doesn't have one, I would find a copy of a move-in/move-out inventory. Be very specific on what you find wrong with the apartment. Is there a ding in the bedroom door? Make sure that it's on there! Even put the little things, like a black mark on the wall. Take pictures!! Send a picture of a roach to your recruiter at 5:00 PM, and you're guaranteed an immediate callback or you need a new recruiter!

Confidence

The basics of confidence include knowing your abilities (strong or weak), being confident in your abilities, and being able to take criticism of your abilities. In the travel nursing world, it really is a jungle out there, and that jungle isn't always rainbows and waterfalls. There are big cats that stalk you, snakes that will want to squeeze the life out of you, and gorillas that want to stomp you in the ground.

The skills checklist is a great way to take inventory of your nursing skills. You want to look good to a hospital, but you don't want to "pump up" your skills checklist. This is the time to be truthful with yourself on what you really can and cannot do. If you have never worked with an intracranial pressure monitor don't put that you have lots of experience related to the fact that you have read every article on ICP monitoring, but no actual clinical experience. By misrepresenting yourself, you are not only putting your license in danger, but you are also putting a patient's safety in danger.

There is a fine line between being a "know-it-all" and having confidence in yourself. You must prove yourself with your actions and not your words. Don't tell them all about your experience with arterial lines and balloon pumps, but get in there and show them that you can set one up and monitor it the correct way. The problem all starts when a travel nurse goes into the hospital and announces that they have so many credentials, certificates, and experience that she should just be called, "Super Nurse."

I worked with a nurse who thought that she was better than everyone else because she loved her high level patients with an arterial line, balloon pump and who were always intubated and unconscious. She was too high tech of an RN who was WAY smarter than any of the rest of us. After making the rest of the staff look stupid for a couple of weeks, she was eventually told that the hospital no longer needed her.

Accepting criticism is one of the hardest aspects of travel nursing. Here you are a thousand miles from home and "no one likes you." You have to get past this and make your patients a number one priority.

My two worst assignments both involved being criticized almost to the point of breaking. It really amazes me how you can do the exact the same thing at different hospitals and you're a genius at one and an idiot at the other one. Tough times, yeah, but I probably learned the most from those two assignments.

My first toughie was in Oklahoma. When I interviewed for the job, I was asked if I took care of post cardiac catheterization patients. Sure I have, not a problem. My first cardiac cath patient came back with this piece of green plastic sticking out of their leg… Oh! That is what a sheath looks like. I'd heard of them, but all our patients came back with an angioseal at the other hospital.

From then on, I was known as the travel nurse making all the big bucks but getting all the easy patients because I didn't have any experience with a sheath. I poured myself into my patients and their care instead of listening to all their bickering.

My second worst assignment was in North Dakota, which is really a shame, because I really liked some of the people that I worked with. During my first two months it was amazing how everyone knew the protocol, but none of them did it the exact same way. Every shift I was told about every little thing that I did wrong; although, I was doing it how the others had oriented me to. Then the nursing supervisor started following me around to catch everything that I did wrong. I started making every effort to stay away from her until one day she attempted to throw me under the bus, and I went to the nursing supervisor about working in a hostile environment.

I say all this to say that when you are a traveling nurse, you are taking a chance of being attacked by the hospital staff. That is why it is very important for you to have great nursing skills, be confident, and know when to stick up for yourself. Don't let anyone beat you down to your breaking point.

Professionalism and Integrity

You may think that integrity and professionalism are automatic since we are all have a professional nursing license, but I'm still shocked at some of the things that I see out there in the travel nursing world.

The first step to professionalism is the way you look. It's not mandatory, but having your hair up off your shoulders is a good start. Have it neatly trimmed and pulled back nicely. Make sure that your uniform is nice and clean without wrinkles. I know that should be a given, but you would be surprised at how many times I have seen unkempt uniforms. Remember on your first day, that you only get one chance to make a great first impression.

Another aspect of professionalism is to not get involved in the unit's politics. After all, isn't that one of the reasons we travel? The easiest way of doing this is by not hanging out at the nurses' station, talking about tummy tucks, boob jobs, and boyfriends. You need to be down the hallway with your patients. Patient care has to be number one.

As a supervisor one of the things that really bother me is the use of pet names. The patients are not your honey, sweetie, papa or momma. They have a name, which is usually written on the board at the bedside now. It doesn't take very long to see that the patient prefers to go by Suzie instead of momma.

A readiness to help is another aspect of professionalism as a traveling nurse. I don't want to ever hear a professional travel nurse state, "That's not my patient," or "They didn't help me." It may not be your patient, but that patient has needs that need to be taken care of, and if you are not busy and can help out, why not? Yeah, we all have those patients who are on the call light constantly. Why not tell the nurse, you'll get it this time? Give the other nurse a break. I have found that usually what comes around goes around.

And what about that professional attitude? Yes, we all have bad days, but we don't have them all the time. Every day, you need to come to work with a smile on your face and an attitude that today is going to be a great day! Yeah, I know, this can change within the first 10 minutes of the shift, but at least you got there with a great attitude. Some mornings and evenings, half the battle is getting to work with a great attitude!

The best definition of integrity is, "Doing what you know is right, even when no one is looking." If a pill hit the floor and no one is looking do you pick it up and put it back in the container or do you go get another one? What if it's a narcotic? Is it really worth the effort to find someone to waste it with you and get another one? I know, this seems to be a no brainer, but you would be surprised!

You also need to have integrity when it comes to working with the hospital and travel agency. If you say that you are going to be at orientation on the 11th at 7:00 AM, you had better be there at 7:00 AM ready to fill out more paperwork! If you tell your company that you will have your titers done by the start date, then you'd better get them done and resulted by then. I also expect the same integrity from the hospital and agency. If a travel company tells you that you will get a bonus for completing 90% of your hours, I expect to see that bonus. I don't expect the company to come up with some lame excuse that you just missed it without a full detail of why you missed it. Empty verbiage does not translate into integrity.

If the hospital states that you will float 25% of the time, I expect them to honor that, unless there is a further agreement between you and the hospital that you will float more than that. I expect the hospital to have the integrity to give you the guaranteed hours that you are required to have.

Again, do what is right, even when no one else is looking.

Adaptability

As a traveling nurse, you must be able to adjust oneself readily to different conditions. This is where the ole saying, "When in Rome, do as the Romans," comes into play. So many times, I've heard travel nurses stated, "Oh, I don't do it like that, because this is how I learned in nursing school and have always done it that way."

Things change...times change...the process is always getting improved. The newest terminology we hear now is evidence-based practice. In 1992 when I got out of nursing school, we didn't do something related to evidence-based practice, we did it because that is how that particular school had been doing it since the new disposable syringes came out! Now there has been such a great leap into evidenced-based practice and nursing research that that's how 21st century nurses have to roll.

As a traveling nurse, one of the most valuable things that you can do when you first get onto the nursing floor is find the policy and procedure manual. Yes, there are basic nursing procedures that never change from hospital to hospital, and with other things there are changes from hospitals to hospitals. One of the policies that come first to my mind is contact precautions for MRSA and VRE. Some hospitals you need full gown, mask, and gloves. Other hospitals you need only gloves unless you are going to be changing the wound where the MRSA is located or emptying the foley catheter where the VRE is located. To change an IV setting or to hit the restart do you need full gown and gloves? The answer to that can only be found in the nursing policy and procedure.

Another aspect of travel nursing and adaptability is accepting the cultural differences of the areas in which you travel to. This can be anything from a poor town to a rich city, small town to big city, and different ethnic groups. Social classes are seen in all areas, not just poor towns and rich cities. Some patients expect everything to be given to them the minute they ask for it, and others are very patient and understand that you are very busy, and thank you for taking time out especially for them. The differences in a small town or big city are most often the nurses' choice, and this adaptability is up to you, the travel nurse.

Currently my home base is in a town with a whopping population of 1,000 people. In just about all the places I have traveled to, I have been in towns anywhere from 10,000 to under 100K. That isn't to say that I haven't taken assignment in a larger market (I'm currently writing this in the "Inland Empire" of the Greater Los Angeles area). There are differences in the population of Southeast Idaho and the population of Southern California!

People here have a hard time understanding that in my little corner of Idaho, we have 1 African-American family and 3 Asian families, but we do have a Hispanic population of 150. Here in the Hemet, CA, there are a total of 40,000 people with 2,600 African-Americans, 13,000 Hispanic, and 1,700 Asian families (City Comparison, 2014). It was just such a reverse shock to them, that some parts of the United States weren't as culturally diverse as other areas. They also couldn't believe that we only have about 5,000 in our county with 1,000 people in my town. In the RV Park that I'm in, there are more people than there are in my hometown. Nothing wrong with either lifestyle, but it does take some getting used to.

You also have to adapt to the specialty idea if you are from a small town. At home I worked Critical Access (where I was doing ER, ICU, House Supervisor, Med-Surg, Post-Partum, Rehab, and PACU). It is very difficult to explain to recruiters and interviewing managers exactly what my "specialty" is. Anyone who has worked Critical Access (25 beds or less in a rural area), knows that most of the time, you have to know a little of everything and you can't specialize in anything but quality nursing care! I'm very thankful for my small town experiences; not many house supervisors out there have not only BLS, ACLS, and PALS, but NRP, AWHONN, and TNCC. Coming to a hospital of 100 beds, I had to adjust to doing less bedside care and more supervising and staffing.

No matter what your specialty is, each hospital is different and you must adapt to the new policy and procedures. As stated before, it is so important to do as the Romans when in Rome!

Dependability

Dependability is another great attribute that a traveling professional must possess. This means that you must be reliable and show up when you are supposed to. Part of being a travel nurse is showing up every day and doing your job. This seems like a no-brainer, but you would be amazed at the number of hospitals I have been to that are astonished when I show up and do my job.

At one of my assignments, they had gone through several travelers who did nothing in their spare time except shop online, play games on the computer, or sleep. I got there and they were so impressed that I showed up, did my job, and was a true leader, in that, when I wasn't busy in the emergency room, I helped out the others on the medical floor. No, I'm not a super hero, I'm just someone who actually shows up and works.

Dependability is also shown by showing up to work on time. When you first get to your assignment (if not before in the interview) make sure that you know what time orientation starts and what time report starts. Most shifts are 7:00 AM to 7:00 PM, what time is report? Some hospitals do the 0645 to 0715 for report, while others may have report from 0700 to 0730. If report is at 0645 and you show up at 0700, your first impression may not be the best.

Some hospitals are not the best at letting you know about changes. As a travel nurse, you need to check the schedule at least weekly to see if there are any changes. Another thing that makes you really look good is by being available to trade days on occasion. Personally, I don't usually don't have any connections or big doings going on while I'm on assignment; therefore, I'm pretty open to working whenever. No, you don't need to do this all the time, but even being available to trade a few days a month makes you look very adaptable and by actually showing up, very dependable.

Dependability is staying until your shift has ended. If your shift is not over until 0730 and it takes you an hour to get to the dentist, don't schedule your dentist appointment at 0800, which would require you to leave when day shift got there right at 0700. Again, this may seem to be a no-brainer, but I've seen this over and over with both travelers and staff nurses.

Make every attempt to have all your work done by the end of the shift. Yeah, I know, charting as you go at some hospitals is only a dream. As much as you try to keep up with charting, sometimes you just have to stay a little longer to complete everything. I find this especially true if you work that OB floor. Babies have a habit of coming into the world just before shift change! Staying late to get all your charting done isn't the best of situations, but it does happen.

Don't leave things undone! All hospitals are 24-hour facilities and some things you just don't have time to do. Make sure that the oncoming shift knows if you have things that you haven't completed or if you're an ER nurse, make sure that they know exactly what you have and have not done. "Triage, assessment, and EKG have been done, but I don't have an IV line in yet." Don't make it a habit of leaving things undone, by having the attitude, "I've had enough, I'm done, day shift can do that."

Dependability is also shown by not calling off for any reason. The Garth Brooks show is in town and you didn't realize it before the schedule came out, so all of a sudden you are having "eye trouble" (just can't see coming in to work). The best plan is to make every attempt to trade a day with another nurse. If you have already made it a habit of trading days with the other nurses, then they are more apt to trade a day with you when you would like a day off.

Find yourself in a bad assignment? The appropriate thing to do is talk it over with your recruiter. Although we are contracted nurses, most contracts have it in there that you are an "at will" employee that can be cancelled with a two-week notice. This concept goes both ways. In an assignment that was misrepresented to you? Talk to your recruiter about the appropriate length of time, give your notice and go on with life. The wrong thing to do is to call off every day until the end of the assignment.

Independence

Oh the freedom of travel nursing. The freedom to pick your destination: mountains in the winter for snow skiing, lakes in the summer for water skiing, becoming a snow bird at the age of 35 instead of 65! The freedom to pick your own culture: living the life in the big city with all its hustle and bustle, going to the country and seeing the stars at night, or living in the burbs with quaint shops and local pubs. The freedom to pick your own work environment: large teaching hospital with opportunities to specialize, smaller community hospital where you have the opportunities to experience other units, or smaller hospitals where you get a wide variety of experiences.

Although you may have limited choices related to your specialty and available assignment by one travel company, you are more than free to check out other travel companies that have an assignment where you want to be. No one can tell you that you HAVE to go to Texas in the summer or North Dakota in the winter. You have choices.

Adventure and Wanderlust

This is what travel nursing is all about! Wandering the country and living the adventure. With travel nursing, you don't have to hike the same old trail. You don't have to play the same old golf course. You don't have to take the same old weekend adventure.

One of my first goals was to travel up and down the Pacific Coast Highway. On my second assignment in California we went from Monterey down to Los Angeles and then making the trip from Monterey up to Garberville, CA. We eventually connected the southern dots by taking a trip from Los Angeles down to San Diego. While on assignment in Seattle, we made the trip around the Washington peninsula to Astoria, OR. While assignment in Oregon, we made the trip south to Garberville, CA and then went north to Astoria, OR. Oh, the great pictures that I have of lighthouses along the Pacific Coast Highway!

I have a friend who is on assignment now in Phoenix who picks a different trail to hike on her days off. The Blogs and Facebook are loaded with pictures of all kinds of nurses taking all kinds of side trips. This is a top reason that travelers love their lifestyle…the adventure of it all!!!

Reference

City Comparison. (2014). Retrieved from Home Fair: http://www.homefair.com/real-estate/compare-cities/results.asp?Zip1=83241&Zip2=92545

Chapter Three

How Travel Nurses Need To Behave

Travel nurses are no different than the other nurses in the fact that we should all behave ourselves. The thing that is different with travel nursing is that travelers are stereotyped more than staff nurses. Any behaviors that a travel nurse expresses will be recognized and expected for other travel nurses. Although this is a short chapter, it is one of the most important in that it affects ALL travel nurses! We need to focus on positive behaviors and just say "no" to the ones that will affect the reputation of a traveler.

When In Rome, Do As The Romans Do

This is like the golden rule of travel nursing. Never, ever tell anyone that they are doing all wrong because they don't do things like you do. There are several ways to change a dressing, and, as a traveling nurse, you will learn them all.

The most important book that you can find once you get onto the unit is the policy and procedure manual. This is usually found on the computer now, but hard copies can still be found on the unit.

Yes, this is a two edged sword in the fact, that you have to do procedures the way that you learned them or have found to work best, but always be open to change.

The one thing that does make it difficult at times is the different way that different nurses at the same hospital do it the "right way," but that's not how others have trained you to do the same routine. You also have to figure out the routine or the procedure ways of the physician, especially if you work in the ER or the OR.

Just Say No To Gossip

Okay this has to be one of my very biggest weaknesses. There are just some things out in the world of travel nursing that will make you scream and it is so easy to fall into the trap. We all want to interact with our fellow nurses but we have to be careful not to fall into the trap of gossiping about the other nurses.

People are naturally curious; they want to know what's going on. Don't be a victim to sitting at the nurse's station discussing the new handbag from Louis Vuitton, your new Prada shoes, or what new cosmetic procedure that your best friend had.

The biggest way to keep your mouth shut is to get back to work. Your number one priority should be patient care and not sitting at the nurse station. The more you do for your patients the less time you will have to sit around and gossip.

This will also give you less time to sit around and discuss salaries for what other traveling nurses are making. The danger with discussing your salary with other nurses is that different companies give different benefits, and while your benefits may be great you might be making less hourly wage whereas another nurse may not have as good of benefits but they will be making more hourly wage. There is just no good way to compare apples and oranges over chips and salsa.

Hit The Floor Running

A big complaint that I have seen on travel nursing forums is the fact that someone didn't get enough orientation. As a traveling nurse, you have to be able to hit the floor running. This is the main reason that you should have at least one to two years in your field. There is no time to lean on someone else. You have to be able to stand up by yourself.

Generally, orientation is anywhere from four hours to a week. During this time, you are expected to learn the routine of the unit. You should expect to be shown where the clean and dirty utilities rooms are, the medication room, the kitchen, and be given any codes to get into those different rooms. Orientation should also entail the general routine of the unit and what is expected of you. In no orientation will you learn everything that you will need to know. In fact, I'm constantly finding out new things during my last week on assignment.

Thinking Fast On Your Feet

As a traveling nurse, you need to have the ability to problem solve while on the run. Critical thinking skills are a must for a traveling nurse. There are times when you have to figure out the best case scenario. Once again, this is the reason why you need to have more than a year of experience before attempting travel nursing.

Critical thinking skills are a must for travelers related to the fact that you are not going to have someone hold your hand. After a short orientation, you will be taking care of your own set of patients. When there is a change in your patient's condition, you have to be able to recognize the problem and start working towards the solution.

This is the main reason why hospitals and travel companies won't even look at a nurse until they have had at least one to two years of experience. Being able to think fast takes some preparation and mastering of your nursing skills. You can't think fast until you build up the stamina to do so. You have to devote yourself every shift to making sharper and faster decisions about your patient's care. Always think about what is best for the patient. Rome wasn't built in a day and neither was a great travel professional. You have to be confident and self-sufficient.

Willingness To Go On The Fly

Another trait of a great travel nurse is the willingness to do things at a moment's notice. In fact, this happens frequently in some assignments with the floating aspect. You must be able to walk onto a floor, take your assignment, see what needs to be done and take care of your patient's in a proper manner.

This can also be true at the beginning of an assignment. Not all arrangements for the assignment are made weeks in advance. Unfortunately, hospitals and staffing companies will ultimately find something that needs to be done the week before the assignment. Although a lack of planning on their part doesn't necessarily constitute an emergency on your part, you still need to make every attempt to get things completed as soon as possible. We have to remember that travel companies, hospitals, and nurses are not always perfect.

Masters of Change

Traveling nurses and therapists thrive on change! If you are even just a little afraid of change, then don't even think about becoming a travel healthcare professional.

Every travel nurse needs a plaque on the wall of the serenity prayer.

"Grant me the serenity to accept the things I cannot change, the courage to change the things I can, and the wisdom to know the difference."

Some of the things that we can do to cope with change and our continuously changing life style are the following:

- Take time to relax. Too many times we get stressed out between all the titers, test, and paperwork that we forget to relax. It is important to find a relaxation technique whether it's meditation, reading, listening to music, or just veggin' out in front of the television.
- Get out and be active. I love it when I see people online getting together to do fun things like hiking, biking, and golfing while on assignment. It doesn't have to be a sport either! Try going out to eat or seeing a movie with another traveler on assignment in your location.
- Remember to take care of yourself. This is one tough thing for nurses. We take care of others really well, but seem to fall short when it comes to taking care of us. Make every attempt to get out and walk for 30 minutes and try to eat healthier. Cheeseburgers and pizza aren't bad, when taken in moderation!
- Kill them with kindness at work. I cannot say it enough; you only have one chance to make a first impression. Go in with a great attitude and show them that you are there not to change them, but to work and help out.
- Guard yourself with a support system. There are several great groups on Facebook that allow travelers to vent their feelings. If you don't feel comfortable in a group, find a smaller group or a person or two that you can chat with when times get tough.

Powering Through When Times Get Tough

Even at the best of assignments, I've had a tough day to get through. No one said that travel nursing was a field of roses all the time. It can be very demanding and trying at times. You will find yourself in situations when you power through the day or maybe you have to power through the entire 13 weeks.

You have to have the ability to bounce back from adversity. Not everyone is going to be your friend at a new location. When things get tough, the tough get going! You have to meet the adversity head on and tackle the tough jobs. If it's a problem with a co-worker, remember to kill them with kindness and keep on smiling.

Focus on the tasks at hand. You are there to help out in the time of crisis. If things were perfect at that hospital, they wouldn't need travel nurses. Your task is to go to a location and make a concentrated effort to help out in any way you can, on the days or nights that you are scheduled. The reward of doing a great job at work is all the adventures that you will have on your days off. Some days you just want to give up, but you have to keep on focusing until the end of the shift, the end of med pass, the end of the hour.

Keep your eye on the end target. When you get into a bad assignment or even just having a bad day, just keep on thinking about the end. Only 10 more assignments, only 5 more hours... In most cases, we can do anything for 13 weeks. My toughest assignment was a 20 weeker in North Dakota, in which some days I definitely counted down the hours until the end of the shift. I made it through those 20 weeks, but it was a toughie! That is why it's so important to have a great recruiter that can help you power through the tough times.

Don't forget to trust in yourself. You are a great nurse and you know it! You didn't spend all that time in nursing school and pass state boards just to be a dummy. You have worked hard to get to the point of being a travel nurse. Believe in yourself and don't lose that confidence.

Personalities In Travel Nursing

The personality of a great travel nurse should include one that is outgoing and spirited. If you are shy and meek, you will be run over like a matador during the running of the bulls at the festival of Sanfermines.

That's not to say that you have to be bouncing off the walls, but you do have to be able to stand up by yourself and take up after yourself. You have to have a strong personality that can stand up in the face of diversity.

This is another subject that is a favorite of mine, the personality between the travel nurse and the recruiter. If you and your recruiter have very different personalities, you may need just to switch recruiters instead of changing companies all together.

I think that so many times the biggest problem we have in nursing field is the different types of personalities that we work with from patients, to families, to co-workers and even managers. Again, being a travel nurse is an advantage to the personality game in that if we can't stand the personality of a co-worker or recruiter, we do the best we can for 13 weeks and then we change hospitals and or recruiters!

In Conclusion

Travel nursing is a very rewarding career, but you definitely have to be the "travel nursing" type, or you are going to be miserable. Not a bad nurse, just not happy with the lifestyle. It is very important for nurses to understand what it takes to be a travel nurse before thinking about hitting the road.

Chapter Four

The Good, the Bad, and the Ugly

"Along the fairways of life, you must stop and smell the roses; for you only get to play one round."

This is one of my favorite quotes from the great golfer, Ben Hogan. What does this have to do with travel nursing? The road traveled has many rewards, but it also has its thorny drawbacks, and it even can throw us completely off-course with an ugly disaster.

Some of the good things about travel nursing include: making new friends, getting a feel of a city before making a move, enhancing your resume, better pay for travel nursing, and getting to eat all the great regional food. The bad includes housing nightmares, politics, leaving friends behind, obtaining all those state licenses, and starting at a new hospital with little orientation. Then it gets ugly with moving every three months, being lonely, staff grudges, sick days which cost you big time, and getting a contract cancelled.

Making New Friends

One of the biggest unknowns going into a travel assignment is what kind of people work for the hospital. When you walk onto the floor everyone is sizing up the new traveler. They want to know how long you have been a nurse, how long you have been traveling, and of course, where are you from. This scenario also works in reverse. One of my first objectives is to find out who is traveler friendly. In every assignment there is usually one nurse that you will "connect" with whom you use as a resource nurse. This is someone who is traveler friendly and seems to be genuinely concerned about making your travel nursing assignment a good one.

Now that we have Facebook, with every assignment my friends list gets bigger and bigger! Except for a few assignments at the beginning of my career, when Facebook wasn't around, I have at least one or two of the nurses from each assignment that I'm still connected with.

With the event of social forums our network of other traveling nurses is also growing. In fact, by networking with an older group from Delphi Forums, I have met some of the best travelers that have turned out to make a big difference in the world of travel nursing. It was from this group that some traveling nurses got together with an idea to create a conference on travel nursing. From that group, Michelle, Candy, Phil, Joe, and I are now the directors of the biggest gathering of traveling nurses once a year at the Travelers Conference.

Making a big move?

Some nurses use travel nursing as a way to explore where they would like to permanently relocate. If you have hesitations about moving to Phoenix, Minneapolis, Seattle, Boston, Los Angeles, or New Orleans, getting a travel assignment there is a perfect opportunity to test out the waters.

By doing this, you learn a lot about what parts of the city are best for you and your family. This can be done in the larger markets by working short 8 to 13 week assignments at different locations in the city. Not sure you want to stay in Phoenix? Then take a break and find a summer assignment in Minneapolis or maybe even Boston.

Do you prefer a small town, suburb, or big city? This can also be explored with travel nursing. I have always lived in towns 10,000 people or less. Do I take assignments in the city? Yes, but I usually find myself out in the suburbs. Would I ever work a downtown assignment? Yes! Why? Because I truly have never lived the city life. In fact, one year, I looked at an assignment at the University of Utah in attempt to try out the city life. In exploring the community and surrounding area, we found an apartment close to the facility where I could take the bus to work every evening and then back in the morning. I have one travel nursing friend who has always lived in the city with mass transportation, and doesn't own a car or even have a driver's license. She gets along fine, but not having a car would drive me nuts! Travel nursing gives me the opportunity to try out that lifestyle.

Enhancing Your Resume

One of the biggest misconceptions about travel nursing is that your resume is going to look like you're unstable related to the fact that you have had 14 travel assignments in 5 years. On the contrary, what this points out to someone who is looking for a temporary nurse is that you are very adaptable to different situations.

Along the travel nursing highway you will also have plenty of opportunities to expand that resume. My assignment in Florida is a great example of that. I was working telemetry floor, but had some small ER and small ICU background. When they needed someone to float to ICU, I was the first to go for "step-down" type of patients, patients that would be transferred from ICU to Telemetry the next day, until the day that I walked in and the ICU nurses were bickering about who was going to float to the ER. They had floated me to ICU to have one of the ICU nurses float to ER. It was then that I spoke up and volunteered to go to the ER. I went to the ER and took off just like riding an old bicycle. From then on, my husband and I would play the guessing game of which unit would I work on that day. Telemetry, ICU, or ER? In the end, this was a great assignment related to the fact that the next 13 weeks, I was chosen to open up the admission unit, where all we did was admit patient's from the ER to Telemetry or Medical floor. My resume then expanded to ICU Float and Admission Unit.

I'm frequently asked by travelers if they can "switch" specialties while on assignment. As a traveling nurse, the easiest way to do this is to take a permanent job at a local hospital and get a year's worth of experience in the new specialty. Given a greater amount of time, this can also be done while traveling by floating to increasingly more difficult floors. I'm not suggesting going from telemetry to ICU, but instead an assignment in step-down and offering to help in ICU. When I was in Tennessee, I frequently floated to ICU to take the low acuity ICU patients. I was considered a "secondary" ICU nurse, which means that I always had a primary ICU nurse as a resource when needed. Most of the time, this was the charge nurse who helped with things that I wasn't familiar with. The most important factor is not making a big jump, but be aware of smaller jumps that can enhance your resume. Always ask yourself, by taking this float assignment, am I putting the patient in danger?

Better Pay

One of the biggest misunderstandings by hospital staff is that travel nurses are making the big bucks. It's true that our bill rate (what the hospital pays) may be higher than what the other nurses are making, but staff nurses don't always understand that we are not pocketing all of the bill rate.

On average, a smaller to medium company will take 10% to 15% of the bill rate for overhead costs, insurance, benefits, etc. On average, I have found the larger companies take 15% to 20%. And, if you are working through a subcontract, your company is usually pocketing 15% while the vendor is pocketing 5% of the bill rate. Not all staff nurses understand this.

My personal best example of this goes back to Oklahoma City (OKC) and a miscommunication. When I interviewed for the job I was asked, "Have you taken care of post cardiac cath patients?" Needless to say, this ended up being a trick question! Yes, I had taken care of post cardiac cath patients, but all of our patient's came back to the floor with a 2x2 and tegaderm over an angioseal. My first post cardiac cath patient in OKC came back with a green piece of plastic sticking out of his leg. My thought: "This is what a cardiac sheath is." That is when I learned that the patients on this floor came back with sheaths, and it was my job to figure out their ACT and when to pull the sheath, which was totally foreign to me. Upon letting the manager know that I didn't pull sheaths, I was automatically labeled as the travel nurse making the big bucks that got the easy patients (didn't have to pull sheaths). Now, by the end of the contract I learned to pull sheaths, but it was 13 weeks of hell (which didn't make since because I was always willing to be the second RN with my tele/ER background).

Then we get to the discussion of knowing your bill rate and knowing if the travel company is cheating you. There has only been one assignment that I have known my bill rate, and upon doing the calculations, I found that I was making 20% on a subcontracted assignment. I was making 80%, my company was making 15%, and the vendor management system was making 5%... sounded reasonable to me.

Then you look at what the nurses are making. Just from "rumors," I know that the nursing assistants are making what I made at "home" in Idaho as an RN, and the RNs are making what my bill rate is. But, I have all the tax exemptions because I'm a traveling nurse with a tax home. Am I getting a fair deal? Maybe so, maybe no, but the bottom line for me is that my take home for one week is the same as my take home every two weeks back home. Yes, I have housing coming out of that, but I'm also getting an extra non-monetary bonus in the adventure factor.

My point is...don't look at someone else's bottom line. What do you need to live comfortably? What do you need to have monetary wise to make ends meet? The pay is better, but it's not always monetarily... you have to look at your assets in lifestyle.

Regional Food

You know that saying, "When in Rome, do what the Romans do." In travel nursing we have the saying, "When in Italy, eat what the Italians eat." One of the best parts of travel nursing is eating what the locals eat!

This may be the best part of travel nursing...finding where all the good food is! San Francisco is known for their clam chowder and the best chowder, of course, is found in a sourdough bread bowl. There is nothing like a trip down to Pier 49 and having clam chowder in a sourdough bread bowl, but what other kinds of food can you find in the local region?

The Northwest is best known for Seattle's Best Coffee and Starbucks. But what about other local flavors? You are truly missing out if you don't go by Salty's for the best seafood or shopping at Pike's Market for the best local salmon and local clams.

The East is famous for the shrimp burgers that can be found in North Carolina, Brunswick Stew, Boston Baked Beans, and a "dog" from Coney Island.

Florida is best known not only for its key lime pie, but other tropical and swamp favorites such as mango chicken and fried alligator. When in Miami you have to try out the local Cuban restaurants. Fried plantains are the best!

In the south you will find a great combination of fried chicken, mashed potatoes, gravy, and cornbread, along with some fiery Cajun jambalaya, etouffee, and blackened catfish.

The Midwest is known for its homegrown corn and beef. Some of the best barbeque can be found in the Kansas and Missouri regions, along with the best steaks coming out of Nebraska. And if you are in Iowa during the state fair, don't forget to visit the cow made of butter!

A trip to the Southwest will bring you the best in Tex-Mex, chilies, burritos, and other flavors with a kick, which are influenced by our neighbors to the south. In Phoenix, we also found the best in Greek food!

Housing Faux Pas

Life is like a box of chocolates, you just never know what you are going to get. The same with travel nursing housing. In my ten years, I have done everything from a hotel with a refrigerator and microwave, to an extended stay with a kitchenette, to a studio apartment, to a one bedroom apartment, to a 3 bedroom, 2 bath house on the bay. Of course, my favorite was the 3 bedroom, 2 bath house on Tillamook Bay.

There is a big difference in what you need in housing and what you want in housing. In North Dakota, my husband and I survived the winter in a fishing cabin on the lake with a refrigerator and microwave. I had also brought my small 2 person crock pot and we bought a microwave pasta maker, so we were good for the 5 months we spent there. In our 3 bedroom house on Tillamook Bay we not only had the crock pot and microwave, but an fully furnished kitchen with an outdoor grill. Just goes to show you, that housing can be different on every assignment!

This is where communication with your travel company plays an ultimate part in your happiness as a traveling nurse. Did I know about my glorified motel room in North Dakota at the fishing resort? Yes! Did I plan for it…yes! Did I know about my house on the bay on the Oregon Coast? Yes! Did I plan for it…yes!

Housing can take many shapes and sizes. It is your responsibility as a traveling nurse to find out exactly what the company is providing and what is available in that area. With my husband traveling with me, we need something more private, but with single nurses traveling alone, sometimes a sublet or roommate situation is best.

Housing can be found on Craigslist, vrbo.com (vacation rental by owner), or corporatevacationbyowner.com. These are the best sources of rentals if you are doing housing on your own.

Taking the housing that the company offers is also an option. While traveling, I always took the housing that the company offered. This isn't to say that I didn't assist the housing department in finding my own housing (that is how I got the 3 bedroom, 2 bath on the bay on the Oregon Coast).

Now I have realized that the best housing option is a travel trailer! I truly believe that if you are thinking about long-term travel nursing, you really need to think about a home on wheels. Whether it is a small travel trailer for one, a larger one for two, a fifth wheel for the family, or a motor home for the single traveler, RVing is really the way to go for long term traveling. No matter where you are, your home is always in your rear view mirror!

Politics

Politics is the number one reason why nurses turn to travel nursing. In fact, that is the exact reason why I started travel nursing then went back to it 10 years later after a 2-year break. In 2003, I was passed over as a house supervisor related to the fact that they had no one to take my place on the rehab floor. Again in 2013, I was passed up as a director of nursing related to the fact that they had no one to take my place on night shift. Both times they had to replace me, because I quit and went on the road.

As a traveler, you do not have to worry about who is going to get the unit manager position, who is going to be the next house supervisor, or who is going to get the holidays off. If I want the holidays off, then I just make sure that my contract ends on December 15th and schedule my next assignment to begin on January 15th.

The politics of travel nursing include choosing the right company and choosing the right hospital. Every company that you walk with thinks that they are the best company out there. The truth of the matter is, a company that may be right for me, may not be right for you. I don't know of any one company that someone has not had a bad experience with. Same goes with hospitals. The ER maybe wonderful at the hospital, but the Medical floor may be a total terror.

All the testing that goes on is another form of politics along with all the Associations that have come up. We will be talking about these things more in depth (PBDS, BKAT Joint Commission, NATHO).

Going Away

Leaving an assignment can be very difficult also. I'm sure we all have had those assignments that we just clicked in, and have even thought of staying on full time. These are usually the assignments that we end up extending six months or more. For instance, my assignment in Iowa was only 3 months in length related to the fact that they found someone else to take my place as a night nursing supervisor. This assignment was very hard to leave! After all, I had made several friends (thank God for the invention of Facebook now), and the job was very rewarding. I really enjoyed my time there, but in 3 short months that was all gone. I found every excuse to get them to let me stay there, but I also knew that my time there was done.

Oh, and now we have the Facebook Factor! This really has made leaving an assignment easier. My North Dakota assignment was not the best of situations; in fact, it was my second to the worst assignment in my 11-year career. But, the truth is, I made some amazing friends in a not-so-friendly environment. My Northern Iowa assignment was great, and I still keep up with some great friends that I made there.

At times it is very hard to leave, but think of all the friends you have met along the way, and all the friendships that are yet to come.

Obtaining States' Licenses

One nuisance is the time that it takes to get a new license in each state, and then having to decide whether or not to renew that license. What used to take a few hours to fill out and send in now sometimes can take days if you have to work with a police station that only does fingerprints on a certain day, and time consuming if the local place to get photos in thirty miles away. Not tough to do—just time consuming. And then, instead of renewing one license every two to four years, you may have several that need to be renewed, or you may need a new license for the next assignment.

This has become somewhat easier with the creation of the compact licensure system, but not even half of the states are "compact." This is a national coalition of states that recognize each other's licenses. The nurse has to be a resident of a compact state then she can travel to other compact states without having to get a new license. For instance, since my home is in Idaho, my Idaho nursing license is a compact nursing license. When I went to Iowa, Arizona, Tennessee, and Mississippi, there was no need to get a new license; I just gave the hospital a copy of my Idaho license.

I also carry a few other states: California, where I worked for four years and Oklahoma, where my parents live. When it comes to renewal time, I will have three licenses that need to be renewed (CA, OK, and ID). I have also had licenses in Florida, Oregon, and Washington, which I have chosen to let lapse. I'm 3,000 miles away from Florida, so the chances of me renewing that one is remote, but I have really considered renewing my Oregon and Washington license since I live in Idaho.

That is what you need to evaluate. Do you think that you are going to ever work in that state again, and how close is that state to your home? Another major factor is what does it entail to get that license broke back from inactive to active? I've heard stories that California can be a bear to renew, so I would never let that one go. As of current, it is taking up to 6 months to renew a license in California. Also, it's taking very long to get a California license verified for transfer to another state. So, therefore, you would really have to think about the advantages and disadvantages of renewing a California or any other state license. In some states, like Montana, you have to verify EVERY license that you have ever had. California wouldn't be a good license for you to have, since you'd have to get that verified and the board stating that you were a good nurse while practicing in California.

Little or No Orientation

For travel nurses, a change is as good as a vacation, but change can also be traumatic to some nurses, especially the "newbies." Nurses start travel nursing because of the excitement and adventure, and then they have to face the reality of catching on quickly and hitting the floor running.

The ideal traveler needs to be able to follow someone one day and take off on their own the next. At times, nursing orientation is as short as a few hours, while other orientations last for a week.

For instance, in Oklahoma City on the intermediate care unit, I had four hours of computer class and four hours of on-the-floor orientation, and then I was on my own. In Plantation, Florida for the telemetry floor, I had five 8-hour days of orientation, then three days on the floor. Now as a traveling house supervisor I usually have one week to follow the other nurse, one week to split the duties, and one week where I'm on my own with a resource nurse.

In some cases I have had the nursing managers ask me what type of orientation I am used to and go with my style of orientation, but others have their own way of doing things, and that is fine also. Part of being a travel nurse is being a fast learner and going with the flow. You MUST be able to hit the floor running! Personally, I want one day to follow and then let me go, but I know that others would like to have the full three days with someone else.

If you do not feel comfortable after your orientation, you need to talk to your manager about what you don't feel comfortable with, and then learn what you can look for next time to make your orientation go smoother and quicker. Just remember the basics of nursing: assessment, planning, implementation, evaluation, and follow-up.

Moving Every 3 Months

This can be a very ugly problem if you cannot pack lightly. My poor husband...I have to pick on him here. He is a pack rat, and this travel thing has been so stressful on him because he can't find all these "basement bargains" at the thrift store and bring them home. Of course I don't have a problem, since all I bring is all the office stuff and books. Now you know why we had to travel with a cargo trailer at one time! Now we just pack it in the RV. If it doesn't have a place to call home, it doesn't go.

Find out in advance what the apartment is going to come with. Sometimes you will have full linen and kitchen utensils if you are in corporate housing, but if you have an apartment, then these things usually aren't available. That is where the thrift store shopping comes in handy.

Most of the time, though, you will have a dresser, side table, and bed in the bedroom, with a couch and chair in the living room, with a dining room table and chairs in either the dining area or the kitchen. Don't forget to take your vacuum, a television, a microwave, and potholders.

What you pack and whom you travel with can also make a difference. When our son was traveling with us, we tended to travel a little heavy. We not only have the office stuff, but hubby has his "workshop" in the front of the trailer to do small repairs, along with all the son's books and schoolwork supplies. Not to mention the fact that we probably have way too many kitchen and cooking items.

A lot of the travelers I have recently met either drive pickups with lockable shells or sport utility vehicles. It can be done in a car by choosing what you take carefully. Also, I have traveled in my car with a topper on. Pack up the topper with non-breakable items just in case it takes a tumble and then pack with care with all the more fragile goodies. Take a first assignment within a few hundred miles to get a good idea of what you need if you require a test run.

Space savers include space bags and rolling instead of folding items! You can also limit your travel items with the plastic container system. You can have one container for the bathroom (a smaller one), one for the kitchen, one for the living room, and one for the bedroom. If it doesn't fit, it doesn't go!

Moving companies are usually too expensive to help you move every time if you have a family, but it can be feasible to hire someone from a temporary agency to help unload your own trailer or a rental trailer, if need be.

Loneliness on the Road

It was the best of times, it was the worst of times, and it was the loneliness of times. Traveling gives you a lot of experience with different cultures, climates, and personalities, but even with all your acquaintances that you meet on assignment, there are still times when you miss your family and friends.

It doesn't matter whether you travel alone or with a family, loneliness will find you. One of the biggest things is to keep in touch with those that matter to you the most. I miss my family in Oklahoma, but have very strong ties in that I call my parents two or three times a week, and my brother every Tuesday. My husband calls his brothers usually about once a week.

And then there is social media! With the invention of Facebook, MySpace, Skype, Instagram, and Pinterest, we are always meeting up with our friends online! Some of my best moments have been chatting on Skype or Facebook with friends back home in Idaho. It's also become easier and easier to get involved with other travel nursing groups and friends who are in the same area that you are. In fact, Phoenix travelers have their own Facebook page to assist travelers in organizing Meet and Greets.

If you live in an RV, meeting up with other RVers is also very easy to do. The parks in the south have all kinds of things going on. If nothing else, sit outside and read a book. Look up on occasion and tell the walker passing by, "Hello." You just never know what kind of conversation is going to come up next!

Then you can also do things the old fashion way by taking time to get in involved in other activities such as a church, friends of the library, or the neighborhood Bunco game!

Sick Days w/ Charge

Another downside related to money is losing out when you are not feeling so great. Not only do you not get paid for the day that you miss, but some companies even charge you for housing costs, their reason being that they are paying for housing for you to work thirty-six hours a week, and when you don't live up to that obligation, they do not get their money from their hospital bill rate; therefore, they are losing out on income, hence you will lose also.

Some of the smaller companies are starting to let nurses have paid time off and/or vacation pay, but this is a very new concept. Most companies that I have dealt with will require you to make those days up, either during that week or the next week. If a whole week is missed, the days may be added to the end of the contract.

This is one thing that you need to make sure that is clear in your contract. Is there a penalty in there? Once you sign it's a done deal. You miss a day without making it up, remember that you are the one who signed the contract with the terms.

Staff Grudges

Some of the ugliest situations I have seen are staff grudges. Now that you are making all these "big bucks," some regular staff think you need to be assigned the most difficult patients, because travelers are there just for the money anyway.

There is also this misconception in some places that the hospital's bill rate (what they are paying out) is also what the nurses are getting; therefore, I have had some nurses want to know if I really do make fifty dollars an hour. They do not understand about the company getting their share and the travel company paying out for housing and other expenses.

Traveler "hostile" hospitals are out there, but they are few and far between. Some nurses have expressed the fact that they get the tough bed assignments because the staff believes that since the traveler makes more money, they can have the group of patients with persistent nausea, vomiting, diarrhea, the gastro-intestinal bleeds, and the Alzheimer's patients.

I have only been in one hospital where the hospital management wasn't hostile, but the nurses were; and then again, the nurse management was also "relieved of duties" half way through the assignment.

Cancelled Contract

This is one of the biggest fears of a traveling health professional—having a cancelled contract. Unfortunately, this has become a bigger and bigger concern over the last few years. Hospitals hire more travelers than they can afford and end up canceling someone's contract. This is also where you see the biggest difference between a good travel company and a great travel company. This is why it's so important to choose a traveling company and a recruiter that is going to have your back.

The greatest expense to a company that can directly affect you is having a 3-month lease on an apartment. If you are cancelled, then the company still has a place for you to stay for 3 months. The best of travel companies will make every attempt to find you something else within driving distance, but if you are in a smaller city with only one hospital, this can be very difficult if not impossible to do. A great travel company in this case would forgive the rest of the lease, but some of the companies who are all about the money will make every attempt to have you pay for the cancelled lease.

This also puts the traveling health professional out of a job and out of a monetary resource. This can be a dire emergency if you don't have enough in the bank to survive up to a month without a job. I encourage everyone to have at least one-month of reserve, and it is most definitely better if you can save up to 3 months' worth of reserve.

This is also the biggest downside to getting your own housing. Then you are completely responsible for the lease, unless you have a super company that will help you out with the rest of the lease.

On the other hand, this is the biggest advantage of traveling in an RV. Usually your space rent is on a month-to-month basis with no lease; therefore, you just pull the slides in and take off to the next assignment or vacation!

In conclusion

There are many good things, a small amount of bad things, and few ugly things you should know about travel nursing. Your mission, should you choose to accept it, is to make a list of all the good and bad things that you need to consider to further evaluate if this way of life is right for you.

Travel nursing is definitely an adventure. You just have to be tough enough to take a few bumps in the road.

Chapter Five

Location, Corporation, and Documentation

Time to get started looking for your first assignment. In order to have a successful first assignment we must find a great location, the right travel nursing company, the right hospital, and have all of our ducks in a row when it comes to our credentials. This part of travel nursing is very stressful, but it can also be a lot of fun trying to figure out where you want to go and work.

Depending on your specialty the location or the travel company can be picked first. If your specialty is a common one–labor and delivery, ICU, med/surg/tele–then you can pick your travel company first and where you would like to go next. If you are in psych, rehab, or a house supervisor, you are going to have to find the company that has the most jobs at the time, and you will have a narrow field of locations to choose from.

Location

If location is the most important thing to you, you will need to find the travel company that goes where you want to go. Almost all companies now have their jobs posted online. The one thing that you need to watch out for is companies that have posted jobs with a start date of a month ago. Chances are that company doesn't keep their job listings current.

Another way to find a job in a certain area is to call the hospital and talk to human resources. Ask them which companies they use for the travel nursing contracts. Some hospital systems have their own company or use one of the larger companies. Hospital Corporation of America (HCA) has their own travel company, Parallon, and Kaiser Permanente in California uses AMN Healthcare to fulfill their travel nursing needs. When these companies can't fill the jobs themselves, then they will subcontract out to the smaller companies.

The next step is investigating the hospital and community that you are looking at. Search the Internet for more information. Search area chat rooms and do a search on a messaging program for people in that area. The Chamber of Commerce, City Website, and Craigslist are good places to start.

The best place I have found to gain information about a new location is at *www.homefair.com*. It is there that you can find information on a cost-of-living comparison, city report, school reports, crime statistics, moving calculator, choosing the right school, and rental furniture. The first place that I start is with the city report. This will give you a good idea of what to expect regarding crime rate, city size, climate, age demographics, and the major employers. There is also *www.crimemapping.com* and has a list of all the crimes that have occurred in a certain area. Other useful information that you can find at HomeFair is the average rent on an apartment and what to expect in salary from the salary calculator.

Another excellent source for information is on *www.apartments.com*. This is especially useful if you are assisting a company in obtaining your own housing. You can also compare what your company is setting you up into other housing available in that area. You can also check out *www.apartmentratings.com* to see if there is anyone happy with the place. Just remember to read the comments and don't necessarily go by the rating. Another thing to remember is that people who are upset are more likely to post a rating than a person who is happy with the place.

This brings up another critical element in choosing a travel company: look at, and ask about, the type of housing each company provides in the area that you are looking at. A lot can be told about a company by their housing. Are you getting a deluxe company with a deluxe apartment, or are you getting an older shack?

The companies who really care about their nurses know that a nurse will only be happy if they feel comfortable and safe in their surroundings. Get to know your surroundings online before accepting any job assignment!

Find out what amenities are available at the apartment or motel. Do they have a pool or spa? What about a workout or weight room? Do they allow pets, and if so, how much does it cost for a pet deposit?

If you travel in an RV, you definitely will want to find out if there are any RV parks close by that accept long-term visitors. I am finding out now that some of the newer parks will only accept you if your vehicle was made in the last ten years.

I work nights and my husband is disabled; therefore, our two main priorities are a hot tub and a place that is quiet during the day.

If you have a child, you might want to find out about what schools are available or what support systems are available for home-schooled children. I also want to know where the local church is and what kind of teen program they have.

Now that we have a company and an area that we would like to go to, the next critical step is to investigate and interview the hospital.

Ask yourself, "What type of hospital am I looking for?" Do you prefer a large hospital, a teaching hospital, or a smaller community hospital? Or...does size really matter?

Are you looking to go to a specific region in the country? Make a list of what you are looking for in a hospital. Even though I came from a small hospital, I really enjoyed my time at the level one trauma center that I worked at in Phoenix, Arizona.

Yes, I definitely was more stressed out, but I was treated as a name and not a number. I had a large support system there, which helped out also. Most importantly, I learned that although I prefer a smaller facility, I should not be afraid of a larger facility.

Get out another piece of paper and take notes on your hospital interviews. Keep the notes of all your interviews together in a folder or on a clipboard. If a nurse manager brings up something that you hadn't thought of, add that to your list.

Always know the exact location of the hospital. Know what area of town the hospital is in. Then use that information to check out the crime rate of the hospital area.

I might consider working in a higher crime rate area, but I would not want to live there. Do you have a "high crime" plan of action? My husband would definitely be taking me to work and picking me up. I would much prefer to work in an area of low crime, but the amenities of a bigger hospital and town might be worth the 13-week assignment.

For example, I looked at going to a suburb of Los Angeles back in 2004. This was after I had spent 13 weeks in Phoenix. No, I wasn't too thrilled about staying and working in a place like that, but the amenities were the reason I would spend 13 weeks there. I would love to take my son to all the sights around Los Angeles, such as Disneyland and

Universal Studios. Now fast forward 10 years, and here I am in the "Inland Empire," just outside of Los Angeles and having a great time going to the horse races at Santa Anita, spending days off at the beach in Capistrano, and taking a balloon trip over wine country in Temecula.

What system do I use? I call it my "Glendale" system! While working in Northern Phoenix, I lived in the Glendale area. This was about as much crime as I would ever want to get into. So, when I'm looking at a place to go, I always compare it to the Glendale, Arizona crime rate. Maybe you would want to use your hometown as a measure.

Corporation

How big is the unit will you be working on? How many nurses are on duty? What is the nurse-to-patient ratio? Depending on the number of patient and nurses, the charge nurse is required also to take patients. This affects the amount of time they are going to have to assist you if needed. Do they have licensed vocational/practical nurses and/or certified nursing assistants? It makes a big difference if you are a registered nurse and not only have all of your patients to take care of but you also have to take care of all the intravenous medications of another nurse.

Think of unit specific questions also. In the intensive care unit you might want to know the average number of ventilators, how many surgical patients, how many medical patients, or how many cardiac patients are there on a "usual" day.

As an emergency room nurse, I would want to know if nursing or respiratory therapy does the electrocardiograms. I want to know if I have an emergency room tech to assist me with dressings and splints. Am I responsible for my lab draws, or do the lab techs come to the emergency room and draw?

In this technology and information age you might want to know what kind of charting is done. Do they chart on paper or on the computer? Most hospitals have gone to computer charting, but in 2013, I did work for a hospital that still used paper charting!

What type of computer program do they use? Cerner? Epic? Meditech? Paragon? Do they have care plan problem charting or subjective, objective, assessment, and plan (S.O.A.P.) charting?

What about the medication system? Do they have a computerized system like a Pyxis? Accudose? How do I obtain medications "after hours"? The time it takes for you to get that medication may be a little slower if you have to have the house supervisor get the medication, or if the hospital has a 24-hour pharmacist available.

One of the most important questions to as is, "How often do the nurses float and what area would you be expected to float to?" Tell them up front if there are any floors that you would not be willing to work on. Be aware also if you are an ICU nurse, the latest trend is for hospitals to hire ICU nurses that can and will float to ALL areas of the hospital. You will not be an ICU nurse, but you will be a FLOAT nurse.

Next you will need to know about meals. This is especially true if you work nights. At the small hospitals, the night shift is usually responsible for bringing their own supper, but in one place where I worked the night shift received their meals free. Plates of food were left in the refrigerator and we just warmed them up in the microwave at break time. At the larger facility I worked at, the cafeteria was open for an hour or two.

The next thing that I can think of to ask would be about special uniforms or the color of uniforms. I worked in one nursing home where the nursing assistants wore colors and the medication nurses wore a different color. The charge nurses could wear colored pants, but we had to always wear white tops, because the elderly associated "white" with a professional nurse.

Next, you might want to ask about the town, although you should have done some homework on the town already. What is the population? Do they have a seasonal fluctuation? In central California, I worked in a small city in which they had a great influx during the harvest season. During that time of the year it was also very difficult to find a place to live.

What is the average temperature for the time that you are going to be there? Do they have four actual temperature ranges and seasons, or just hot, hotter, hell, and whew, I can breath again! Is it cold, colder, polar bear, and then a few months of defrost? Personally, I'm trying to get this snowbird thing worked out… north in the summer and south in the winter!

What about natural disasters? How many major earthquakes have occurred in the past few years? How many tornadoes or hurricanes? How many times does the creek rise to flood stage? I arrived in Central California the first of November, and during my 13-week contract we had the December 22nd Paso Robles earthquake, then I had a repeat adventure the first of May 2014 with the 5.1 in Habla, CA. I landed in

Fort Lauderdale on October 23rd and Wilma landed there October 24th. Although I did miss the Tornado near Nashville, TN by a month, and a tornado in Iowa by 75 miles; therefore, I'm probably not the best to give advice on diverting away from natural disasters. Oh yeah, and don't ask why Seattle's worst snowstorm ever was when I was on assignment in Puyallup, WA! HA!

Documentation

Out of all the sections that you will read in this book, this is THE MOST IMPORTANT ONE!!! I cannot stress enough to read, read, and then read again this section until you have it down. This could be the difference between a great contract and a disaster!!!

You've talked to the hospital, and now you are ready to head off to your new destination. Our recruiter talks to the hospital and the deal is done on their end, but what about the deal on your end?

This is where things get fun. This lovely document, my friend, is called a "contract" or an "agreement." Everything is settled upon verbally, and then the contract is drawn up and sent to you. Your first assignment before you get to your destination is to read the fine print of the document that will dictate what your career will be like for the next 13 weeks.

Negotiations with the recruiter can sometimes be a tedious job, but every detail must be dealt with. Your first indication might be to think, "We discussed everything, and it's in there." NO! I guarantee you that the first time you do that will be the last time that you do that. I have yet to have a contract that I didn't need to add something to.

Sit down in a quiet place and read your contract, word for word and between the lines. If there is any part that you do not agree with, or have questions about, do *not* sign it until those questions have been answered.

If you have a vacation planned, or if you need certain days off, make sure that you get those dates in writing. It has been my experience that if it is not in writing you may have to just live with the consequences. If it *is* in writing, you are guaranteed those days off.

When you open up your new-hire packet you will find several pages of legal jargon that states that you are going to a hospital or facility to work for a certain amount of time for a certain dollar amount. It says that you are going to act like a professional and that the client-hospital and your travel company are going to treat you like a professional.

The employment relationship is the legal arrangement of the contract. As a staff nurse, you were used to being an "at-will" employee, which means that your continued employment was at the discretion of you and the hospital. As a travel nurse, you will become a "contracted at-will employee." Yes, they can still let you go, but as a contracted employee they are obligated to compensate you for breech of contract.

Another type of relationship between nurse, hospital and agency is called "match-hire," in which the nurse is matched to the hospital, but the nurse is paid directly by the hospital. In this situation, the agency matches you to the hospital. The hospital not only gives you a regular paycheck, but they give the agency a preset dollar amount for your services. Be careful of this situation, because benefits can be very tricky here. The agency can't give you certain benefits because you don't get a regular paycheck from them, and the hospital doesn't give you benefits because you aren't a full-time employee. This situation can cause further confusion between nurse and travel agency when it comes to longevity benefits.

We should all know our professional responsibilities, but because some nurses do not act professionally at all times, those paragraphs have to be added. This part of the contract states that if you cannot show up for your assignment, then you need to call at least two hours before your shift starts. This section also draws the lines of when you, in effect, "voluntarily quit." Although some companies allow for a "lenient" day, most of the time, if you do not show up for the first day, they consider that a voluntary quit. As a protection to the travel company, a clause is added that states that if you act in a careless manner that affects patients or the client hospital, you can and will be turned into the local authorities and state nursing board.

The professional responsibility section is also where you agree to follow the standards set up by the Joint Commission Accreditation of Hospitals Organization (JCAHO), the Occupational Health & Safety Organization (OSHA), and the Nurse Practice Act. This section also includes the fact that you must keep your credentials and licenses that are required for the assignment current. These include documentation that might be needed relating to your nursing qualifications, including ACLS, PALS, TNCC, and State Licenses.

Next you will find your start date, the end date, the facility to which you are assigned, your shift, your on-call time, and your flexibility or floating capabilities. This section might also include whether or not you have guaranteed hours. Make sure that this section is filled out the way you want it! Especially your guaranteed hours and/or the number of days that they can cancel you per contract/per week.

If you do not want to float or do not want to be put on call, then make sure that is put into writing. If you do not feel comfortable floating to a certain floor, like O.B. or O.R., then state that in your contract. When reviewing this section of your contract, you must also be mindful that part of a travel nurse's job is to be flexible. This is *your* contract, and you must protect yourself!

Your travel arrangements and lodging arrangements should be next. Listed here will be your permanent home address, and even your temporary address. If applicable, your travel housing stipend amount should also be listed here.

When it comes to your work salary and housing, get everything in writing, and don't ever take anything for granted. If there are days off that you want guaranteed, ask for them in your contract. If floating is a possibility, specify the situations that you will not float; as in the fact that, "I don't feel comfortable in ICU or OB," so you put in your contracts that you will not float to ICU or OB. If you want every weekend on or every weekend off or you're willing to work every other weekend, specify that in your contract if that matters to you. Put it in writing whether you wish to work overtime or not.

If there is to be any deduction in pay related to a missed shift that should also be included. If you are put on call, these deductions should not apply. Make sure that the on-call stipulations are there in the contract.

Included also might be what you are to be paid for a per diem rate. This rate is a fixed rate that is paid to you for food, parking, and other ancillary expenses that you will incur while away from your home state. As of writing this chapter, the maximum allowed by the government is no more than $30 per day. Taxes should be taken out of your hourly rate, but not out of your per diem rate. Companies most often call this a "tax-advantage" program. You will file your taxes in your home state, and will get back most of the money that you paid into another state, but also expect to pay into your own state taxes.

It will also indicate what is included in your housing arrangements. With some companies you will pay for cable and local phone, most of them will not pay for those extra utilities. But then again, everything is negotiable in this business!

You cannot get paid unless you turn in your time slips. These time slips are usually faxed to the company that you are contracted with. Some companies have you also mail the original to them, while other companies have you give a copy to the nursing manager. If a company wants certain information on this form, it is also included in this part of the contract.

The last part of the contract might include more legal jargon about benefits, injury on the job, alcohol use, illegal drug use, and the confidentiality clause. All of these important items are included in your contract to protect both you and the company.

In fact, that is the sole purpose of any contract that you have with any company: it is to protect you, the employee, and the company. In this business, verbal agreements mean nothing. Have you ever watched those court shows in the afternoon? *Always,* the judge wants to know if you had it in writing. If it isn't in writing, you just lost. A nice recruiter may be a pleasure to work with, but just remember that they are working for the money they get from handling your contract. Remember, they are no more than nursing salespeople.

And You're Off!

After you have picked out the hospital and travel company you need to prepare for the next assignment. The company will send you another employee packet with many official forms that need to be filled out: forms required by the Occupational Health and Safety Authority, the Internal Revenue Service, and other miscellaneous company forms.

You then need to make sure that your living arrangements and transportation arrangements are all squared away. The travel company usually makes flight arrangements, but you need to also arrange for your personal items to get there. Can you get everything in three suitcases? Some things may have to be shipped by UPS or by a moving company. However, having things moved by a moving company can take away a lot of extra money.

Travel nurses are some of the best shoppers at thrift stores! Take only the bare necessities and then go shopping when you get to your new assignment. If you are going to be living at an apartment complex and do not mind used stuff, watch for what is left beside the dumpsters.

Many treasures have been found there. Not that the items are "bad," but when others move from these complexes you would be amazed at what they leave behind. Just like you, others do not want to drag around stuff, so they leave it behind.

On my first assignment my husband and I found a vacuum cleaner and a futon bed. The lady who put them there came out of her apartment just about that time and asked us if we also wanted her television cabinet. Wow! The cabinet turned out to be a corner television cabinet made out of oak, with room for my son's video games below.

After making the thrift store rounds, *then* go to a discount store to purchase the rest of your necessities. When you leave, take the important and/or expensive stuff with you as much as possible, sell what you can, take it back to the thrift store for tax credit, or set it back out at the dumpsters for the next traveler.

If you are moving to an extended stay or motel, things are much easier. They usually have pots, pans, and dishes. If not, go back to the thrift store and get a small and a large pot to cook with, and one or two dishes and cups. Do not forget to also get a microwave-safe cooking dish. Before you leave, make sure that your recruiter or housing supervisor tells you exactly what "furnished" will mean for that assignment.

If you are staying at a hotel or extended stay, a necessity is definitely a slow cooker. They will usually have a microwave already in place at the motel or extended stay. With a microwave and slow cooker, you can have hot meals ready when you come home from work.

If you're dragging or driving your home with you, you do not have as many things to "pack up," but you need to load the RV with the necessities before you add your other wants and needs of comfort. Included in your RV, you do not want to forget your coffee maker and slow cooker. It has also been my experience that we ladies cannot forget a bag—or two, or three—with our craft and sewing items. I have even been to a few travel trailers with sewing machines right next to their computer on the "dining" room table. Scrap-booking materials are also necessary for some travel nurses.

Be sure to pack your necessary nursing documents, such as your last tuberculosis test, your hepatitis C immunization records, and any other immunization records that your company required you to list on the forms that you sent in. Even though you probably sent them a copy, always have them available.

Pack at least copies of your certificates, and carry your nursing license with you at all times. Be prepared to produce any other documents that human resources may ask for.

Be sure to call the place where you are supposed to stay and inquire as to whether all the necessary arrangements have been made. There is nothing worse than getting to a place and have them say, "We weren't expecting you." Make sure that the landlord of the apartment complex knows when you are expected to arrive, and arrange a tentative time to meet with him/her. I cannot stress enough the importance of getting all your housing arrangements guaranteed before you get to your assignment. This is where the great recruiter part comes in! Oh, and do not forget that wonderful recruiter's phone number.

Chapter Six

The Nitty Gritty About Taxes

One of the most challenging aspects of traveling will be the tax issues that you will encounter when filing your annual returns and navigating the laws that apply to travel reimbursements. At the time of this publication, there were over 20 healthcare staffing agencies under IRS audit and many others in industries that employ mobile professionals. There are many travelers who have had their returns examined as a part of the evidence gathering that the IRS performs when probing corporate travel reimbursement programs. Some agencies under audit have all the personnel files of travelers placed in an area accessible to IRS agents so they can randomly examine documents regarding tax home status, agency policies, pay rates and reimbursements. To add fuel to the fire, the average recruiter has no idea how the tax laws apply to travel reimbursements and many travelers, who are equally clueless, unknowingly violate the regulations. And of course, there are a fair percentage of travelers that purposely flaunt the rules to their advantage by misrepresenting their status to the staffing agency, encouraging others to do the same. Every industry has its bad apples, but since much of healthcare staffing compensation involves tax-free reimbursements in a multistate context, the burden of tax compliance is weightier.

Tax Home and Permanent Residence Rules

Why is this so important?

Travel reimbursements, which consist of lodging/housing, meals and transportation, can be excluded from taxable compensation (tax fee). The average traveler working a full year of contracts saves between 6 and 9 thousand dollars in taxes when they have a legitimate tax residence. When you multiply that by the number of travelers, the value of conceded tax revenue is eye popping. Not to mention, the pay savings the agencies enjoy, as there are no employment taxes assessed reimbursements as opposed to wages. To receive travel reimbursements (lodging, transportation and meals) on a tax-free basis, you must be working temporarily away from your *tax residence*. This is where most people begin to misinterpret the rules, as a tax residence and a permanent residence are not the same thing although they are often the same place.

Permanent Home, Permanent Residence, Domicile

A permanent home or a permanent residence is your legal home. It is often called a domicile, which is distinguished from "residence" as one can maintain two homes. One can have two residences, but only one *domicile*. It is also the place that a person intends to return to after a temporary absence. A permanent residence is determined by the legal ties one has to an area. A driver's license, car registration, voter registration, resident professional practice license and to a lesser degree, church memberships, mailing address and bank accounts. These connections all point to a permanent residence in a state and more particularly, a specific community. However, none of these ties together rise to the level of a tax residence.

Tax Residence, Tax Home

A tax residence or tax home is one's Economic Home, and the tax regulations define a tax home as one's principal place of income/business. In other words, it is the general area in which the taxpayer earns the majority of their income on a year-to-year basis. One can have a permanent residence in one place and a tax home in another. If they drive 100 miles to a permanent job, then their tax home is the area of the job, not their personal residence. A good example is a professional sports player. If they play for the San Francisco Giants and have their house, spouse and kids in Atlanta, then their tax home is San Francisco. When traveling to Atlanta on road games, they are working away from their tax home despite the fact that they sleep in their own bed at their permanent residence. The expenses incurred for transportation, lodging and meals are still deductible since they are incurred in Atlanta, for business away from the tax residence.

Determining the Tax Residence

Since a tax residence is defined by one's principal place of income/

nining the location of one's tax home is relatively simple . If they have one permanent job, then that is their tax e they live is a personal choice regardless of distance b site. There are no deductions for simply commuting ardless of distance. Some people may have two or more ncurrent jobs or work seasonally in one place while maintaining a regular job at home. Nothing really changes as far as determining the tax residence. Just follow the money/income. IRS publication 463, pages 2-6, has a general discussion on this and is helpful since it uses examples drawn from tax court cases.

But what about travelers? True travelers have NO principal place of income. They mobilize from job to job and do not stay in the same metropolitan area when they take on another assignment. Note the term "mobilize"—travelers are not "moving" as they are working *away from home*. They may extend their assignments, but they do not work longer than a year in one area. This is an important distinction and even shows up when travelers are stopped for speeding. If the officer sees out of state license plates and you say that you have "moved", then the officer may issue a citation or a "fix it ticket" requiring you to re-register your car and change your driver's license to the work state. Not a nice way to spend an assignment. To actually fix this, you would need to go before the judge and show them your temporary contract etc.

The Exception to the Tax Home Rule

For individuals who have no principal place of income there is an exception to the tax home rule that applies to many travelers and other mobile professionals. Navigating this *exception* can be like working through an ACLS algorithm. A traveler needs to stay within the specific bounds of this exception as their actions can inadvertently place them back under the tax home rule without prospective planning.

The exception works like this: for those who do not have a primary place of income, whose job locations are constantly changing and only temporary; the Tax Residence is allowed to default to the Primary/ Permanent Residence/Domicile. For this to work, it requires the traveler to satisfy 2 out of 3 of the following criteria:

1) Have significant income at home
2) Have substantial expenses maintaining their dwelling that are *duplicated* when they work away from home on a temporary job. Duplicated in that they incur expenses to maintain their primary residence and have expenses for the lodging at the

assignment. (Note that the goal of these rules are to mitigate the duplicated living expenses of one who is required to travel away from their home to perform their job duties.)

3) Have not abandoned their traditional place of lodging and working—they have family members at the residence (lineal or spouse) or use the residence frequently for lodging.

Most travelers do not work at home, and in healthcare, it is almost impossible to maintain a job that you work so infrequently. Some do, but the balance of travelers satisfy the requirements through criteria two and three.

Expenses keeping a home

Notice that the exception requires expenses to maintain a home. A *home* is not a storage unit, a mailing address, where your friends are etc. It is a home you own or have a mortgage; an apartment you rent; or an alternate arrangement with a friend/family member. If rent is paid to a related party (family member), then the arrangement must look, smell and taste like rent and not be a "stick house." A rental arrangement with a family member should consist of rent paid at fair market rental value or a detailed split of the expenses required to maintain the residence. It should also be memorialized on a written contract and there should be a financial paper trial to follow. Finally, rental income is taxable so the person you are paying rent to has an obligation to report the income on their tax return unless you are sharing the expenses evenly with other adults. Determining fair market rental value of a residence is easily done via classifieds, Craigslist, or some other third party reference.

Abandonment

This is a highly subjective criteria, however there are some important parts of this to grasp. First, a traveler who never returns home despite spending millions to maintain their home has basically abandoned their home. We like to see our clients at home 30 days or more a year, and it doesn't matter whether that is all at once or scattered through the year. Some agencies even require travelers to return home 45 straight days after two years of traveling. That requirement is not an IRS rule; it is simply a way in which the agency seeks to stay compliant with the rules. An agency can establish stricter policies than the minimum set forth by the IRS if they wish.

When a traveler quits their main job, moves a considerable distance from the old area and then begins to travel, it poses an audit risk as it can potentially weaken the taxpayers argument that they maintain a tax residence. Once the traveler has left their old place of work, there is nothing established at the new place. For example, say a traveler has worked in Baltimore for the last 3 years at a permanent job, and then moves to their parents in Colombia, Missouri and begins to travel. They have nothing to abandon in Columbia, because they have no recent history of work/residence in the area prior to traveling. There is nothing established, hence, nothing to abandon. This can be remedied by taking a job in the area of the new home for a short period of time (like a fully taxable, local travel assignment) and establishing an income base.

The Agency Role

Staffing agencies are required to screen a traveler's tax home status before paying tax-free allowances for lodging, meals and transportation. This is often done though a tax home statement or some document in which the traveler is required to attest to their status. Do not confuse the agency requirements with your own obligations to the IRS. An employer has a lower threshold of compliance than the individual traveler and many travelers have learned the hard way in audits. Just because it's cool with the agency does mean it passes the smell test with the IRS. We will see an example of this shortly.

Illustration

To illustrate the exception to the tax home rule, suppose Jane lives in an apartment that she is renting while working in Phoenix. She travels to a three day trauma conference in Denver. While she is away from home in Denver, she will satisfy all three factors of the tax home exception. She will return to her job, she continues to maintain her apartment and she has not abandoned the Phoenix area. All of her expenses for transit, lodging and meals are deductible OR reimbursable by her employer since she is away from home on business.

While she is in Denver, she meets a recruiter for a travel nursing agency who convinces her to travel. Jane gives up her job but does not relinquish her apartment. She signs a three-month contract and mobilizes to the Denver facility. She has the same transit, lodging and meal expenses, but since she satisfies two out of three of the criteria to default the tax home to the permanent residence, her expenses continue to be deductible or reimbursable by the agency.

Let's take this one step further. Suppose Jane gives up her job and her apartment and then moves into her parents' home in Phoenix before mobilizing to Denver. She does not pay rent. satisfies one of the three criteria and only has a perm in Phoenix—not a tax residence. In this case, ALL rei transportation, lodging, meals, and even the value of housing are taxable as wages. The fact that the agenc housing does not change this—it is constructive receipt of income property for services. Jane has one alternative. She could maintain a PRN or seasonal job at home. If the income is significant, she could still maintain a tax residence by satisfying criteria one and three of the exception provision.

Limitations

One-Year Rule

A traveler must be working "temporarily" away from their tax home to receive tax-free allowances for lodging, transit, and meals. The term "temporary" is defined as any assignment that does not last longer than one year in the same area. This is a prospective concept. If one has already worked in the same area for 10 months and signs a three-month extension, the moment the new contract is signed, the traveler has committed to 13 months of service. At the signing of the extension, the tax home shifts to the work location and all tax free reimbursements become taxable from that point forward..

Short breaks at home do not restart the clock since there is continuous income in the same area. This is another area where agency policy and a traveler's obligation are different. When approaching one year of service in a particular geographical area, the IRS's internal guidelines require a minimum 7-month break between 12-month stints, preferably a 12-month break. Our guideline for clients is to never spend more than 12 out of 24 months in the same area. The rationale for this is simple—a tax home is one's principal place of income and when maintaining tax residence under the exception provision, frequent, repetitive engagements in the same area will back a traveler out of the exception and into the rule since there is an identifiable principal place of income. Annual returns to the same city/area can cause the same issue unless there is income at home to offset the income at the frequently visited city. Many agencies impose a 30-day, 3-month, or some other break in service rule before allowing a traveler to return to the same area after 12 months of service and continue in travel status. An agency can establish such a policy and, so long as it is followed, the IRS will not ally take issue with it; however, the agency is not the IRS and is expected to police your tax status. Just because the agency imposes 3-month break in service does allow the traveler to do the same if they intend to protect their tax home status. Whenever in doubt, consulting with a tax professional dealing with mobile professionals is imperative.

50-mile rules and other myths about being away from home

Some agencies toss around a 50 mile rule or some other mileage benchmark to determine if a traveler is far enough away from the assignment to receive tax free allowances for lodging. Unfortunately, there is no such rule. The time tested rule determining *away from home* travel that has been applied in tax court cases is the *overnight stay* rule. The assignment must be far enough away to require one to get rest or sleep at the assignment location to fulfill their duties. Logically, why should one receive a tax-free lodging allowance without incurring lodging expenses away from home? This is why truckers who sleep in their cab cannot be paid tax-free per diems for lodging. The same rule holds for meals. Everyone needs to eat so an expense for food is implied; however, to receive a tax-free meal per diem, one must still be away from home overnight.

Renting your residence while traveling

If a traveler rents their residence to another party, they have converted the home to a business property. It does not necessarily matter that the rent only covers the mortgage—it is the use of the home that is in focus. Accordingly, one can partially rent their home keeping a bedroom for themselves or rent it on a vacation basis to a tenant and still keep the dwelling as a tax residence. One can also have family members in the dwelling that share in the expenses. The point is whether you use the home as your place of lodging.

Storage Units

Even though some storage units are gated communities, they, along with vacant land, empty mobile home pads, etc., are not residences. Having a storage unit just means you have too much stuff.

RV as a residence

Using an RV as a second residence is a great way to travel, however, a traveler is still obligated to duplicate lodging expenses and be away from home overnight. A traveler whose only home is an RV and who takes the RV to the assignment is not *away from home*. The home is going with them. As noted above, an empty pad for an RV or mobile home is not a residence.

Facts and Circumstances

One thing to note about the 3 criteria used for the exception provision. If an individual meets all 3 criteria, the the IRS presumes the tax residence is where the taxpayer lives and keeps a home. If they only meet 2 of the 3 requirements, they are still subjected a "facts and circumstances" review if they are audited. This is why it is important to keep all permanent residence ties consistent with the area that the traveler calls home. For example, if a traveler spends $500 a month to maintain a home in Denver, but has their drivers license in Washington and their car registration/tags in Iowa and voter registration in Texas, it begs the question of whether the traveler really has a home. In these cases, the IRS may consider the traveler an "itinerant." This is the label the IRS and courts use for someone whose tax home is like a backpack, going wherever the taxpayer works. Again, careful planning and the advise of a tax professional that is knowledgeable in the area of tax homes is imperative.

Multi State Tax

While the discussion on tax residence has probably sent you to the ibuprofen, the really pesky task is your state filings. Outside of rare exceptions, you will file a return for your home state and every state that you work in. It does not matter that you did not earn any income in your home state as your domicile/permanent residence state determines where you file your home state return. The mechanics of state tax filings are relatively simple but it requires planning to avoid traps that are common to travelers, especially those domiciled in high tax states.

Your home state will tax ALL income earned anywhere regardless of where it was earned. The state you work in will also tax the earnings within its borders. Fortunately, to offset any double tax, the home state will credit you for the taxes paid to the work state. If the home state has a higher tax rate than the work state, you will have to make up the difference. If the work state has a higher tax rate that the home state, you will have no additional tax to pay to the home state even though you will still report the income on the home state return.

There are a number of states with no income tax. This does not exempt residents of these states from paying taxes to states that have an income tax and neither does the reverse apply. The states without an income tax are Alaska, Nevada, Washington, South Dakota, Texas, Tennessee, New Hampshire, and Florida. DC cannot tax a non-resident and the Virgin Islands collects tax through an allocation with the IRS– these jurisdictions function like a state without an income tax

There are some exceptions to this rule most of which involve border states that consider income earned by a border state resident to be treated as if it was earned in their resident state. The other exception is a weird compact between Indiana, Virginia, California, Arizona and Oregon. Basically, the formula for multistate tax is reversed. The non-resident state gives a credit for taxes paid to the home state on the same income. For example, an Indiana resident that works in California will claim a credit against California tax for the amount paid to Indiana on the same income.

Some states like PA, IN, and OH impose a tertiary tax for municipalities, school districts, or cities. Of these three, the worst two are OH and IN. When a PA resident pays more tax to the work state than they pay to PA, they are allowed to take the excess credit to the municipal level to offset the local income tax. Not so with OH and IN. The only way to offset OH municipal income taxes is by working in another area that has a municipal tax. Indiana has a county piggyback tax that can only be offset by working in an area that imposes a local tax as well. Maryland has a similar arrangement which is currently being challenged in court.

Travelers from states with high income tax rates, those from states with municipal income taxes, and those who work in states without an income tax often wind up with large amounts due at tax filing. It is not wise to wait till year-end to pay these taxes. Tax agencies expect a taxpayer to pay at least 90% of their tax obligations as they earn the income, not at year-end. When 90% is not paid, the jurisdiction will impose an "underpayment" penalty or interest just like a credit card late fee changed when a cardholder does not make their monthly payment. To avoid this, the traveler should make estimated payments through the year to their home state or see if the agency payroll operations can handle a second state of withholding. Agencies are only obligated to report and withhold for the work state and many payroll platforms cannot handle more than one designated state. However, it never hurts to ask the agency if they can do this if a traveler is domiciled in a state with a higher tax..

Residency Issues

Filing the correct residency status on the tax return is extremely important. A traveler should always file as a resident of their home state and a non-resident in the work state. Many tax preparers and travelers attempting to do their own returns file as part year residents where they work, caring more for the refund than the accuracy of the return. This creates major problems with nurses holding compact licenses, as a home state filing is often required as a part of the renewal process. All tax filings produce paper trails and having random residency filings can create a big headache and trigger state audits.

All that is needed for states to pursue residency audits is a driver's license, car registration or professional license. Many mobile professionals get disturbing letters from state tax offices asserting residency tax assessments due to legal ties that were mistakenly established in work states while on assignment. NEVER change your driver's license, car registration or voter registration. They should all stay at your permanent resident state.

Lastly, many states now cross reference professional practice licenses with tax return filings. About 4 years ago our office contacted all state nursing boards and state revenue agencies asking whether they cross referenced data from each other–almost all said they could and many said they did it as a regular practice.

Deductions, Per Diems, and Paychecks

No discussion on taxes is complete without a review of the tax free reimbursements for travel expenses that many travelers receive. As mentioned earlier, the starting point for this discussion begins with the tax home status of the traveler. If you do not have a tax home, then everything provided by the agency is taxable. The goal is then to minimize the tax burden by taking the taxable stipend and finding housing that is cheaper. Otherwise, when the agency supplies the housing, the taxes paid on the value of the housing come out of the rest of the compensation.

For those that have a tax residence the discussion that follows applies.

Reimbursements

An employer can reimburse for business expenses that the employee could otherwise deduct on their tax return. For staffing agencies, travel reimbursements are the largest source of reimbursements. Most contracts are broken down between taxable wages and allowances for housing, meals and transportation. Lodging and meals are often reimbursed under what is known as a "per diem basis." Per diems are very confusing to those that have never encountered them. Basically, per diems are substitute for receipts. The Federal government maintains a listing of standard allowances for lodging and meals broken down by specific geographic location. These amounts are the maximum that an employer can provide to an employee without an exchange of receipts, so long as the employer has performed their due diligence in screening the employee's tax home status and have a reasonable belief that the employee will incur the expenses to perform their duties. Since the amounts that are published are a substitute for receipts, the fact that the employee spends less than the allowance is ignored. In other words, you keep the difference between the allowance and what you spend. Sound too good to be true? Talk to any trucker and they will tell you that they find the cheapest accommodations to maximize the value of their lodging per diems.

Expenses in excess of reimbursements

Since the reimbursements you receive are broken down by category, whenever your expenses in a particular category exceed the reimbursement, you have deductible expenses. Lodging is almost always covered (and then some) under a per diem method and as we mentioned, the excess is not taxed as the per diem provided functions as the receipt. For meals, you can use the Federal per diem rate. When the published rate exceeds the meal reimbursement, you can deduct the difference. The same applies to travel pay, and since most travel pay is a capped amount, many travelers have deductible transportation expenses.

Short list of deductions

Travelers can deduct the following assuming the tax home requirements are satisfied: transportation, lodging, and meal expenses mobilizing to the assignment less travel pay; expenses for meals, reasonable local business transportation, and lodging at the assignment less reimbursements (remember that lodging per diems are their own receipt); and finally, the expenses returning home or to the next assignment. There are other costs such as shipping, tolls, etc. that are allowed as well. A traveler can also deduct trips home during an assignment or between extensions, but these deductions ca what they would otherwise deduct had they stayed at the location. One thing to note—if an agency pays a per diem/ stipend and does not specify an allocation between lodging a the payment is deemed to be 60% for lodging and 40% for meals. The reason for this is that meal reimbursements are only 50% deductible and the employer cannot arbitrarily assign all per diem to lodging. The IRS views per diems as a combination of lodging and meal payments unless the lodging is paid dollar for dollar or provided directly. In that case, a meal allowance is optional.

How agencies construct their pay

When agencies assemble a contract, they always start at the bill rate they receive from the hospital/facility client. The proceeds from this bill rate are then divided between an admin fee (about 20–25%) to cover costs/profit, taxable wages and reimbursements. This creates a tight matrix. When more is paid in reimbursements, taxable wages and/or profit must give etc. Some agency business models seek the lowest taxable wage possible and the highest per diems to make the contract more valuable to the traveler and save the agency payroll taxes. Some travelers have contracts paying $8–10 and hour as a result. On the other end of the spectrum, there are agencies that pay only for the actual cost of housing and a high taxable hourly rate. The majority function in the middle of these extremes.

Some travelers mistakenly believe that an agency is bound by the published per diem rates, or even more incredulous, they think that per diem payments come from a mysterious government subsidy for healthcare travelers. As mentioned earlier, per diem rates are the MAXIMUM that an agency can pay without receipts—it is not the standard or the minimum. An agency can provide anything up to the published rate or nothing at all. This is important when you are negotiating a contract as tax-free allowances are worth more bottom line than a taxable wage, however, there comes a point when the rate is too low to be acceptable.

For the average traveler, a tax free dollar is worth around $1.40 based on a 15% Federal tax bracket, 5% state rate and 7.65% FICA/Medicare tax. This value rises with higher incomes and tax brackets so it can only be determined accurately when using expected income for the year and actual tax on that income. A tax-free dollar is worth more because taxes reduce the net take home amount and $1.40 represents

..at one would have to make before taxes to have $1. This value is a good tool to use when comparing contracts, and since a tax-free dollar varies in value for different wages, consulting with a tax advisor may help make the comparisons more accurate.

Caution on low wages

One may walk away from this discussion thinking that the best contract is one with the lowest taxable wage and the largest per diem; however, the lower the wage, the more risky the terrain. The fact that a professional nurse is getting $12 an hour is not the litmus test of a bad contract or agency, but it certainly draws a lot of attention from the IRS and state labor departments, especially when the agency allows their recruiters wide discretion as to the final wage. To illustrate, say Agency X has 4 nurses working in the same area of the same hospital. Nurse A gets 20 taxable/20 non-taxable, Nurse B gets 15 taxable/25 non-taxable, Nurse C gets 25 taxable/15 non-taxable and Nurse D gets 10 taxable/30 non-taxable (per diems are not supposed to be paid as wages but we will use this for illustration). Everyone is being paid $40/hr. All changes in wages are directly proportional or traceable to the change in the taxable wage. The IRS calls this wage recharacterization—the practice of shifting a taxable dollar to a non-taxable reimbursement. Realistically, this goes on behind the scenes prospectively before a contract is presented to the traveler; however, this cannot become the substance of the negotiations where a traveler is offered a choice between a dollar of taxable wages and a dollar of tax-free reimbursements. The IRS views an acceptable wage construct as follows:

Taxable Wages + Reimbursements = Total compensation

Looks simple, but reimbursements are paid to offset the costs incurred to carry out an employee's duties—not as a substitute for wages. An agency aggressively pursuing the lowest wages constructs a contract in this manner:

Total Compensation - Reimbursements = Taxable Wages (specifically—whatever is left over)

If the IRS sees that an agency has a policy similar to the second one outlined above, it can assess some massive penalties and restate all the non-taxable amounts to taxable wages, requiring employment taxes from the agency on the reconstructed income. This is currently happening in some of the audits that we mentioned earlier.

"Tax Advantage" and other nonsense

Though the practice has tapered in the last few years, a number of agencies have marketed the tax free reimbursement component of their compensation as a "tax advantage" program, drawing attention to the higher take home pay that is supposedly reaped from the arrangement. The IRS is not ignorant to the practice. A number of years ago, an agency that had never had such a program, announced their new "Tax Advantage" plan with a full media blitz, touting an increased take home pay. An advertisement for this change was seen by an IRS attorney in Washington who was responsible for the annual update of the per diem policies. We can only imagine what was done with the information. We have also seen marketing documents touting an agency's Tax Advantage program as a way to qualify for needs based education grants, Earned Income Credit, and even a way to dodge child support payments. Again, most agencies work hard to be compliant with the tax laws, but there are always a few in every industry that don't.

The point of this is that it is not kosher to market higher pay due to more tax free reimbursements. When a recruiter quotes an "after tax equivalent," they are marketing their reimbursements, not their contract or services. When an agency markets their "Tax Advantage" program, they are marketing their reimbursement as a wage. The lower the wage the greater the risk. Consider the following: 1) Mortgage applications are generally based on your taxable wage, not reimbursements, 2) car loans are based on taxable wages, 3) a 10K a year mortgage interest payment (reported to the IRS) and 20K of taxable income begs the question of whether other income streams exist, 4) Social Security is based on the highest wage years, and 5) Workers Compensation, Unemployment, and Disability are often based on taxable wages. Again, this is not to say that all agencies are up to mischief as the majority are well-run, stellar players in the industry. As in any group of companies however, there are those with questionable practices just as there are bad apples on every tree.

Missed shift charges

Both traveler and agency are looking for profit and we would be short sighted to think that an agency should just swallow the costs when a traveler fails to fulfill their contract obligations. This is not necessarily a tax issue for the traveler, but it touches the tax free per diems that a traveler receives and it does have an impact on the agency's tax compliance. In short, the best way this is handled is through a t by withholding per diems. The numbers arrive at the nation, but since per diems should not normally be paid as e best approach for the agency is to pay the per diem for the nd then apply a missed shift charge. Withholding per diems by h s missed indirectly treats per diems as wages.

Take Aways

Traveling is a great way to see the country, expand your horizons and your career. However, you can count on the fact that your tax filing requirements will be no cakewalk and change dramatically. Anything rewarding requires work, and the work of traveling is worth it. I traveled over 20 years ago, and my wife and I are still reaping the benefits of a wonderful 3 years. When you have doubts about your tax situation, consult the advice of a tax professional that is knowledgeable in the area of both multistate filings, per diems, and is available during the year to assist you as each opportunity arises. The chain preparation firms have staff that can handle travelers but you have to ask for them. With chains, a new client is usually paired up with a new preparer and many only work three months a year. The extra effort, and even expense, will go a long way in helping you avoid mistakes, take advantage of any tax benefits available to you and protect your license.

~*~

This chapter was authored by contributing author, Joseph C. Smith, RRT, EA, MS Tax of Travel Tax® His experience as an IRS Enrolled Agent and respiratory therapist makes him a valuable asset for travel nursing tax information. Not only does he prepare tax returns, he also holds regular free seminars all over the United States for traveling professionals. As an Enrolled Agent, he defends the returns that he completes. If you get a letter, just send it to him and he handles the case. If the case does go to tax court, he will refer you to an attorney that works with him. His firm is well known and respected by many individuals and is a leader in the travel medical professional tax world. That, and he is just an all-around nice guy. Check out his website! www.traveltax.com

Chapter Seven

Politics in Travel Nursing

Although most of us go into travel nursing to get out of the hospital politics, there are a few things that affect travel nursing in a political fashion.

Three of the most recent developments include: JCAHO accreditation of healthcare staffing agencies, the Nursing Compact, and NATHO. This chapter will explore these new elements of travel nursing and how they will affect your career as a travel nurse.

Joint Commission

The Joint Commission has recently set new standards for healthcare staffing agencies. This new certification process will mean big changes in the travel-nursing field. What does this means for staffing companies? New standards have been placed on the travel-staffing companies and on travel nurses. The staffing companies will have to clearly define the company leadership hierarchy.

The hierarchy of the travel company will include the administrator, director of nursing services, recruiters, and traveling nurses. The recruiter most likely will have a regional supervisor, an account manager, or a recruiting manager. Also in the mix will be the accountant, payroll supervisor, information systems technician, human resources, and a housing supervisor. The new JCAHO standards will mean that travelers have to get used to the formal processes, but it will also prevent finger-pointing at travelers and in effect will assist in the protection of the travel nurse's license.

The administrator, nursing director, accountant or chief financial officer will also be in charge of the development and monitoring of an annual budget. This budget will include costs of certifications, cost of management, costs of the nurses, costs of the benefits, and how that amount compares with the accounts receivable through the hospital bill rate. Where is this going to lead?

With the implementation of JCAHO certifications, the initial cost of owning a staffing company just increased. This cost is proportionate to national versus regional coverage and the overall size of the company. The cost of JCAHO certification is determined by the number of branch offices the staffing company is operating. Although the initial cost may be in the thousands of dollars, the efficiencies that certification puts in place increases the effectiveness that keep both hospital and travelers happier in the long run. Staffing companies have found that since the implementation of JCAHO standards more contracts from hospitals have been offered to the staffing companies; therefore, the jobs available to nurses have increased.

Most certainly, not all staffing companies will be able to survive all these costs; therefore, companies either will have to do more subcontracting through companies that can afford the JCAHO certification or the smaller companies will be forced to comply with JCAHO standards through subcontracting to JCAHO certified firms. Either way, eventually all firms will have to be JCAHO compliant.

A top priority addressed by the JCAHO certification team is a code of ethics—a code that says the staffing office will take every precaution to provide a work environment that is free of harassment, treats everyone equally, and, in short, treats people like human beings.

As a nurse, I expect companies to treat me like a name and not a number. Along with treating me as a name, please have the decency to call nurses by the name that they wish to be called. Not every nurse goes by their given "first name." Since 9–11–2001, first names have become more of a security issue. You can put my first given name on my paycheck and office IRS documents, but when I call the office I expect you to call me by my middle name, which I have gone by for over twenty-five years. It totally amazed me when I called the larger company that I traveled with for over a year and they couldn't find me in their system under the name that I go by, but they found me in the system by my social security number. I was definitely just a number and not a name to everyone else but my recruiter.

Respect and ethics have other faces, including sticking with your nurses when the times get tough. Nurses must respect their agencies to be truthful and honest in every situation. Nurses must have ethics and professionalism every day on the job, and the expectations should also be there for the staffing agencies.

Another issue addressed by JCAHO pertains to getting business through other unfair means, including contract discrepancies, making your travel assignment your permanent assignment, and other conflicts between the hospital and the nurse. JCAHO now mandates that travelers be protected in their contracts, particularly for professional liability insurance, floating, orientation, and incident or complaint reporting. Contract discrepancies can include anything from unsuitable housing to pay being contracted as one thing and paid at another rate, and a pay rate that is verbally agreed upon then changed in the written contract.

Conflicts can also occur when a nurse wants to continue on as a permanent staffing member instead of as contracted staff. Some companies put a six-month to one year clause in there that says you cannot go from travel to permanent after a certain period of time. Staffing companies must have a plan to deal with the above situations and any others of the like that come up. When there are problems with the nurse's performance, the hospital has a right to terminate that contract, but there is usually a conflict between how much the employee is penalized monetarily for housing and travel. If the employee feels that they were wrongfully terminated, they have the problem of a wrongful contract termination. There must be a plan of action to assist with this conflict, which includes incident reporting that JCAHO requires from the hospital.

There are always two sides to every story, and conflicts can only be solved through a structured plan and the assistance of mediation, if needed. Conflicts and problems do not always occur Monday through Friday, 9:00 AM to 5:00 PM. There must be a twenty-four-hour support telephone line available. The problems that do occur must be promptly solved. The longer the problem lingers, the greater the problem becomes.

The next big issue is that of quality nursing care. Quality must be assured by skills checklists, orientation skills checked off, and standard safety proficiency. Safety issues are addressed initially with the use of skills checklists, which are completed by the nurse upon application for the position. If a hospital reports that clinically a nurse is not able to perform as stated, then it is the agency's job to work with the nurse to either find different placement or help the nurse to obtain the credentials. These skills checklists must also be updated every year.

Another aspect of JCAHO standards is the issue of quality assurance and making sure that the credentials and experience correlate to the work history record. For example, if the nurse says that she knows about Swan-Ganz arterial lines, wouldn't it make sense that she must have worked in critical care? Standard safety issues, including blood borne pathogens, fire safety, back safety, and safely getting from the hospital parking lot to your floor and back at the end of your shift are also things that need to be addressed in orientation and yearly educational programs. There are rules now about required yearly continuing education, which will hopefully eliminate repeat paper work at your assignment.

A big safety issue that is a prominent concern is nurse-to-patient ratios. It is the travel nurse's responsibility to assure that they are not being put into an unsafe situation during the interview with the hospital. It is the staffing agency's responsibility to stand behind the nurse with these staffing issues. This is accomplished by the new JCAHO complaint reporting laws. If the nurse-to-patient ratio is not as stated in the interview, then the staffing company and nurse need to do some conflict resolving with the hospital's management team.

Evaluations from supervisors are also an important tool in safety and quality of care. These evaluations are used to determine if the job is really going as well or as bad as the travel nurse states it is. Then again, we have to remember there are two sides to every story, but usually if things are bad, things are bad on both sides, and conflict mediation may be needed to continue quality nursing care.

JCAHO standards also involve continuing education. Continuing education, as well as experience, is what make a good nurse even better. Education must also be provided for age specific aspects, patient confidentiality, HIPPA Privacy Compliance, Infection Control, and how to help the patients who have been involved in a domestic abusive situation. This is most often correlated in the orientation process and quality of care issues that were mentioned above. A nurse's skills must be kept up-to-date and new education opportunities taken advantage of in the area of expertise.

When these quality measures become issues, then a staffing company must have an organized approach to improve the nurse's performance. This can be done through educational opportunities and other opportunities for improvement. If required, verbal warnings, written warnings, and termination may be inevitable if these opportunities are not taken advantage of. If there is a conflict between what is stated on paper and what the nurse's performance is, the hospital has the responsibility to report it to the staffing agency. What was the problem? What attempts were made to solve the problem? What was the outcome? What is the percentage of travel nurses that stay with the staffing company? Why did the travel nurse leave the staffing company? Were their problems with the company or just problems related to location or benefits?

All this information provided by the hospital, the nurse, and other information from the staffing company pertaining to the employment of the nurse must be kept in a secure and confidential environment. A plan must be in place in order to maintain confidential information about the hospital that is being staffed also.

Along with all of this goes the process for maintaining continuity of information. The records of each nurse must be safeguarded. The information must be available to the nurse, if needed, for other staffing opportunities. Profiles only need to be submitted upon approval of the nurse. Profiles must not be lost within the system! I had a situation where I was transferring to a different office. One week after I had moved, my file mysteriously disappeared from the office. Was my information in a safe and confidential place?

Ummmm…Another nurse told me the same type of story with the same company. Maybe, with the new JCAHO certifications and regulations, this problem will not continue to occur. Files won't get lost and employees won't get lost in the system.

What is the future of travel nursing? Many travelers that I have talked to have raised concerns that the staffing agencies will have to be JCAHO certified in order to place nurses in JCAHO certified hospitals; however, the cost of this certification will usually increase the bill rate to the hospital, so pay should remain proportionate. The agency will have to renew their certification every two years. Travel nurses should be accountable for themselves and have personal quality control and ethics; those who are in it for the money and not concerned about patient care are the ones whom this will affect the most. Over all travel nurses are quality nurses, who have great expectations placed on them.

I was recently discussing this with Greg Allen, president of Cirrus Medical Staffing, and he feels that many of the nurses may become discouraged because of all the paperwork required to remain a traveler, since their company is JCAHO certified. All updates must occur on a bi-yearly basis. Though travelers are used to the standard licensure, certification, and medical updates yearly, they will now have to update other tests, such as medication tests, age competency tests, abbreviation standards, various required continuing education requirements, and the list will continue to grow as JCAHO certification becomes the standard for staffing firms and other safety issues are identified. The best way to handle this is to request copies or make copies of all required paperwork and keep them for yourself at all times. This will make switching companies much easier when needed.

Another impact may be that the travelers must become more open to and willing to float to other units, which hospitals will be forced to show evidence of an appropriate orientation of another similar unit for the traveler to the traveler's company for JCAHO compliance purposes.

I believe these regulations were created to assure quality of care is provided to the hospitals that use travel nurses. I just don't like the fact this may be at the expense of the smaller travel companies that provide the best customer service to the nurses.

Excellence in patient care should be the number one goal, and setting the same standards for healthcare agencies that the hospitals have to follow also may be just one more warranted step towards providing greater standards for all involved in the field of temporary staffing.

The Nursing Compact

In the year of 2000, Maryland, Texas, Utah, and Wisconsin formed what is known now as the Nursing Compact. These four states were soon followed by many others to form a mutual recognition system. To date there are twenty-four states that are in the Nursing Compact, with three others that have a bill signed by the governor, but which have not been put into effect. At this time Illinois, Oklahoma, Minnesota, and Massachusetts have legislation in progress to join. For a current list of all compact states, see the National Council of State Boards of Nursing's website at *www.ncsbn.org*.

For a traveling nurse, this is the best thing since the invention of the mobile phone. This means that as a resident of the state of Idaho, I can travel between twenty-three different states without having to obtain a different license. This is only because my home residence is in a Compact state. If you live in Montana, which is not a Compact state, but have an Idaho license, it is *not* eligible for multi-state recognition. If you go to Texas and state that you are working under your "Idaho Compact

License," you are actually practicing in Texas without a license, because your home is in Montana instead of in Idaho.

If you have a multi-state license in one state and you move to another state in the Compact, your first license will no longer be valid. For instance, when I moved my residence from Arizona to Idaho, I received a letter from the State of Arizona stating that my Arizona license had been inactivated due to the fact that I now have a multi-state license in Idaho. If your home state is a Compact state, your license will show "multi-state license" or something to that effect.

Your home state is the place where your house is or where you receive your mail if it's at a relative's house. Although the rules for home state aren't as strict as the tax home rules, I would still have as much supporting information as possible to support your claim of a Compact state being your home state. This might include voter's registration, care registration, driver's license, and mail sent to your address.

Another confusing issue about the Nursing Compact is your state of original licensure. Your state of original licensure has *no* bearing on whether or not your license is a multi-state Compact license. In effect, if I moved my permanent residence to Montana, I would no longer be Compact eligible, even though my original license was granted in Idaho related to the fact that I'm no longer a resident of the state of Idaho.

The biggest safety advantage of the Nursing Compact is that nurses whose licenses have been revoked or suspended in one state will automatically have a record through a national database; therefore, making it more difficult for a nurse to get a new license in a different state after being convicted of a crime in another state or any other disciplinary action against their license.

When it comes to legal issues, although you practice under your Compact license, you are still required to practice until the rules of the state in which you are practicing in are effective. For example, although I have an Idaho Compact license, I am currently practicing in Tennessee. Therefore, at this time I would be held liable if I did *not* practice under the rules of the Tennessee State Board of Nursing, whereas Idaho State specific rules do not affect me at this time.

Be aware also that if you have a license in a non-Compact state that goes Compact, you will need to notify both boards as to which state is your home state. In other words, I also have an Oklahoma license where my parents live that is *not* Compact. When and if Oklahoma ever joins the Nursing Compact, I will need to notify both Idaho and Oklahoma that Idaho is my state of residence; otherwise I run the risk of my Idaho license being cancelled because I received my Oklahoma license a few years after my Idaho license. Some states will send you a request for your home state verification, but others will just cancel your oldest license. This has happened to some travelers who had to pay to get their legal home state licenses reinstated. It is imperative that you keep each state board of nursing informed of your permanent address at all times for this reason.

I have attempted to answer the basic questions about the Nursing Licensing Compact. If you have further questions, it is always best to call the state board. If you work in a state that is Compact and your license is not a multi-state license, this will not only affect your license in that state, but *every* nursing license that you have. Ignorance is *not* bliss this time.

~*~

The National Association of Travel Healthcare Organizations

In 2008 a new non-profit association of travel healthcare firms was formed to promote ethical business practices in the healthcare travel industry. It benchmarks the new gold standard for behavior that is aligned among member agencies on behalf of travel candidates and clients.

The organization functions to educate the healthcare industry on the benefits of travel healthcare staffing, establishes a set of service standards among travel healthcare companies, shares resources among member organizations, offers formal dispute resolution process between NATHO member firms through an arbitration committee, and assists members in cultivating market growth.

NATHO members are held to a strict code of ethics that was developed specifically for the travel healthcare industry. It is important for travel healthcare professionals and healthcare facilities to keep this in mind when selecting a company to provide services.

NATHO membership allows healthcare staffing firms to access information unique to the travel healthcare industry to include insurance and risk management resources, public relations, shared marketing resources, federal and state legislative issues, ethics and arbitration guidelines, credentialing standards, standards of practice, industry benchmarking, industry statistics, and group purchasing.

Membership criteria includes Joint Commission certification, proof of insurance (professional liability, general liability, and workers compensation), and a payment of the minimum membership fee of $1,000 annually.

The Code of Ethics states that the members are responsible for maintaining and promoting an ethical practice. The Code of Ethics will serve to clarify the manner in which each member of the organization may fulfill its responsibilities to the general public, to clients, to candidates, to other recruitment organizations, and to other travel healthcare organizations. If a dispute occurs between members, the first obligation is for the members to resolve the issue among themselves. It is understood that disputes between members will then go to the Ethics Committee or Arbitration Committee (if it is a dispute over a fee) for resolution.

The ethical rules state that a travel company shall fulfill all agreements made with the hospital and shall not make promises that the travel company believes they cannot keep in full. The travel company has to represent the nurse as accurately as possible with the nurse's employment history and qualifications. The travel company cannot send a profile to a hospital if he or she does not have the approval of the traveling nurse. If a travel nurse's file is submitted by one or more travel companies, the travel company that receives the job offer from the hospital will be honored as the company representing the nurse, regardless of the timing of submittals. If a hospital makes an offer to more than one member, the traveler will choose the company to represent them.

The travel company must provide services that remain in compliance of any applicable law, including complying with federal, state, and local laws governing hiring practices. A travel company must adhere to the credentialing standards established by the Joint Commission.

The travel company shall not knowingly make a false statement about a job opportunity to include responsibilities, compensation, hours, and other pertinent information concerning prospective opportunities. A travel company cannot knowingly deceive a traveling nurse or encourage a nurse to breach a current obligation or future contact. The travel nurse is not allowed to switch companies, but must remain at the same hospital without a 90-day break.

During an investigation by the Ethics Committee, the travel company shall fully cooperate with the Committee or Board of Directors concerning violation of the Code in a timely manner. The two travel companies with the conflict must inform NATHO Headquarters that they have made an attempt to solve the matter between themselves.

In their use of advertising and marketing, they must not make a false or misleading statement about the healthcare staffing company or the services. They cannot publish material misrepresenting the spirit of the Code of Ethics, and they cannot publish something that would make the statement misleading. The travel company cannot compare other company's services to theirs when the facts cannot be factually substantiated. A member must ensure that the jobs they advertise are factual and available.

The staffing company should never discredit the reputation of another competitor, and they must honor agreements between other members of NATHO. They must refrain from defaming, maligning, or falsely accusing another member or competing firm. They also must refrain from intentionally misrepresenting another member to a prospective candidate, client, or another staffing agency.

The Code of Ethics also demands that all staffing company representatives act professionally and in a businesslike manner, not engage in a deceptive or misleading manner, and they must honor both oral and written agreements made with other members. It must never engage in activity that brings dishonor to the healthcare staffing industry.

In accordance with the ethics policy, all staffing companies must abide by strict accounting and taxation standards as set forth by the Internal Revenue Service. It is also understood that violating accounting and taxation laws to gain a competitive advantage is not only an issue of unfair competition, but also puts the client hospitals and travelers in serious risk of sanctions for violating labor laws and regulations. They perform proper use of the non-taxable per diems or lodging, meals, and incidentals allowances or reimbursements. They must also use appropriate classification of the temporary healthcare employees as non-exempt and W2 employees with proper withholding of all taxes, including state income taxes. They must abide by all overtime laws.

The NATHO Ethics Committee will field all complaints to the president and the Ethics Committee. The Ethics Committee will consist of the chairperson and a minimum of three other members. The chairperson is appointed by the President of NATHO for a three-year term. All of the members shall be individuals employed by active member organizations of NATHO and appointed by the Ethics Committee chairperson with the board of directors approval for a three-year term. The chairperson and committee members may succeed themselves. The Ethics Committee shall be responsible for reviewing and acting upon reported violations of the NATHO Code of Ethics or may, on its own initiative, institute an investigation of apparent violations.

In February 2010, NATHO formed a technology committee to assist in the development of software standards for healthcare staffing agencies to share data with vendor management services. The aim of this committee is to provide staffing firms with a database in which venders can enter job order information and firms can match up travel nurses with the information entered from their application profile. At this time, staffing companies have to enter the candidate's information into each vender management system for each job that comes up. By integrating the system, the candidate's information will not have to be entered into the system repetitiously.

Most recently, NATHO sponsored KPMG to conduct a hospital labor cost study to compare the salary and benefits cost of hourly full-time employees in comparison to a temporary traveling nurse. According to their press release on June 8, 2011, the all-in cost of a full-time direct care hospital registered nurse (RN) is on average \$98,000/year (\$45/hour), of which only \$55,739 is base wages (\$25.84/hour). Fully-loaded payroll, which includes base wages, employer taxes, and paid time-off represents 76–78% of the total cost of the RN labor force at facilities. The balance comes from non-productivity costs (12–13%), insurance costs (8–9%), recruiting costs (1–2%), and other costs (1%). In other words, the actual cost per hour for a full-time nurse is on average 176% of their base hourly wage. These are important factors in evaluating whether to add staff, increase overtime, or use contingent nurses to meet patient needs.

There are also significant additional "hidden" nursing labor costs, which are mainly the result of non-productive labor hours and associated opportunity costs, as well as attrition and time required to fill a permanent direct care RN position, the KPMG study reports. Non-productive labor hours on average represent 13% of total hours, according to respondents.

Two-thirds of the hospital executives responding to the survey say they are currently using travel or per diem nurses. The key reasons for using traveling nurses were supply-and-demand and the quality of these nurses. These appear to be even more important decision factors than cost. Some of the reasons given, which enable some hospitals not to use traveling staff, include the use of extra full-time staff, part-time employed staff, incentives to limit turnover, and to encourage working overtime, as well as the current economic downturn leading to limited turnover. Many of these factors may be of a temporary nature and increase costs and turnover over the long term. Respondents also stated that the ideal balance is 90% permanent staff and 10% supplemental labor.

Two other studies that are in the beginning stages include a study on the use of the PBDS testing, which is used to evaluate the "competency" of a traveling nurse, and a study on travel nurses who switch companies, but do not switch hospitals.

The study is to determine if the PBDS (Performance Based Diagnostic System) test is being used suitably for traveling nurses. If the test is found to be inappropriate, then NATHO will encourage those hospitals using the test to have it get rid of it or use it more appropriately.

They are also studying a way to prevent travelers from going from Travel Agency A to Travel Agency B while still working at the same hospital. While there are times when nurses have a genuine reason for switching companies, there are many more who switch companies for trivial reasons.

This chapter is only the tip of the iceberg. NATHO offers so much more with articles of interest for traveling nurses, agencies, and hospitals. These articles include up-to-date news on the nursing shortage, mandated staffing ratios, the economics of travel nursing, travel tax answers, how to choose a reputable agency, how to be professional while on the job, landing the best assignments, and many other tips for the traveling healthcare professional.

All in all, NATHO is making every attempt to create a positive image for the traveling healthcare industry by developing a peer review process that is based on excellence, honesty, and fairness between travel healthcare agencies. This, in turn, will provide better quality service to hospitals, traveling nurses and ultimately patients.

**Mission, ethics, and standards of practice information were acquired from the website and press releases of the National Association of Travel Healthcare Organization used by permission. This chapter has been reviewed and approved by NATHO president, Mark Stagen. For more information, please check out their website at* www.natho.org.

Chapter Eight

Testing In Nursing

Tests, tests, tests...you thought the NCLEX was the last test that you would have to take in nursing, but it was actually just the beginning. When you decide to make travel nursing your career, you just locked yourself into nurse testing up to four times a year.

Unfortunately, there are some tests that will be required for each hospital that you go to. I'm warning you now, your company will have you fill out all those tests and competencies before you get to your hospital in Paradise, and don't be surprised if you have to fill out all that information again on the hospital's forms or computer system.

Basic Company Testing

There are some tests that are required by the travel company that you will have to take before ever landing a travel assignment. These are tests that are required usually by regulatory agencies once you get to the hospital (Joint Commission, Medicaid, and Medicare).

Mandatory tests that you can expect to take include HIPAA, age specific knowledge, hazardous chemicals, fire safety, newborn safety, infection control, drug use in the workplace, ethics, environmental safety, fall prevention, biological terrorism, patient rights, body mechanics, restraints, prevention of medical errors, cultural diversity, disaster preparedness, sexual harassment, violence in the workplace, and violence in domestic situations.

You will also have to fill out a skills checklist for your specific specialty. Some of these tests include general registered nursing, progressive care, NICU, PICU, telemetry, medical, surgical, intensive care, dialysis, psychiatric, and emergency room. Other added tests may include pharmacology, basic rhythms, and intravenous therapy.

Other forms that you will be expected to fill out at the time of application, which are not necessarily tests, might include permanent resident/home declaration, background check, employment history, travel or mileage reimbursement forms, a physician's statement, immunizations statement, and a declaration of employment eligibility/ citizenship.

Also be aware that in most recent years your background check will not only include your criminal history but could also include a credit history. Most companies that I'm aware of have this capability, but only few will actually complete a credit history that can be detected when you receive your yearly credit report.

Performance Based Development System

This is a wonderful test that was developed by Dr. Dorothy delBueno in an effort to test a nurse's critical thinking, interpersonal relation, and technical skills. The test consists of several short videos that are played in which the nurse is required to recognize the problem, assess what interventions need to take place, what he or she would expect the physician to order, prioritize how and when those interventions are to take place, while also taking into consideration conflict resolution, customer satisfaction, team building, safety in performance, and use of equipment.

The travel nurse will be required to take the test that most closely corresponds to that of their specialty. To date, testing is provided for adult Med/Surg, critical care, OR, OB, mental health, and ER. In the hospitals that I have researched, those whose specialty is pediatrics, rehab, or telemetry, are required to take the Med/Surg test. Those whose specialty is step-down, surgical intensive care, medical intensive care, coronary intensive care, or neurological intensive care are all required to take the critical care test.

Here is where the first problem lies: there is no test developed for every nursing field that exists. If I'm hired for telemetry and take the Med/Surg test, how does that prove my competency for the telemetry floor? If I'm hired for rehab and I take the Med/Surg test, how does that prove my competency for things such as how to manage the care of a patient who is trying to walk again versus a patient who is having an acute stroke? Some hospitals just give everyone the Med/Surg test as a "basic" nursing test, even though the nurse has been in the Psychiatric or OB field for ten years or so. Therefore, if they are going to use this for a competency-based assessment, they need to have it for the specialty that we say we are competent in and have been practicing in.

When you take this test, you will be shown about a twenty second video of a patient who is having some kind of an acute distress, and you are supposed to figure out what is going on with that patient, what you should do first, and then progress from there until the patient is stable.

Here lays the second problem in the fact that you are expected to write every little thing down that you can think of to do. You also have to come up with a diagnosis that you think the physician is going to assign to the patient. Remember, you have to do all this after viewing just once a short video, approximately 20 seconds worth. Since when are nurses trained to diagnose what is wrong with the patient? Do you take notes or watch the video? I would think it is very difficult to accomplish both at the same time.

There is also a section that concentrates on prioritizing in "must do," "should do," or "could do." If a patient has a potassium level of 6.2 and another patient has a troponin level of 0.144 with a CKMB of 4.5, which is going to be my priority? Although the potassium level may cause some cardiac arrhythmias and would be considered a "should report," the elevated troponin and CKMB levels are more important and a "*must* report," related to the fact that they are indicative of a myocardial infarction.

These tests require you to write down not only what you would do in step-by-step format but also why you are doing those things. One of the catches here is that you must write down all the little things. For example, for the an elevated potassium level you would not only notify the physician, who will probably order Kaexy late, but don't forget to also write down that you would hold the morning and evening doses of potassium.

To help study for this test, think about some of the situations that you have been in that require prioritization. What would you do or say if the charge nurse asked you to do orientation of a new nurse, but you have a really busy day and all of your patients have different procedures to go to on which you might have to accompany them? What would you say when a nurse comes up to you and asks you about another nurse, and what would you do if you witnessed a nurse yelling at a patient in the room?

Diseases that you might want to be familiar with and write out a care plan to study include heparin drips, insulin drips, diabetic coma, stroke, acute myocardial infarction, chest pain, increased intracranial pressure, digoxin toxicity, pneumothorax, congestive heart failure, chronic obstructive pulmonary disease, pulmonary embolism, renal failure, hemorrhage, pylonephritis, bladder retention, ilieus, thrombocytopenia, peritonitis, pain control, and sepsis.

What effect does this test have on travel nursing, and why is it so controversial? It is because the test was designed to assess a nurse's strengths and weaknesses for an orientation process that is tailored to that nurse, but what the hospitals are now doing is using the test to "weed out" travel nurses that are "incompetent." This includes several nurses that have been "practicing incompetency" for twenty years. Excuse me? The state board of nursing says that I have been competent to practice nursing for twenty years, but a 20-second test says that I'm a danger to my patients?

I have heard numerous stories where the first week of orientation was going great, the hospital really liked the nurse, the nurse's professionalism and competence was being proved daily with everyday situations, and then their contract was cancelled because all of a sudden some test says that they are incompetent. Now she has no job, but she still has a three-month lease on an apartment.

Let's just say that I have accepted a job in Naples, FL (several hospitals there are known for using the PBDS testing for travelers). To date, the average apartment lease is $1000/month plus a $200 deposit, and I will have to lease the apartment for 3 months in order to move in. This will be at a cost of $3200. After I lease the apartment, then I have to drive there from my home in Idaho. At the current rate of $0.48 for the 2600 miles, this would make my travel expenses $1248. At a rate of 500 miles per day, it will take me approximately 5.23 days to get from Idaho to Florida, which will mean 5 nights in motels at an average of $75/night for a total of $375. Then we will need to add $40/day for food, for a total of $200. That would mean my total for the trip and the three-month lease, not including rental furniture that will need to be returned, will be $5023.

My question now is, what nurse in his or her right mind would take a $5000 gamble on a test that is not being used as it was originally designed? Unfortunately, there are some nurses who do take this gamble, and that is why the hospitals continue to use this testing system. I don't have a problem with a testing system to prove competency, but it needs to be arranged before a nurse drives across country only to have her contract cancelled. I don't even have a problem with the PBDS test, as long as it is being used to see where nurses are lacking and orientation is customized around what the nurses are lacking in. Travelers are expected to receive very minimal orientation and hit the floor running; therefore, extended customized orientation is not an option.

Basic Knowledge Assessment Took

The BKAT is a Basic Knowledge Assessment Tool used to test a nurse, usually in an orientation setting. According to the author's design, it is not to be used as a "weeding-out tool" for hiring purposes. It was designed to validate the knowledge of nurses who have previous experience in medical/surgical nursing, pediatric and adult intensive care, adult and pediatric emergency care and telemetry nursing. Clinical specialists and educational coordinators are to review the tests and gear educational in-services to those questions that nurses have missed.

The tests were originally created by Jean Toth, PhD, RN, MSN, CV-CNS, BCCC, from the Catholic University in Washington, DC, over thirty years ago. It was created by using analysis of literature, clinical proficiency, and a panel of master degree level nurses who excel in their specialty. The test can be copied, but it cannot be altered in any way.

It is an educational tool that, according to the author, Jean Toth, is to be used for determining the educational requirements of nurses. There are BKAT's for ER, Peds, etc. The author states in her preamble to the "test" that it is *not* to be used for hiring or firing.

According to nurses who have taken the test, the questions are very similar to those found on the NCLEX exam. It is a very practical exam and tests your knowledge of every-day situations. The questions are very basic and should be relatively easy to an experienced nurse, and should be very passable for even a new graduate.

The medical/surgical BKAT is an eighty-eight question test that measures the knowledge of nurses in the areas of cardiovascular, endocrine, renal, neurology, gastrointestinal, pulmonary, and wound care, along with a few questions on pain control, fall prevention, infection control, communication, spiritual care, emotional care, drug calculations, advance directives, blood transfusions, hypothermia, and obesity. This test takes about forty minutes to complete.

The Adult ICU-BKAT is a ninety question test of critical care nursing knowledge of cardiovascular, pulmonary, monitoring lines, neurology, endocrine, renal, gastrointestinal systems, along with a few questions on infection control, hypothermia, burns, and spiritual care. The test takes approximately forty minutes to complete.

The telemetry/progressive care BKAT evaluates the nurse's knowledge of cardiovascular, neurology, endocrine, renal, pulmonary, gastrointestinal/parenteral items, along with a few questions concerning infection control, hypothermia, monitoring lines, and emotional/ spiritual care. There are eighty questions that take approximately forty minutes to complete.

The pediatric BKAT is a ninety-six question test that tests the nurse's knowledge about pediatric cardiovascular, monitoring lines, pulmonary, neurology, endocrinology, renal, gastrointestinal, and other areas, including play therapy, drug overdoses, and family-centered care. This test takes approximately forty minutes to take.

The Neonatal ICU-BKAT is a seventy-five question test that evaluates the knowledge of the NICU nurse. The questions cover cardiovascular, pulmonary, gastrointestinal/parenteral, neurology, renal, monitoring lines/catheters, family/spiritual care, with a few questions on developmental care, sleep, pain, and blood incompatibilities. This test takes approximately forty-five minutes to complete.

The ER-BKAT is a one hundred question test that determines the basic knowledge of the critical care nursing aspects in the Emergency Department. Items on the test include: cardiovascular, pulmonary, neurology, endocrine, renal, gastrointestinal/parenteral, OB/GYN, pediatrics, with a few questions on drug abuse, trauma, psychiatric situations, rape, and mass casualties. It takes approximately forty-five minutes to complete.

The Pediatric ER-BKAT is an eighty-question test that assesses the basic knowledge in pediatric emergency care. The content measures the knowledge of the nurse in cardiovascular, neurology, pulmonary, trauma, endocrinology, gastrointestinal, renal, and miscellaneous items to include drug abuse, sepsis, and psychiatric situations. It also includes a question about blood transfusions, burns, child's play, conscious sedation, drowning, immunization, mass casualty, and obesity. This test takes about forty minutes to complete.

A copy of the test can be obtained by sending $15.00 and the agreement form to Jean Toth, PhD, RN, MSN, CV-CNS, BCCC, BKAT

For Critical Care Nursing, PO Box 6295, Washington, DC 20015. Nurse staffing agencies are not allowed to request the tests—only nurses who are subject to taking the test. More information and the agreement form can be found at *www.bkat-toth.org*

Chapter Nine

Preparing For an Adverse Reaction

With each travel assignment, we prepare for the adventure, live the escapade, and then our journey ends, only to perpetuate us on to the next quest. But along our path, we cross over many bridges in the form of emergencies, troubled waters, and even the end of the road. These things are more difficult to face as travelers related to the fact that we are out there on our own and don't have a community or family right there to surround us with comforting thoughts. However, a determined travel nurse doesn't give up; we just pack up and move on down the highway of destiny.

Emergencies Along The Road

In case of a medical emergency, we are taught to dial 911, but whom do you call when you are hundreds of miles away from home? Be prepared! Be very prepared!

The first line of defense in case of an emergency is to have an emergency planned for. Not that we really want one to happen, but we don't want one to happen and get caught, as they say, "with our pants down." We certainly don't want to panic.

The first order of business is to have someone to call, like AAA, Good Sam's Emergency Road Service, or OnStar®. Keep those numbers, usually found on your membership card, in your wallet, above the sun visor, or in your purse. Other important phone numbers to have with you include your nursing recruiter, your bank's number, your car insurance agent's number, and a network of friends along the way.

A network of friends is not only handy to have as a safety feature, but could also be a convenience feature. I have several friends around the country with whom I have worked before that I keep track of and have even had a few invites for supper and a place to stay. I wouldn't recommend staying with someone whom you have only met online, but I would definitely stay with someone that I had worked with before. Of course, meeting other travel nurses along the way for supper is great fun. I have even met other travel nurses after work for breakfast!

If you have not invested in a good nationwide cell phone, now is the time. For years I refused to get one because I had a C.B. and it was free. Although very handy at times, some people just aren't comfortable with a C.B. When I was driving forty miles every day to work, the C.B. was all that I had. The few times that I had problems, I would holler at the trucks to send a policeman or highway patrol.

Have a friend or relative lined up to call every time you stop for gas. I always call my parents along the way so if something does happen to me they have some idea where to start a search. Of course, you would also want to let that person know what route you are taking.

Although taking some cash is a good idea, taking too much is not a good idea. Keeping a national ATM card, with access via a pin number, is a must. I carry no more than a hundred dollars cash, and attempt to pay for everything off my debit card, which comes out of my bank account. This also gives me documentation for the tax man.

Before embarking on that next adventure, it is also a necessity to visit your local mechanic to get the oil changed and the fluids checked, along with tire pressure. In the trunk of your vehicle you should keep extra food, blankets, and water, in the event that you have a roadside emergency.

Make sure that you have a good map or a great GPS. The best maps with nationwide truck stops can be found at the major "chain" truck stops, and some even provide a list of rest areas. If you are traveling in an RV there is also a map put out by Good Sam Rand McNally Road Atlas. This is a great map that not only finds all the tourist traps, but also gas stations for RVers. Another great resource is the location of tourist information centers as you go into a state. They not only provide you with free maps, but they also have interesting facts about the territory you are about to travel through. GPS is a great tool! In fact, as a traveling nurse, I won't have a vehicle without one. There are some really good portable ones out there on the market, and even cell phones have them.

When on a long trip and you haven't ever been that direction, you should always start looking for a gas station when you reach one-half of a tank. By doing this, you don't risk getting too low before finding a place to stop. This is especially essential if you are pulling a travel trailer or traveling in a big motorhome. It is also important to remember that your gas mileage is a lot different when you are pulling a trailer.

When getting out of your vehicle to fill up with gas or go to use the restroom, always be aware of your surroundings. If someone makes you feel uncomfortable, stay in your vehicle and travel to the next rest area if possible. If you are a female traveling alone, it is not advisable to drive at night, although I do know some women who aren't afraid of traveling alone because their safety is insured by Smith and Wesson.

That brings up the point that, if you do have a concealed weapon, be sure that you know the concealed weapon laws in the states you travel through. Other personal safety items to keep in the vehicle consist of a large flashlight, which not only provides light but can be used as a weapon. They also make a small light that goes on your key chain with an ultraviolet light that will blind someone, giving you time to get out of a dangerous situation.

Another great tip is to carry a device in your glove compartment that will allow you to break the glass or cut your seatbelt in case of a traffic accident.

And last but not least for on the road, always make sure that your spare tire actually has air in it! You won't be too happy if you find this out along the Interstate.

Once you have arrived at your assignment, a phone book with the yellow pages is a must. Look in it to find the nearest urgent care center, the grocery stores, the laundromat, and, if you have a pet, an emergency vet. Once you are making good money as a travel nurse, get some of your bills paid off and save up at least enough money to float you for a few months.

In my case, it sure was nice when my dad became sick last year that I had enough saved up to take two months off. In the event of a family emergency, quick airline tickets can be found at *www.hotwire.com*, *priceline.com*, and *bereavementair.com*.

By using these tips and others, you can travel from state to state with peace of mind. By preparing for an emergency, you will know that if something does come up. You won't be the first to hit the panic button because you will have everything under control

Surviving The Assignment

My patient is screaming down the hallway about how it is time for his pain shot; the nursing supervisor just called and my admit will be here in ten minutes; when I called the surgeon about his patient that is bleeding through his dressing, I got yelled at because I didn't call sooner; and if the patient in room 19 doesn't quit hitting at the staff, then I'm going to have to call his doctor to get an order for restraints; and, of course, there is no one to help me because I'm the traveler, making "all the big bucks." Are travel nurses supposed to think that this is "normal" behavior, or is this nursing abuse?

Pain management is getting to be a bigger and bigger issue. Yes, there are patients who have legitimate pain management needs, but how many patients are we taking care of where this is their second admission this month because they need their dilaudid fix? This is a bigger issue in the emergency room than I see on the medical-surgical floor. The 1-10 "oucher" scale was supposed to help this, but some patients have figured that out and will rate their pain as a 15.

What are nurses to do about the abuse of the system? We just have to continue to assess our patients in a timely manner and provide them with their medications, as ordered by their physician. There is nothing that we can do about this abuse of the system because we are not that patient and we have been told that we have "no right" to judge how much pain a patient is really in.

Working with physicians that are verbally humiliating, degrading, and have a total lack of respect for us as professional nurses is also a fact in the life of a nurse. In a recent study published by the Association of OR Nurses, over 90% of nurses that were polled were subject to verbal abuse by a physician. Is that true just in the operating room? I don't think so! Try calling certain physicians in the middle of the night.

What can we do about verbal abuse? What usually happens is that we vent to a few of our co-workers, we keep the patient in mind, and go on and do our job to the best of our abilities. Remember, the patient is why we are there. We must call that physician in the middle of the night to protect our patient, as well as for protection of our license.

Abuse of a nurse by the patient is also a common problem that nurses face during the work day/night. The patient is under the influence of narcotics, illicit drugs, or alcohol and we're supposed to be understanding because they *are* ill. Would they still be ill if they weren't under the influence of all those substances?

We must protect our own health, and when a patient gets violent we need to seek assistance as soon as possible. If we are injured, this needs to be reported to the nursing supervisor as soon as possible, along with getting medical treatment for ourselves.

Do we have the right to press charges against that patient for assault? In some states, a hospital employee definitely has the right to press charges against that patient. There should be no difference if that patient injured us inside the hospital or if he injured us out on the street. If nurses get hurt, who is going to take care of us?

Of course we have to deal with all these things, plus "crises" that occur, and not make any mistakes on these hectic floors. Time management is the key to survival! Come out on the floor, check out your patients and then get a routine going. No, you can't stick by your routine every day. Things happen—patients have surgery, patients have to be admitted—but if you have your routine set up, then it is easier to accomplish these other tasks without getting overwhelmed.

When an overwhelming situation comes along, ask for help. Hostility may be amongst the nursing tribe because you are a travel nurses "making all the big bucks," but you can't do everything by yourself. You need to ask for help. If you can't get anyone to help you, approach the charge nurse and then work your way up the chain of command, all the way to the nursing supervisor. If hostility occurs, contact the director of nursing and your recruiter.

Travel nurses are in hospitals all around the United States and select foreign countries. They are there to help. They are not going to these different places to be abused by other staff and patients. You should be flexible in helping your co-workers, but you don't have to take severe abuse. Keep on working hard, and remember that you only have thirteen weeks there.

Don't be afraid to stand up for yourself. If you become overwhelmed with the pressures to the point that your license is in danger, you must get out of the contract. You were looking for a job when you found that one. Life may have its speed bumps, but just keep on trucking down on the travel-nursing road. The next assignment has to be better!

Looking back at all the tough assignments that I have had, I asked myself, "What are some of the techniques that I use when things are getting tough?" As we all know, travel nursing isn't always fun. We have plenty of good times and adventure, but there are also times when we want to run and hide.

Yes, survival is what it is all about. It's a jungle out there, and a travel nurse must be prepared to tread through the trenches and come out a victor! Come on, there can't be much difference between surviving in a jungle and surviving a terrible nursing assignment. Here are my eight tips for survival in Travel Nursing:

- Shield yourself with a "net" by putting a smile on your face. How can you be sad if you are smiling? Sure, you might be smiling only on the outside, but that is a start. You can shield your patients from knowing that you are having a bad day by wearing a smile!
- Get rid of the leeches! Stay away from the people who are most commonly the causes of the frustration. Sometimes you can't ignore them, but by getting more involved in nursing care and farther away from the nurses' station, these leeches will bother you less.
- Delve into the trenches. One of the best diversion tactics that I rely on is to spend more time with my patients. Take time out just to visit with them. What can you do for your patients instead of sitting up at the nurses' station, listening to what all is wrong with the unit?
- When the rainfall is heavy, find shelter. You need to have someone that you can talk to. If nothing else, call your recruiter or get online and find a travel nurse support group. Sometimes things will resolve themselves if you just tell your frustrations to someone who is going to give you a little reassurance.
- In a violent storm or monsoon season, it may be necessary to find a lifeboat. Talk to your recruiter about what is going on. Talk to the unit manager or someone who is over the person that you are having trouble with. If you really feel like your nursing license is in danger, go talk to your recruiter and/or an attorney about getting out of your contract.
- Finding the light in the midst of darkness. Find something that makes you happy and surround yourself with it. Go on a little shopping trip and get something that you have always wanted. Find a place of serenity and immerse yourself in meditation. On bad days I tend to come back to my little "ol'" RV, sit outside, and watch the waterfall that I have in my pond. I would definitely suggest that a travel nurse have some kind of small water feature to travel with her.
- A positive attitude can keep some of the mosquitoes from getting

to you. Go into each day with the thought that you are going to make it the best that you can. That may change twenty minutes into your day, but at least you started out on the right foot.

- Count down the days. Seeing the light at the end of the tunnel is always refreshing. Mark on your calendar the number of weeks left, or even the number of shifts left. Twenty-seven days sounds a lot better than two months!

These tips and tricks may not work for everyone; but for me, they keep me going through tough assignments. Remember that you are there because of your love for nursing, without all the politics. Remember that you do care, and that there will always be the next assignment and another exciting adventure in travel nursing.

Using Laughter To Survive Your Assignment

We've all heard the saying, "Laughter is the best medicine," but just how can it help you through your day as a traveling nurse?

Our first two weeks at a new assignment has to be the toughest. It is at this time that I am trying to adjust to my new surroundings, and I want to make an impression that I really do know what I am talking about. In the first weeks I have to prove that I am not into travel nursing just go to from company to company to see how much I can get away with. It is only after establishing that professional relationship that I start mixing in a little humor.

A little humor can go a long ways in making an assignment the best that it can be. Even with my worst assignment, humor is what made my day worth getting up for. Not humor with the other staff members, but humor with my patients. Even though the staff was under a lot of stress and anxiety, my patients were well taken care of and smiling because I was busy taking care of them with a little bit of everyday humor.

On the second day that I have a patient I can usually gain a smile by asking, "Can I listen to see if your heart is beating today?"

This simple attempt at humor will give me a feel about how well the patient is going to accept humor. With some patients that is the start of a wonderful humor relationship, and with others they let me know right quick that they are not in the mood for my little antics.

Some of my most memorable patients haven't been those that are grumpy, but those patients that I have laughed with through their many days at the hospital. Not only does this elevate my patient's mood, but it also has been proven to make a difference in muscle relaxation, neuropeptide release that affects depression, vasodilatation that reduces hypertension, and it also has the most effect on the hardening of attitudes.

Many of the places I have been want me to extend, not only because I'm there to work and do my job, but because of the humor and positive attitude that I bring to the unit.

Someone was fumbling with the foil surrounding a suppository the other day and I just calmly walked over and asked, "You know why they include the directions to take off the foil… because you *know* that someone did *not*." That little chuckle took away some of the stress that she was having opening that silly packaging.

You don't have to be a comedian to be a humorist. Just keep your eyes open to everyday occurrences. Did you ever wonder why they put the instructions on the hemorrhoid cream, "Do not take PO"? Yes! Because someone, somewhere, was eating the hemorrhoid cream and complaining to the company that it wasn't helping their hemorrhoids, and that they couldn't eat anything larger than a jellybean. And whatever possessed the hospital to contract "Seymour Butts" to design hospital gowns?

Now that you're smiling…take that smile to work and make your co-workers and patients smile right along with you.

Unexpected Contract Termination

What is a nurse to do? What constitutes valid grounds for the nurse to break a contract? What constitutes valid grounds for the travel company to break a contract?

A travel nursing contract is a legally binding contract and cannot be broken for just any old petty reason. Part of the nursing shortage problem can be from working conditions. Again, document this on your interview information sheet. Unsafe living conditions can include housing that is inhumane or insecure.

As a travel nurse, you need to do your homework on your accommodations before signing the contract. By using *www.apartments.com* or *www.homefair.com*, apartment and general housing location's crime rates can be checked out. What crime rate is an acceptable crime rate for you? Do not hesitate to call security to escort you to your vehicle if you decide to take a job in a higher crime area.

The trend for big problems usually arises with the larger companies that place corporate politics over taking care of their nursing staff. Recruiters can only do so much for their nurses in a larger cooperation. If the problem does not get solved, give them written notice as to why you believe that the contract has been breached, and that you are terminating your contract due to their breach of contract and their inability to resolve the problem. Health reasons can also be considered as a legitimate reason not to complete a contract.

Serious health problems, such as orthopedic and/or medical problems that require surgical interventions, motor vehicle accidents, or medical problems that will take an extended period of time to recover (i.e. hepatitis) are legitimate reasons to end a contract. If you are not able to complete your contract because of health reasons, the request to terminate the contract early must be in written form, which also needs to be accompanied by a physician's statement.

Health reasons for immediate family are also considered a legitimate reason to ask for early termination of a contract. In 2004, I had this happen to me when my father came down with Guillian-Barre Syndrome. I was lucky enough to be on week 11 of a 13-week contract. The manager asked me when my last day was, and put on my records that I completed my contract on that day in good standing. Now, that being said, my company was very good also in letting me out of my contract two weeks early, but this will not always happen! The company can make an attempt to collect housing costs for the days that are left on the lease.

I don't know of any travel nurse who can say that they have never been homesick at some time in their travel-nursing career. Keep your ears and eyes open for other travel nurses at work.

You have an agreement with the travel company that is a legal and binding contract. Problems can usually be ironed out along the way by talking to the nurse manager or your recruiter. Related to the fact that there are so many problems with contracts, I have decided that this subject requires a whole new chapter about contracts. Therefore, I invite you to read on about other problems that contracts in a whole new chapter!

Chapter Ten

Traveling as an LPN

Long before I was a registered nurse I practiced as a licensed "practical" nurse. Although I never traveled as an LPN, I remember hearing all the time, "If only you had your RN license." At the time, I was doing just fine as an LPN. I never had a problem finding a job, I made more money than I did as a nursing assistant, and still had the satisfaction of assisting the elderly.

That was twenty-two years ago, and I still don't think things have changed that much for LPNs. You still have LPNs who are happy to be just who they are and who don't want the added stresses of being a registered nurse. To tell you the truth, there are some days when I wish that I was "only" an LPN. I still believe that the LPN is a great asset to the nursing community.

With all that being said, the real question comes to this: how does being an LPN affect you as a traveling nurse? Should LPNs be able to travel? Of course. I've met a lot of them that I would much rather work with than some RNs, but there are some hospitals that are phasing them out. This may elevate the degree of difficulty in finding a travel nursing job, but it *doesnot* make it impossible. To explore this option for LPNs, I asked for now traveling LPNs to answer a few questions. The following is what I found out.

When asked if they felt like LPNs were being phased out, most believe that no, they were not, and that LPNs should be able to travel as well as RNs because nurses are needed everywhere. The real trick is to gain a lot of experience and have a willingness to travel to limited areas. One nurse stated, "Being an LPN is a financial move; it covers the bases and as in any structured situation, the higher you get the less scutt work you wish to do. Oddly, many good LPN's don't see things the same way. Nursing is about getting away from the bedside, and that is understandable; it can be a horrible place to be, but an LPN knows she /he will always be there, so they take it much more to heart than the "office nurse," and they are always the last in line for respect. It's a sad way to make a living."

At the time of writing this chapter it seems like Core Medical Group, Medical Staffing Solutions, and Supplemental have the most jobs. I would suggest that you find two or three companies and always keep your file updated so you can be ready to go when there is a job that comes up.

When it comes to reimbursements, the jury is split 50/50. Half of the nurses told me that their compensation was no different than an RNs, and half of the nurses stated that their compensation was a little less. From this I gather that it all depends on what company you travel with. Your travel pay, including your housing stipend, meals and incidentals, should be the same whether you're an LPN or an RN. The thing that will be different, as usual, is your regular hourly rate.

When it comes to education, the travel companies do not seem to supply much more than your BLS/ACLS. A few hospitals have offered nurses staff positions in trade for financial reimbursement for additional schooling to get their RN license. Personally, I went to school for my RN through the University of the State of New York/Regents/Excelsior program while practicing as an LPN instead of having a hospital pay my tuition in trade for two years of service. That is a great option if you really want to further your education, but you do not have to get your RN to be a great travel nurse.

Most LPNs struggle with finding good assignments and the lies, misrepresentation, lack of respect, and lack of recognition. Other facts that challenge LPNs are reimbursement issues, and they believe that facilities do not want to put their money on LPN's.

Some of the rewards of traveling as an LPN include meeting new people, receiving more pay, traveling to places that are happy to see you, and the occasional recognition. Other LPNs stated that serving the healthcare community and seeing areas of the United Stated that they have never previously visited is what makes it all worth the while to them.

According to most of the company websites that I visited you must have at least two years of experience, with at least six months of recent hospital experience, and LPNs in a hospital setting must be IV certified. As with traveling RNs, you will still have to file a work history, background check, mandatory education (Blood borne pathogens, OSHA, Fire, HIPPA, etc.…), and your skills checklist.

When it comes down to finding a nursing job, I would try one of the companies listed below to find a job. I have personally tested these companies out and they do have jobs!

~*~

LPN/LVN Travel Companies

Advantage Medical Staffing - Advantage Medical Staffing specializes in locating travel nursing jobs across the nation. Find out how you can get paid to travel and work with top benefits and pay. www.advantagemedicalstaffing.com

AWM Staffing, Inc. - AWM Staffing, Inc. is the leader in quality medical staffing services, and we service our medical facility clients by hiring medical professionals who have demonstrated the highest level of service and professionalism. www.awmstaffing.com

Cirrus Medical Staffing - At Cirrus Medical Staffing, they specialize in the placement of traveling medical professionals. If you're ready to earn top dollar, leverage your skills and enjoy the adventure of a lifetime, this is where your journey begins. www.cirrusmedicalstaffing.com

Core Medical Group - Their highly experienced staff works with the country's best hospitals to obtain new LPN jobs daily. www.coremedicalgroup.com

Fresenius Medical Care - Fresenius Medical Care provides LPN services for dialysis patients around the United States.

Juno Healthcare Staffing, Inc. - Juno Healthcare Staffing provides staffing solutions that meet the employment needs of hospitals, nursing homes, and other healthcare facilities by offering supplemental staffing of nurses, physical therapist and allied healthcare professionals. It offers temporary, full-time, per diem, and traveling nurse jobs for RNs, LVNs, LPNs, CNAs and PTs. You can search for jobs online or get in touch with their recruiters for personalized service. www.junohealthcare.com

Maxim Staffing Solutions - Maxim Staffing Solutions provides medical staffing solutions and employment opportunities for contract, temp to perm, per diem and direct hire healthcare jobs. Maxim is the leading healthcare staffing agency in the nation. Maxim staffs nursing jobs, allied health jobs, physician jobs, health information management jobs, government health care jobs, administration jobs, and more. www.maximstaffing.com

Medical Staffing Solutions - A temporary staffing agency owned and operated by medical professionals with just one mission: Matching the right opportunities with the right people. Local registry jobs as well as national travel assignments are available. www.mssmedicalstaffing.com

Meridian Medical Staffing, Inc. - Offers supplemental staffing solutions to premiere healthcare facilities in all fifty states. www.meridianmedicalstaffing.com

Radius Healthcare Staffing - Works with hospitals, clinics, and skilled nursing facilities to help provide the best quality candidate for permanent or contract positions. www.radiushealthcarestaffing.com

RN Network - Travel Nursing Jobs from RN Network, the first company in travel nursing to give you first-day benefits for both LPN and RN travel nurses. www.rnnetwork.com

Soliant Healthcare - Soliant has opportunities for LPNs in hospitals, nursing homes, private homes, ASCs, and assisted living facilities. www.soliant.com

Supplemental Healthcare - When quality, service, and performance matter, health care professionals turn to Supplemental Health Care first. Placing RNs, LVNs, CNAs, therapists, and technicians nationwide with travel contracts, per diem, or permanent placement positions.www.supplementalhealthcare.com

The Right Solutions - A select group of travel nurse and allied health staffing agencies which has travel contracts for license practical nurses that are IV-certified in military, veteran, and Indian health services. www.therightsolutions.com

Total Med Staffing - A local healthcare staffing company that recruits, screens, and places qualified professionals in various healthcare organizations. www.totalmedstaffing.com

Travel Max - Find direct placement and travel nursing jobs with TravelMax Nursing, a travel nurse staffing agency. Search for Registered Nurses (RN) and Licensed Practical Nurses (LPN) for both direct placement and travel nurse jobs. www.tmaxnursing.com

Trustaff - At Trustaff they do more than recruit and staff. They develop futures, deliver opportunities, and build relationships that last. They dedicate themselves to truly matching top talent with top employers nationwide. For organizations searching for first-rate talent, or job seekers looking for a new career, consider them your single-source solution to handle any and all of your staffing needs.

Valley Healthcare Systems Inc. - They understand the value of what their nurses provide and the needs of facilities to have a top-notch staff in an industry that is changing rapidly. It is their commitment to both parties that makes them second to none. www.vhcsystems.com

Traveling as an LPN may be a little more difficult than traveling as a RN, but it *is not* impossible.

Chapter Eleven

Allied Health Traveling

Physical Therapy

Physical therapy is a very rewarding occupation in which you can take an immobile patient and have him up and walking in a relatively short time. As a traveling physical therapist you can travel to acute rehabs, home health, pediatric centers, skilled nursing facilities, sub-acute facilities, and wound care clinics.

Many states now require physical therapists to have a master's degree, and it would be a good idea to have at least two years of experience before hitting the road on a travel assignment.

PhysicalTherapyJobServices.com is a full-service informational website that allows physical therapists easy access to many essential resources when planning for a change in your career path. www.physicaltherapyjobservices.com

Occupational Therapy

When soldiers from WWI came home they needed help to get back to doing even simple everyday activities of daily living. Their "occupation" was getting back to a normal everyday life as best as they could. To help accomplish this, specially trained people called "occupational therapists" were trained to help them get back to the simple tasks of combing their hair, putting on their boots, and feeding themselves.

Occupational therapy has come a long ways since then. Not only can you now help those who need assistance at home, on the job, or in school, but you can do that for several types of people in several locations around the United States.

In order to be a traveling occupational therapist you will need to be certified in occupational therapy and have at least two years' worth of experience at a hospital or rehabilitation facility.

Speech Therapy

A speech pathologist doesn't just deal with how well you speak, what dialect you speak, or mispronounced words; they are much more than that. They find themselves working in acute care, long-term care, and rehabilitation facilities with those patients who are having problems eating and swallowing. Others also work with patients in improving their linguistics, communication, language disorders, phonetics, and language development.

After completing a "swallow evaluation," speech therapists will make a recommendation on what type of food the patient can handle, whether it is whole, cut, soft, ground, or pureed. A speech pathologist or therapists may also accompany a patient to radiology for a barium-swallow test.

Respiratory Therapy

According to the Department of Labor, faster-than-average employment growth is projected for respiratory therapists. Job opportunities should be very good, especially for respiratory therapists with cardiopulmonary care skills or experience working with infants.

The employment of respiratory therapists is expected to grow 19% from 2006 to 2016, faster than the average for all occupations. The increasing demand will come from substantial growth in the middle-aged and elderly population—a development that will heighten the incidence of cardiopulmonary disease. Growth in demand also will result from the expanding role of respiratory therapists in case management, disease prevention, emergency care, and the early detection of pulmonary disorders.

Older Americans suffer most from respiratory ailments and cardiopulmonary diseases such as pneumonia, chronic bronchitis, emphysema, and heart disease. As their numbers increase, the need for respiratory therapists is expected to increase as well. In addition, advances in inhalable medications and in the treatment of lung transplant patients, heart attack and accident victims, and premature infants (many of whom are dependent on a ventilator during part of their treatment) will increase the demand for the services of respiratory care practitioners.

Job Prospects

Job opportunities are expected to be very good. The vast majority of job openings will continue to be in hospitals; however, a growing number of openings are expected to be outside of hospitals, especially in home health care services, offices of physicians or other health practitioners, consumer-goods rental firms, or in the employment services industry as a temporary worker in various settings.

Respiratory therapy travel is one field that is gaining in popularity; therefore, the field of traveling respiratory therapy is also growing at an astronomical rate.

For All Therapies

Once you have the license and experience you can travel to hospitals, assisted-living facilities, rehab centers, long-term care centers, outpatient clinics, and home health agencies.

Therapists receive some of the same benefits as a traveling nurse including housing, meals, incidentals, continuing education, free health, dental, and vision insurance along with some short-term, long-term, and life insurance.

~*~

Allied Health Placement Companies

Therapy Jobs - TherapyJobs.com is the leading online resource for physical therapy jobs, occupational therapist jobs, and speech therapy jobs. Post your therapy staffing jobs. Therapists, upload your resume and search jobs for free. www.therapyjobs.com

360 Healthcare Staffing - Healthcare staffing resources for healthcare professionals and employers. PT jobs, OT jobs, RN jobs, SLP jobs, MDS coordinator jobs and more. www.360healthcarestaffing.com

Advanced Medical Personnel Services - Advanced Medical Personnel Services, Inc. specializes in connecting people with Physical Therapy jobs, Physical Therapy Assistant jobs, Occupational Therapy jobs, Occupational Therapist jobs, and Speech Language Pathologist jobs. www.advanced-medical.net

Allied Travel Web - Welcome to AlliedTravelWeb.com, employment site where the search for Allied travel jobs ends. Now travel assignments find the travel therapists, traveling techs, and other travel healthcare professionals. Travel companies compete for Allied travelers. www.alliedtravelweb.com

Cariant Health Partners - Travel Physical Therapy, Occupational Therapy, and Speech Language Pathology Jobs. www.cariant.com

Cirrus Medical Staffing - At Cirrus Medical Staffing they specialize in the placement of traveling medical professionals. If you're ready to earn top dollar, leverage your skills, and enjoy the adventure of a lifetime, this is where your journey begins. www.cirrusmedicalstaffing.com

Comp Health - CompHealth is one of the nation's largest providers of healthcare recruiting and staffing services. www.comphealth.com

Core Medical Staffing - Travel Nursing Jobs. Whether you are seeking a travel nurse, permanent nursing job, or seeking an allied health job, they've got hundreds of health care jobs to choose from. www.coremedicalgroup.com

Cross Country Allied - Cross Country TravCorps offers physical therapy, speech therapy, occupational therapy, and respiratory therapy jobs. They also have radiation therapy, speech language pathology, medical lab, and other allied health travel positions with thirteen to twenty-six week full-time contracts. www.crosscountryallied.com

Delta Healthcare Provider - They provide outstanding opportunities that match your skills and location preferences so you can work and live where you want, which all adds up to a better outlook for you. www.deltahealthcareproviders.com

Ethika Group-Ethika Group was founded on a single constant to provide healthcare professionals and facilities with innovative solutions to their staffing needs while upholding the highest level of ethical standards in the industry. www.ethikagroup.com

Healthcare Starz-Specializes in connecting the best Healthcare Professionals with the best healthcare facilities from coast-to-coast including Alaska, Hawaii, and the US Virgin Islands. www.healthcarestarz.com

IPI Travel - IPI Travel excels in the Travel Nurse, Allied and Rehab Industry providing quality healthcare clinicians in all 50 states. Their network of relationships, with top healthcare facilities across the country, will open doors for you where other Travel Companies fall short.www.ipitravel.com

Jackson Therapy Partners - Whether you are interested in travel physical therapy jobs, travel speech therapy jobs, or occupational therapy travel jobs, you will enjoy the same benefits as their permanent partners with the added freedom of choosing the location you want to experience next. www.jacksontherapy.com

Liquid Agents - A comprehensive workforce procurement firm for the healthcare industry. They provide clients with qualified candidates, access to talent database, and cost-effective software. They help nurses and allied health professionals find recognition for their contributions. www.liquidagents.com

Medical Solutions - Travel nursing jobs and travel allied health jobs are found at Medical Solutions, a JCAHO certified travel nurse agency. www.medicalsolutions.com

Med travelers - Discover travel therapy jobs and medical imaging jobs at MedTravelers.com. We offer temporary assignments in many disciplines for qualified allied health professionals. www.medtravelers.com

Next Medical Staffing - Partners with premier healthcare facilities across the country to match your professional experience with their needs at a critical time. They work to be the staffing agency of choice for both healthcare professionals who strive to achieve their career goals and medical venues that expect the best from their specialists. www.nextmedicalstaffing.com

Onward Healthcare - Find the travel nurse job, per diem nurse job, or allied healthcare job that is right for you at Onward Healthcare. They are committed to providing their employees with outstanding customer service and the highest paying travel nursing assignments and allied health jobs in the industry. www.onwardhealthcare.com

PPR Healthcare - Specializing in travel nursing and therapy, PPR Healthcare Staffing is an industry-leading employment firm. www.pprtravelnursing.com

PT Solutions - A staffing company owned by two therapists who provide supplemental staffing coverage; they care about creating placements that benefit both therapists and therapy providers. They specialize in recruiting PT, PTA, OT, COTA, or SLP staff to fill short term or permanent openings. www.myptsolutions.com

Reflectx Staffing - Therapy jobs at ReflectxStaffing. Looking for a therapy job in Physical therapy, Occupational therapy, Speech therapy, or Respiratory therapy, or have positions that need to be filled? Use their staffing resources to fill your therapy needs. www.reflectxstaffing.com

Rehab Options - A rehab-personnel sourcing service for the rehabilitation services field, and they offer free rehabilitation job listings. Physical therapist jobs, physical therapy assistant jobs, physical therapy jobs, occupational therapist jobs, occupational therapy jobs, occupational therapy assistant jobs, speech-language pathologist jobs, speech-language pathology jobs, speech pathologist jobs, speech pathology jobs, and speech therapist jobs are the positions they cater to. www.rehaboptions.com

RTG Healthcare - They focus on providing you the best experience possible. We know you have a choice when it comes to an agency to represent you. RTG Medical is setting a higher standard in Healthcare Staffing. www.rtgmedical.com

Salus Solutions - Since 2004, Salus Solutions has provided Therapy Staffing Services to organizations and professionals nationwide who specialize in the rehab industry. www.salussolutions.com

Soliant Healthcare - Soliant therapists enjoy excellent salaries, robust healthcare benefits, paid housing and travel, saving plans, and much more. www.soliant.com

Sunbelt Staffing - They take pride in successfully pairing you with first-rate facilities nationwide. Their commitment to serving you with warmth and having a real interest in your happiness is what makes them different. www.sunbeltstaffing.com

Supplemental Healthcare - When quality, service, and performance matter, health care professionals turn to Supplemental Health Care first. Placing RNs, LVNs, CNAs, therapists, and technicians nationwide with travel contracts, per diem, or permanent placement positions. www.supplementalhealthcare.com

Trustaff - Placing healthcare professionals in travel nurse jobs, pharmacy jobs, therapy jobs, and more. www.trustaff.com

Chapter Twelve

Traveling When You're From A Foreign Country

Just because you were not born in the United States does not mean that you cannot become a traveling nurse in the United States. It does take a while to get your work visa, take language tests, take a registered nurse competency test, and make the voyage to the United States, but it is a worthwhile journey when you think about all of the new adventures you will be experiencing. Being a traveling nurse once you have at least one year of experience will give you an excellent way to travel around the United States and see all the wonderful sites. This chapter was written to help you accomplish that dream.

Finding a Nursing Job In United States

With the nursing shortage getting bigger and bigger every day, finding a nursing job in the United States is easier than ever. Nurses who are from the Philippines, Canada, Australia, or England can easily gain employment in the United States by following this simple guide.

With the help of CGFNS (The Commission on Graduates of Foreign Nursing School), nurses' qualifications are acknowledged, confirmed, and proven in reference to the education, registration, and licensure of nurses worldwide. Through this commission you will need to finalize a Visa Assessment and Work Screen.

In the Work Visa Screen, an educational investigation and evaluation of the foreign nursing license is conducted. Nurses are also required to pass the NCLEX or the CGFNS International Qualifying Examination and an English Language test, such as the TOEFL or IELTS.

One of the first requirements is getting an associate's or bachelor's degree in nursing and then passing the NCLEX (National Council Licensure Examination), which is a computer nursing competency test.

In some states, if you did not go to an English-speaking school, you will have to take the TOEFL (Test Of English as a Foreign Language) before you can receive your license as a Registered Nurse. This is the most widely used test for workers from a foreign country.

Some states are starting to use the IELTS (International English Language Testing System). It is a language test that measures the ability to communicate in English in listening, reading, writing, and speaking.

After passing the NCLEX, a language test, and obtaining a Visa Screen Certificate you are qualified to submit an application for a nursing license in the state where you reside. Then the fun begins in finding a nursing job.

You would be surprised how many travel companies now welcome foreign educated nurses with open arms. Some of the companies that will assist you include All About Staffing, Assignment America, Global Healthcare Group, Health Careers of America, Nurse Immigration Services, Pacific Link Healthcare, PPR Healthcare, Preferred Healthcare Staffing, Premier Healthcare Professionals, and Worldwide Resource Network.

Coming to work in the United States can be a longer process than you would like, but it is important to keep your eye on the cloud with the silver lining ahead of you. Someday, *it will* all be worth it!

CGFNS

The Commission on Graduate of Foreign Nursing, also known as the CGFNS, is a not-for-profit organization that completed credential evaluations for professional nurses, authenticates and verifies nurse's credentials, and then issues a certification to the state board of nursing for which the nurse is applying to take their NCLEX testing with.

The CGFNS is dedicated to the registration and licensure of all overseas nurses, whether they are from English speaking countries or not. In order for nurses to obtain their credentials they must take the NCLEX (National Council of Licensing's Exam) and pass an English language test.

At the writing of this book (April 2014), the credentialing service had a fee of $350. There is also an additions English proficiency report that has a $100 fee. This report is required by 14% of the states in the United States. There is also a fee for re-evaluation, additional reports, additional report recipients, and expedited service.

For the evaluation you will need to provide your license information, registration information, and diploma information. You must also have a comprehensive educational transcript. All professional schools must be included in this report.

The English language tests that you may take include the TOEFL (Test of English as a Foreign Language) or the IELTS (International English Language Testing System). One of these exams must be completed if your education and textbooks were not printed or spoken in the English Language.

After you have passed the NCLEX and one of the English language tests the CGFNS will review your Visa Application, and if acceptable, will issue you a Work Visa Screen. To obtain this screen you must also visit the consular officer and inform him/her of your intentions to work in the United States.

To do all of this you must also have a Visa Sponsor, which is a travel company that will assist you in obtaining all the requirements for your Work Visa. Usually this will be attached to you during the time that you work for that travel company. (CFGNS, 2013)

Work VisaScreen®

The VisaScreen® is an official document that you will receive from the CGFNS that states that you meet all the legal requirements to work inside the United States and that you are an RN (Registered Nurse). This means that your educational credentials and your competency testing meet the standards for all nurses who wish to obtain a job. The VisaScreen® also certifies that you have met the standards set by the Department of Homeland Security.

This screen will certify that you have taken and passed a language test such as the TOEFL or the IELTS, as described in the section above.

For the VisaScreen® you will need to have a license for registered nursing that is not restricted, transcripts from your nursing program showing that you have passed the national council of nursing's licensing exam, and obtained a sponsor.

It is also important to note that if you wish to become a resident of some states, you have a legal and clear nursing license you may be able to obtain a CGFNS certificate in lieu of the VisaScreen®. Related to the nursing shortage, the Department of Homeland security is making it easier for nurses who have a nursing license in another country to get a United States license and this has shortened some of the processes necessary for immigration.

One thing to remember in this process is that there are only limited amounts of Work VisaScreen® processed every year. The selection is based on the country in which you were born; therefore, going to nursing school in the United States under a student visa does not always guarantee you a work visa.

After all of this is completed you are on your way to getting a great job as a registered nurse in the United States. And remember that after you get a year's worth of experience you will have many opportunities to travel and work as a traveling nurse all over the United States. There is no better way to have a career and work at the same time! (VisaScreen®, 2013)

English Language Testing

When you make application for your work visa, one of the things they will want to know if you did not go to a school with English textbooks is if you are proficient in the English language. This is accomplished by taking either the IELTS or the TOEFL test. This is a must before you can get a job as a registered nurse.

IELTS stands for "International English Language Testing System." It is a test of English language proficiency. It is jointly managed by the University of Cambridge ESOL Examinations, the British Council, and IDP Education Australia and was established in 1989. There are two versions of this test: the Academic Version (which nurses and medical professionals must pass), and a General Training Version used by more than 2,000 universities in the United States.

The IELTS incorporates a variety of accents and writing styles that are presented in text materials in order to minimize linguistic bias. The IELTS tests the ability to listen, read, write, and speak the English Language. Each candidate is scored in four modules: Listening, Reading, Writing, and Speaking. It is scored on a scale from 1 to 9 with a "9" being an expert user. All nurses must score a total of at least 7, classified as a "Good User," which means that he or she has an operational command of the language, though with occasional inaccuracies, inappropriateness, and misunderstandings in some situations, and that he or she generally handles complex language well and understands detailed reasoning. (IELTS, 2014)

The TOEFL (Test of English as a Foreign Language) evaluates the potential success of an individual to use and understand

Standard American English at a college level. It is required for non-native applicants at many English-speaking colleges and universities. Additionally, institutions such as government agencies, businesses, or scholarship programs may require this test. A TOEFL score is valid for two years and then is deleted from the official database. Colleges and universities usually consider only the most recent TOEFL score.

The Internet-Based Test was introduced in late 2005 and has progressively replaced both the computer-based test and the paper-based tests. The IBT is now in use in the United States, Canada, France, Germany, and Italy.

Although the demand for test seats was very high and candidates had to wait for months, it is now possible to take the test within one to four weeks in most countries. The four-hour test consists of four sections, each measuring mainly one of the basic language skills (although some tasks may require multiple skills), focusing on language used in an academic, higher education environment. Note taking is allowed during the IBT. The test cannot be taken more than once a week.

The reading section consists of 3–5 long passages and questions about the passages. The passages are on academic topics; they are the kind of material that might be found in an undergraduate university textbook. Students answer questions about main ideas, details, inferences, sentence restatements, sentence insertion, vocabulary, function, and overall ideas. New types of questions in the IBT require paraphrasing, filling out tables, or completing summaries. Generally, prior knowledge of the subject under discussion is not necessary to come to the correct answer, though a prior knowledge may help.

The listening section consists of six long passages and questions about the passages. The passages consist of two student conversations and four academic lectures or discussions. The questions ask the students to determine main ideas, details, function, stance, inferences, and overall organization.

The speaking section consists of six tasks, two independent tasks and four integrated tasks. In the two independent tasks students must answer opinion questions about some aspect of academic life. In two integrated reading, listening, and speaking tasks students must read a passage, listen to a passage, and speak about how the ideas in the two passages are related. In two integrated listening and speaking tasks students must listen to long passages and then summarize and offer opinions on the information in the passages. Test takers are expected to convey information, explain ideas, and defend opinions clearly, coherently, and accurately.

The writing section consists of two tasks, one integrated task and one independent task. In the integrated task students must read an academic passage, listen to an academic passage, and write about how the ideas in the two passages are related. In the independent task students must write a personal essay.

It should be noted that at least one of the sections of the test will include extra, uncounted material. Educational Testing Service includes extra material to try it out for future tests. If the test taker is given a longer section he must work hard on all of the materials because he does not know which material counts and which material is extra. For example, if there are four reading passages instead of three, three of the passages will count and one of the passages will not be counted. It is possible that the uncounted passage could be any of the four passages.

The paper-based test is given in areas where the Internet-based and computer-based tests are not available. Because test takers cannot register at the testing center on the test date, they must register in advance, using the registration form provided in the Supplemental Paper TOEFL Bulletin. They should register in advance of the given deadlines to ensure a place because the test centers have limited seating and may fill up early. Tests are administered only several times each year.

With the Internet-based test nurses must make a score of 76. The computer-based test is scored on a scale from 0 to 300. Each of the four sections is given a total of 30 points, and then these are all added together to get the total score. For the computer test you must make 207, and for the written you must make a 540.

There were many changes made in 2006, including: (1) Overall, passages have become longer; (2) Part 1 has fewer questions involving photo descriptions; (3) The Listening Section hires not only North American English speakers but also British, Australian, and New Zealand English speakers. The ratio is 25% each for American, Canadian, British and Australian-New Zealand pronunciation; (4) Part 6 no longer contains the error spotting task, which has been criticized as unrealistic in a corporate environment but instead adopts the task wherein the test taker fills in the blanks in incomplete sentences, and (5) Part 7 contains not only single-passage questions but also double-passage questions wherein the test taker has to read and compare the two related passages such as e-mail correspondence.

Another change in 2007 added speaking and writing tests, and some changes were made to the reading and listening test as well that de-emphasized knowledge of grammatical rules.

This test will take you two hours to complete and consists of 200 questions. Half of the questions are on listening comprehension and the other half is on reading comprehension. Each person receives a score from 5 to 495 on each part for a total of 10 to 990. Nurses make a score of 725.

After you have completed and passed one of these tests and the NCLEX you can apply to the state board of nursing in which you reside. Through the CGFNS you will then be given your work visa. After you have received your nursing license you are on your way to one year of nursing experience, and then down the road to a travel nursing job. (TOEFL, 2014)

The NCLEX

The NCLEX is the National Council Licensure Examination, which is used to test the competency of all nurses who have completed their required educational program at an accredited university. This test is also required of all foreign-born nurses who wish to come to the United States to practice. This test will be a part of your Work Visa Screen.

This test of 265 questions is performed on a computer. Once you have reached the amount of questions determined by the national council of nursing to prove that you are competent, your test will announce that you have completed the test. Some nurses have gone to 75 and passed, and some nurses have gone to 75 and failed. Some nurses have gone to 265 and passed and some not. Wherever the test shuts off, you really never know how you have done until you get your results in the mail.

The NCLEX-RN (National Council Licensure Examination-Registered Nurse) is a computer-adaptive test (CAT) of entry-level nursing competence. Passing the exam is required of candidates for licensure as a Registered Nurse (RN) by all US state and territorial Boards of Nursing.

The NCLEX-RN and NCLEX-PN examinations are developed and owned by the National Council of State Boards of Nursing, Inc. (NCSBN). NCSBN administers these examinations on behalf of its member boards, which consist of the boards of nursing in the 50 states, the District of Columbia, and four U.S. territories: American Samoa, Guam, Northern Mariana Islands, and the Virgin Islands. This test is given only in English.

To ensure public protection, each board of nursing requires a candidate for licensure to pass the appropriate NCLEX examination, NCLEX-RN for registered nurses, and the NCLEX-PN for practical/vocational nurses. NCLEX examinations are designed to test the knowledge, skills, and abilities essential to the safe and effective practice of nursing at the entry-level.

NCLEX examinations are provided in a computerized adaptive testing (CAT) format and are presently administered by Pearson VUE in their network of Pearson Professional Centers (PPC). Authorized testing centers are located throughout USA and in selected foreign countries, including the most recently approved—the Philippines and Mexico. Click on their external link and visit the NCSBN for a list of approved countries where the NCLEX exam is given.

All items are developed and validated, using the expertise of practicing nurses, educators, and regulators from throughout the country. The content of the items of the NCLEX examinations is based on a practice analysis conducted every three years. All students considering taking the NCLEX and/or CGFNS exams must keep in mind that the exams are about basic nursing intervention, and not about nursing intervention beyond the level of practice of any entry-level nurse.

The two most important elements when considering and discerning the most correct answer are whether the answer is part of an intervention that is "safe" and "effective." Students should use this as a guideline: if an answer doesn't have the elements of a "safe" and "effective" intervention, whether seeking the physical and/or psycho-social integrity of a patient, that answer cannot be the "best" answer. It can be partially correct, but most likely it is not the best answer of the multiple possible answers. (NCLEX, 2014)

After you have taken a nursing competency test, English language competency test, obtained a sponsor and have applied for your work visa screen you are well on your way to becoming a travel nursing RN. Once you have that license in hand and work at your sponsored hospital for up to a year you will have the chance to take your skills on the road fulltime with a travel nursing job. Travel nursing RN jobs are not only financially rewarding, but they offer the best way to get around and visit the different parts of the United States.

~*~

Travel Companies Who Assist Foreign Nurses

Adex Medical Staffing - Medical Employment/Staffing, US and International Nursing Jobs - ADEX Medical Staffing, LLC specializes in providing quality health care and medical staffing services travel and per diem projects. www.adexmedicalstaffing.com/internationalnurses/

Cirrus Medical Staffing - At Cirrus Medical Staffing, they specialize in the placement of traveling medical professionals. If you're ready to earn top dollar, leverage your skills, and enjoy the adventure of a lifetime, this is where your journey begins. www.cirrusmedicalstaffing.com

Core Medical Group - CoreMedical Group has been placing healthcare professionals in rewarding travel assignments across the United States. www.coremedicalgroup.com

Expedient Medstaff - A leading travel nurse agency that will bring excitement and adventure to all your future nursing jobs. www.expedientmedstaff.com

Global Healthcare Group - Travel nursing agency with branches and affiliates in the UK, Canada, Philippines, India, South Africa, and the Middle East. www.globalhealthcaregroup.com

Medliant - In the business of supplying international nurses to staffing companies all over the United States.www.medliant.com

Nurses Rx - Discover the wonderful opportunities NursesRx can provide for Canadian nurses who wish to work in the US. NursesRx is a leading US travel nursing company. www.nursesrx.com

O'Grady Peyton - Learn more about the allied health and nurse employment opportunities at O'Grady Peyton. We offer travel nursing jobs to North American nurses and long-term positions for health care professionals from many other countries. www.ogradypeyton.com

Onward Healthcare - If you are looking to relocate to the United States as a Registered Nurse, then Onward Healthcare is the company for you! Over the past three years, they have helped hundreds International Nurses realize their goal of moving to the U.S and furthering their nursing careers. Their dedicated international nurse recruitment team and immigration specialists are ready to help you achieve your personal and professional goals. www.onwardhealthcare.com

Parallon Workforce Solutions - High paying per diem shifts, travel assignments, and full-time positions for Registered Nurses and Healthcare Professionals are available now! Parallon Workforce Solutions offers you the best opportunities, benefits and rates in the industry! www.parallonjobs.com

Premier Healthcare Professionals - When you work in the U.S. with PHP, they will assist you with the hassles of relocation so you can focus on enjoying life and practicing your profession. Their dedicated staff will arrange your placement, relocation, housing, insurance, and provide continued support throughout your assignment. www.travelphp.com

Strategic Healthcare - Strategic offers you a variety of unique opportunities to live and work in new places while expanding your professional horizons. Their experienced licensing, immigration, and housing specialists coordinate your pre-employment arrangements and advise you on all aspects of your relocation to the United States.www.strategic-healthcare.com/international-programs.html

Worldwide Travel Nursing - WTS has many travel nursing jobs around the world and is the only travel nursing company that provides true travel nursing jobs to the travel nursing industry worldwide! www.worldwidetravelstaffing.com

~*~

References

CFGNS. (2013). Facts retrieved from CFGNS: http://www.cgfns.org/services/ces-professional-report/

IELTS. (2014, April 11). Facts retrieved from Wikipedia, a public domain governed by a General Public License: http://en.wikipedia.org/wiki/IELTS

NCLEX. (2014, February 8). Facts retrieved from Wikipedia, a public domain governed by a General Public License: http://en.wikipedia.org/wiki/NCLEX

TOEFL. (2014, April 6). Facts retrieved from Wikipedia, a public domain governed by a General Public License: http://en.wikipedia.org/wiki/TOEFL

VisaScreen®. (2013). Facts retrieved from CGFNS: http://www.cgfns.org/services/visascreen/

Chapter Thirteen

Independent Contracting

Many nurses now have put on the hat of nurse entrepreneur. Getting contracts by yourself and doing your own independent contracting is a little tougher than just having an agency helping you with taxes, government dues, insurance, and getting assignments, but there are definite advantages, with more money coming into your pocket and having control over your destination.

One of the basic differences of being an independent contractor instead of an employee is that you will be receiving the IRS Form 1099 instead of a W2 form. This IRS Form 1099 shows the amount that was paid for services rendered. This form will have on it the account number (or unique number), the payer assigned to distinguish your account, the amount subject to self-employment taxes, other income, backup withholdings, and any state of local income tax withheld from the payments.

Another difference is that you will be responsible for obtaining your own contracts. Most commonly, this is done in two ways: First, by calling the hospital and seeing the availability of contracts, which they usually use for contracts, and if they would consider an independent contract, or you can contact a company that specializes in independent contracts. These companies will charge you a few dollars per hour for helping you in obtaining a "subcontract" through them. There used to be four or five companies that you could subcontract for, but in 2014, I can now only find one—Skilled Nursing Inc. www.snistaffing.com.

I know, you're anxious to get down the road by yourself, but there are just a few more basics that you have to understand, such as the type of business you are going to have, formulating a business plan, creating a marketing plan, must-haves for the office, and what to put into the contract. You just never know, after starting your own independent contractor business you may want to expand and let other nurses share in your happiness and wealth.

What Type of Business?

First, you need to decide what type of business you will start. There are several types, including a sole proprietor (the most common), a C-Corporation, an S-Corporation, or a limited liability corporation (LLC).

A sole proprietorship is a corporation that officially has no separate existence from its owner. Hence, the limitations of liability enjoyed by a corporation do not apply. All debts of the business are debts of the owner. It is a "sole" proprietor in the sense that the owner has no partners. A sole proprietorship essentially means that a person does business in their own name and there is only one owner. A sole proprietorship is not a corporation; it does not pay corporate taxes, but rather the person who organized the business pays personal income taxes on the profits made, making accounting much simpler. A sole proprietorship need not worry about double taxation like a corporation would have to.

A business structured as a sole proprietorship will likely have a hard time creating capital, since shares of the business cannot be sold, and there is a smaller sense of legitimacy relative to a business that is organized as a corporation or limited liability company. Hiring employees may also be difficult. This form of business will have unlimited liability; therefore, if the business is sued, it is the proprietor's problem.

Another disadvantage of a sole proprietorship is that as a business becomes successful, the risks accompanying the business tend to grow. To minimize those risks, a sole proprietor has the option of forming a limited liability company. Most sole proprietors will register a trade name or just go by "Doing Business As." This allows the proprietor to do business with a name other than their legal name, and it also allows them to open a business account with banking institutions.

A C-corporation is a form of corporation that meets the IRS requirements to be taxed under Subchapter C-of the Internal Revenue Code. Most major companies are incorporated under a C-corporation. After the corporation is created, it becomes its own entity and has an indefinite lifespan, as long as the yearly filing fee is paid. This is what you would want to file if you were starting a staffing agency that would have several employees.

The main difference between S and C is the fact that a C-corporation is taxed a Federal Corporate Income tax, whereas an S-corporation is not. It may also have an unlimited amount of shareholders, as well as foreign shareholders, unlike S-corporations.

In order to accomplish the task of becoming a C-Corp, you will need to choose an available business name that complies with your state's corporation rules, appoint the initial directors of your corporation, file formal paperwork, usually called "articles of incorporation," and pay a filing fee that ranges from $100 to $800, depending on the state in which you incorporate, create corporate "bylaws," which lay out the operating rules for your corporation, hold the first meeting of the board of directors, issue stock certificates to the initial shareholders of the corporation, and obtain licenses and permits that may be required for your business.

An S-Corporation is taxed as a joint venture, while at the same time it enjoys the benefit of incorporation. This means that, while the S-Corporation itself pays no federal income tax, the shareholders of the S-Corporation pay federal income tax on their proportionate share of the S-Corporation's income. In other words, any profits earned by the corporation will not be taxed at the corporate level, but instead will be taxed only at the level of the individual shareholders.

Unlike C-Corp dividends, which are taxed at the federal rate of 15.00%, S-Corp dividends are taxed at the shareholder's marginal tax rate. However, the C-Corp dividend is subject to "double-taxation." The income is first taxed at the corporate level before it is distributed as a dividend. The dividend is then taxed at the personal capital gains rate when issued to the shareholder.

S-Corp Distributions are only taxed once at the marginal rate of each shareholder who received a distribution. Additionally, the S-Corp shareholder will pay taxes on the S-Corp earnings, whether or not a distribution is made. Having S-Corporation status can prove a huge benefit for a corporation. The corporation can pass income directly to shareholders and avoid the double taxation that is inherent with the dividends of public companies, while still enjoying the advantages of the corporate structure.

In order to qualify, a corporation must be a small business corporation. Requirements that must be met include the fact that it must be a domestic corporation, must have no more than 100 shareholders, and all of the shareholders must be citizens of the United States. The corporation also must have only one class of stock, and profits and losses must be allocated to shareholders proportionately to each one's interest in the business.

If a corporation meets the foregoing requirements, its shareholders may file Form 2553 with the IRS. The Form 2553 must be signed by all of the corporation's shareholders. If a corporation that has elected to be treated as an S-Corporation ceases to meet the requirements, the corporation will lose its S-Corporation status.

A Limited Liability Corporation is a legal form of business offering limited liability to its owners. It is similar to a corporation and is often a more flexible form of ownership, especially suitable for smaller companies with restricted numbers of owners.

An LLC allocates for the flexibility of a sole proprietorship or partnership arrangement within the structure of limited liability, such as that approved for corporations. A benefit of an LLC over a limited partnership is that the rules and regulations required for forming and registering LLCs are much easier than the requirements most states place on developing and managing corporations. Most LLCs will, however, decide to implement an Operating Agreement or Limited Liability Company Agreement to provide for the authority of the Company, and such Arrangement is normally more multifaceted than a corporation's statutes.

One motive that an industry might prefer to be planned out as an LLC is to circumvent dual assessment of taxes. A conventional corporation is taxed on its income, and then when the profits are dispersed to the owners of the corporation or shareholders, those dividends are also taxed. With an LLC, income of the LLC is not taxed, but each owner of the LLC is taxed, based on its pro rata allocable portion of the LLC's taxable income, apart from whether any distributions to the associates are made. This single level of taxation can lead to significant savings over the corporate form.

Another underlying principle that a company might choose to be arranged as an LLC is to take advantage of the tax classification flexibility that LLCs allow. A new business facing losses might opt to function as a sole proprietorship or partnership in order to bypass those losses to the owners. A slightly more established business might operate as an S-corporation to save on self-employment taxes. A large, mature business with many owners might operate as a C corporation.

Formulating A Business Plan

Your business plan will need to include an executive summary, general company description, products and services, an operation plan, management and organization, a personal financial statement, startup expenses and capitalization, a financial plan, and refining the plan.

The executive summary actually needs to be written last. It should include everything that you would put into a five-minute interview, including the fundamentals of the proposed business, what your services will be, who your customers will be, who the owners are, and what you think the future holds for your business. This summary needs to be KISSed…Keep It So Simple!

The general company description needs to include the fact that you are a registered nurse, providing services to hospitals, and how you will provide those services. You will need a mission statement, usually 40 words or less, which explains your reason for starting this company and what philosophies have guided you to make the decision to strike out on your own.

Next, you will need to state your goals and objectives. What goal do you have for your company? Do you want to be in the Fortune 500, or do you just want to provide great service to others, giving them quality service instead of quantity? This will depend on whether or not you decide to remain a sole proprietor or if you incorporate as a C, S, or Limited Liability Corporation.

To whom are you going to market your products? Hospitals, nursing homes, physicians' offices, surgical centers? What is the future of your company? What changes do you see in the future? How will you deal with those changes?

Also, in the goals and objectives you will need to describe why you think that your company is the best company for the job? Customer service? Experience? Skills?

This is where you will also want to state what type of corporation you have filed as and why you decided to file as that type of corporation.

Next, you will describe in-depth your products or services with technical specifications: what set of skills are available, what can you do for the hospital or medical facility? Which of these features will give you the competitive edge and exclusivity? What is the bill rate for your services? Why is your bill rate a good bargain? Hospitals are looking for the best rates and the best quality together. Can you supply that demand? (This will be discussed further in the marketing plan section).

Next is the operation plan. This will explain the day-to-day operation of the business, its home-base location, people, and processes. Some of the things you will want to include in this section are the services you will provide, quality control aspects, and customer service. Where will your home base be located? Unless you are planning on hiring a lot of nurses in a staffing company type of setting, this will be the physical location of your permanent residence. What type of licensing and insurance will you be carrying on yourself and/or personnel?

If you plan on hiring other nurses, you will need to list how many nurses you will start out with, the units of the hospital that you would like to provide services for, how to pay for their services, training methods, requirements for nurses, job description, and any need for subcontracted workers.

How will you manage your accounts receivable? You will have to formulate a plan to bill the hospital, as well as how to receive the payments. Independent contractors typically bill the hospital weekly, but payment is usually made only once a month.

Next, you should state your management members and any consults regularly used. Consults that you are smart to have available include an attorney, accountant, insurance agent, banker, nursing profession consultants, small business consultants, and mentors you feel are needed to help you run a successful business.

After that, you should explain what you believe your startup expenses are, your financial ability to assist with those expenses, and any other capital funds you have acquired or have a plan to acquire. Do your research on exactly how much it is going to cost you to start up a home office. Do you have a computer, fax machine, copy machine, and phone? A fairly inexpensive printer can do faxing, copying, and scanning. Other services can be provided through an office supply store. Once you estimate your start up expenses, it's a general rule to plan on a twenty percent financial pad for unexpected incidentals. How much do you plan to make in a year? How much do you plan to make in five years? What are your long-term financial goals? Do you plan on starting as a sole proprietor and then further incorporate into a Limited Liability Corporation or C-Corp?

Refine your plan to include the key competitive factors in the industry, capacity limits, purchasing and inventory management of supplies, and new services under development. How will you manage rapidly changing prices or costs, and how will you remain on the cutting edge with your services?

The preceding questions can be answered by taking your time and doing an in-depth look into what you really want to accomplish with your services as an independent contractor. Having this documentation will give your company more validity.

Creating a Marketing Plan

The purpose of a marketing plan is to put onto paper why you think your product is better than other products, why hospitals should hire you, why hospitals should hire your staff, and the future plans of your company. This plan will assist you in knowing where you have been and where you are going. It will keep your eyes focused on the job at hand—building your travel nursing company into a prosperous and successful business.

We are going to build this nursing company just like we take care of our patients—through assessment, planning, implementation, and evaluation. To accomplish this, first we need to assess what types of services we are going to provide, to whom we are providing those services, who are our competitors, and how the market fluctuates.

What types of services are you going to provide? This will be directly linked to what your nursing specialty is. Are you going to employ others? If you have multiple specialties, then the greatest demand will determine what services you will have the most success in providing to your clients. You will need to do some research into what hospitals you are going to target at first and determine what their needs are.

You need to research what other nursing contractors are out there and what their targeted hospitals are. What do they provide to the hospital that you could provide better? You must declare what the market is lacking in order to determine how you can fill that place.

By doing some research, you can also find out what your competitors are paying. If you explain that you are a nurse wanting to do a travel assignment and wanting to know what types of jobs they have and what the pay rates are, then you can figure a ballpark range of what the bill rate is by taking what they are paying the travel nurses and adding 20% (take the pay rate and multiple it by 1.2). You can also go to salary.com and see what the nursing salary is for that position. To get an idea of a bill rate from this you must understand that travel nurses make approximately 20% more an hour than staff nurses and the company will also get 20%. By taking the pay rate and multiplying it by 1.4 you can figure out an approximate bill rate.

Your plan will include aligning the price with the apparent value with the customer. If your price seems a little high, drop it a few dollars per hour. If you are unable to get contracts after discussing the bill rate with human resources, you may have to look at changing the price. Keep in mind also that if you provide outstanding service to a customer, you can raise your price a little on the next contract.

Snoop around and see what other competitors are out there. Are there several independent nursing companies available? Are they all providing service to one hospital, or do they cater to a group of hospitals? What are their strengths? What are their weaknesses? How can you capitalize on those weaknesses? Maybe the hospital needs a more flexible nurse…maybe they need someone to work night or weekends. Find out the need and what needs are not being provided for by other nurses and you will get your foot in the door.

You need to plan how you are going to get the word out to these hospitals. There are several ways to get the information into hospitals by using phone calls followed up with brochures and postcards telling hospitals of your new services. Carry business cards with you at all times. You never know when you are talking with people out in the community and you can tell about some hospital, clinic, or nursing home that is, "terribly short-staffed, I just don't know how they make it." Your eyes and ears should be open at all times for marketing possibilities.

What are the goals of your marketing efforts, and in what time frame do you want to accomplish them? Some nurses just want a contract for the next month, some want a contract for the next week, and some want a contract for the next year. Do you plan on helping other nurses find contracts? You might have a goal of 10 nurses this year to work in an attempt to make a good living with your company and propel it to the next level.

You also need a plan to launch your business. Follow your business plan and get your business license, get a bank account set up, and have your marketing plan ready to go. A great way to announce the beginning of your company is to place an ad in the newspaper, or better yet, send out press releases in an effort to have the media do a human interest story about why you are starting your own nursing company. If you have a self-contract, you might contact the local newspaper and offer a free article to the newspaper, with your contact and company information as a tag line.

Next, you can implement your plan in attempt to sway the client from a stage of knowledge to one of contemplation. The client needs to have confidence that you will supply their facility with the best of service.

To do this, you will need a set plan, telling when you can start, how much the bill rate will be, how you plan on doing quality control on yourself, and reinforce the fact that the independent contractors services are the best for that client. Work with the client and negotiate for the best possible deal for both you and the client.

Choose where you want to be, and beat down the doors of every hospital in that area by sending out your profile. The profile will include your resume and a skills checklist, and then start your circle to the outskirts of town. Persistence will pay off, and you will find you a job where you want if you put enough time and effort into it.

What To Put Into The Contract

Independent contracts are very similar to those of an agency nurse, but there are some differences that you need to be aware of concerning certain responsibilities: billing, insurance, and other documentation. The following is a brief description of what needs to be included.

The contractor responsibilities: A contractor (the independent contractor) is to provide nursing services in a certain area of the hospital, according to standards set forth by the Joint Commission on Accreditation for Health Care Organization (JCAHO) and the Nursing Practice Act of the State of Idaho (my home state, you can insert yours).

The contractor certifies and will provide legal documentation of skills acquired in the past 16 years as a licensed nurse, health certificates, personal identification, company identification, and proof of liability insurance with minimum amounts of $1,000,000 per occurrence and $5,000,000 yearly.

This contract will be entered into as an independent contract with the agent not entitled to any benefits accorded to hospital employees, including workman's compensation, disability, vacation, and sick pay.

The client is responsible for providing a safe work environment, including a job description and basic orientation to medication administration, documentation, order transcription, patient safety, and on-the-job employee safety.

You may also put in there the cancellation policy for low census days, areas that you will and will not work based on competency, any guaranteed hours, and nurse-to-patient ratios that are acceptable. Also, add in a phrase about the need to notify you two hours in advance of cancellation and you will notify them two hours in advance of unable to meet the obligation related to an illness.

Next are the financial items, including bill rates, overtime rates, weekend rates, and holiday rates. It is definitely best to keep this simple by charging a basic bill rate, overtime at 1.5 times the base pay, and holiday rates at 1.5 times the base pay. Other things that you can add, if you really feel the need to, are charge nurse pay, weekend pay, and shift differential. Just keep in mind, the more straightforward and uncomplicated the contract appears, the better it is, but don't cheat yourself either.

You should also add in a statement about when accounts are receivable. Some hospitals only pay out once a month, but by offering a 2–5% discount, some will go with a bi-weekly pay rate. Also, add a section on how much interest will be charged if the amount is not received in a timely manner. This may be anywhere from 2–5% of the total invoice for every day that is late. Also include a statement that if things go to court, lawyer fees will be asked for. You must also state when the workweek is—from Sunday to Saturday or from Monday to Sunday. You may have to be negotiable with this and go with the same schedule as the hospital has for their other employees.

Last is the termination clause. This should list how long the contract is to last, and under what circumstance the contract can be terminated. The industry standard is that contracts can be cancelled with or without cause by providing thirty days written notice.

After the basic contract is written, don't be surprised if it goes through a few changes and negotiations with the hospital. It will take you an average of two weeks from the start of the negotiation process to being on the job.

Taxes and Payroll

There are several payroll taxes/costs for the independent contractor to consider ways of minimizing. I'm not including income tax in this definition. Payroll taxes usually refer to FICA, workman's comp, and unemployment insurance.

The biggest is FICA/Medicare (Federal Insurance Contributions

Act), also referred to as Social Security or SSI, or in another context as the self-employment tax. Employers and employees split these taxes; employers can deduct their half as an expense. Each half is 7.65%, and together they add up to 15.3%. ICs are responsible for the entire amount, although half of it is treated as a deductible expense. There is no difference in sole proprietor and corporate treatment.

Workman's comp is technically not required for a sole proprietor (depending on the state, a corporate officer may also be exempt), but if you hire other employees, it is an absolute requirement. The hospital may require it or some other form of accident insurance. I have also read recommendations that ICs should carry workman's comp, regardless of the requirements. It costs perhaps 2% of gross payroll, so it is up to your judgment. Rules also vary quite a bit from state to state.

Unemployment insurance has a state and federal component and also accounts for about 2% of payroll. It is optional for a sole proprietor and usually a corporate officer, but not for their employees. I can't think of a good reason to pay this, and you won't be eligible for benefits anyway. It is also a cost advantage you have over an agency (you could reduce your bill rate by 2% for example to be more competitive).

The easiest way to reduce all taxes is by seeking out and taking all available legitimate expense deductions. Don't spend money just to save on taxes; that is just foolish—the more you spend the more you save theory. Deductions that a travel nurse IC should consider are meals and incidentals from Publication 1542, housing away from your tax home (leveraged with Publication 1542 schedules if you are a corporation), all travel between your tax home and the facility (if an overnight stay) at 37.5 cents a mile (or actual airfare/other costs if higher), commute miles between temporary housing and the hospital, licenses, education R/T profession, certifications, and cell phones. Perhaps you have to hire people to maintain your home while you are away. Anything business related should be considered, including lawyer, CPA, other consultant fees, books about business, incorporation and maintenance costs, and bank fees.

Business structure directly impacts payroll taxes. S-corporations can pass some of their profits to their owners without being subject to payroll taxes. (See Business entities FAQ.) C-corps may likewise be able to figure out a scheme to do this. Be careful and get good advice, though; bonuses for officers or employees are usually considered reportable wages. Dividends to shareholders, while not subject to payroll taxes, are subject to both corporate income tax *and* personal income tax (double taxation).

In Conclusion

This is only a tip of the iceberg when it comes to the world of independent contracting. This, along with other resources including the IRS website, small business associations, and discussion boards on independent contracting or nursing entrepreneurship, will have you headed down the road to success.

***

Big thanks to Ned for allowing me to use portions of his website for some content in this chapter. Ned, RN, is the host of the Independent Contractors forum at: http://forums.delphiforums.com/ICNurse/, a forum that allows independent nurses to network, ask questions, and give advice to other independent nurses and those who wish to become independent contractors in the nursing or the broader healthcare community.

Other aspects of this chapter were written from my personal experience of being a sole proprietor of an eBook publishing company, travel nursing informational site, and being partial owner in an Internet Service Providership, which was classified as an S-Corp along with my husband's experience in both C-Corporations and Limited Liability Corporations.

Although a business plan and marketing plan are not set in stone must-haves, I do believe that it is a great way to plan out what you are trying to accomplish and have available if someone ever questions the validity of your company.

Chapter Fourteen

Traveling With Pets

For many of us our "family" also consists of a few furry children. While not impossible to travel with a pet, it is a little more difficult and does cost more. For dedicated pet owners, that is a small price to pay to keep our four-legged children with us.

First of all, you need to consider what kind of pet you have. If you have a two hundred pound Saint Bernard, he is going to be much harder to travel with than if you have a two pound Chihuahua. Remember, as a traveling nurse, we try to keep things in smaller packages. The biggest problem with a larger pet also is that some apartments now have a weight limit on pets, and so do most motels. The biggest restriction that I have found is for pets that weigh over twenty pounds. They also have breed restrictions that usually restrict pit bulls, mastiffs, chows, and some boxers. Some airlines also have summer restrictions on pets with short noses such as pugs, bulldogs, and shar-pei. I also found where one airline restricts the travel of any pets during the winter months from Jackson Hole, WY; Boise, ID; and Salt Lake City, UT.

When traveling by car, you don't have as many restrictions, but it does mean a longer trip for your furry friend. There are some hotels with breed and weight restrictions, but they are usually more lenient than the airlines. The most important thing about keeping your pet in a motel room is to remember to declare your pet and pay the pet deposit. Most hotels that I have been to charge between $15 and $50 for your pet to stay the night. Sometimes they will also have a refundable pet deposit in case there is damage to the room. On the flip side, if you don't declare your pet upon arrival, then they can charge hundreds of dollars as a "fine," as if you were smoking in a non-smoking room.

A good way to find a pet-friendly hotel is through the Internet or with a downloaded phone app. Both Choice Hotels chains (Quality Inn, Comfort Inn, Clarion) have quite a few pet friendly hotels. LaQuinta has a pet-friendly app for your iPhone.

Upon arrival, always ask for the pet rules. Most hotels do not allow a pet to be in the room by themselves, especially while the housekeeping staff is in the room. These rules usually include the fact that your pet is only allowed in designated areas to do his business. Always keep your pet on a leash and keep those little green baggies handy for cleanup after Rover (a fitting name for a travel nurse' pet). Remember to dispose of the waste outside and not in the bathroom wastebaskets. It is also handy to have a towel to dry paws after being out in the grass. If you have an energetic dog, you can always ask the desk clerk if they know of a park that is close.

Along with your pet's identification on his collar, it is a good idea to get a tag with your cell phone number. Another great dog tag to have is one with his veterinarian's number included. If you have to leave your pet in the room for even a short amount of time, be sure to post your cell phone number in the room, along with when you expect to be back. If your dog is a barker, this may not be a good idea, related to the fact that you may be asked to leave if Rover wakes up everyone when you go out for your midnight snack.

For traveling nurses, there are a few things that you need to check on before you embark on your next adventure. First of all, check out the state laws where you are planning your next assignment. For example, if you are wanting Hawaii in the winter, you need to realize that Hawaii has a 120-day quarantine for all pets that do not meet their "5 day or less" checklist. This 120-day quarantine also comes at a hefty price: over $1000.

Your pet should have all their shots up-to-date, and a letter of health from the veterinarian that has been taking care of your pet. It is also smart to get your pet micro-shipped. It only costs about $60 and is well worth the expense. To have your animal in some states parks (such as Vermont), you are required to have a letter of pet immunization before they will allow your pet inside the park. Once you get to your assignment, ask other nurses that you meet in orientation, or ask the educational supervisor, if they have a recommendation for a local veterinarian.

Although most travel companies will not let you into your

apartment until just a few days before orientation, ask if you can have a few more days before to get moved in and have a few days where you are with your pet in their new environment. Of course, by having their favorite toy or cat claw station, the pet will adjust more quickly to this new place being a safe place.

One handy gadget that I found online was a KongTime automatic dispenser. It has four compartments and you can fill it with a toys or treats. This will give your pet a new toy or treat every hour or two, depending on your settings.

Before you arrive at the apartment, you should touch base with the manager of the facility or your housing coordinator about pet rent and pet deposits. Some companies cater to nurses with pets and will assist you in paying the deposit by taking it out of your check a little at a time. For pet owners that strike out on their own, they may find places that say they don't take pets will take a pet for a larger deposit. There are advantages and disadvantages to company-provided housing and traveler-provided housing. There are some companies that will encourage you to take the easy way out and leave Rover at home, but never give up! Housing can be found if you use the resources found online. With the invention of Craigslist, housing near your assignment is somewhat easier. Still, you may have to look at an extended-stay suite that is pet friendly. For instance, Candlewood Suites is pet friendly to pets that weigh less than 80 lbs. for a deposit of $150. In addition, Healthcare Travelbook now offers housing services to help all travelers, not just pet owners, find safe and secure housing while on assignment.

Upon arriving at the apartment, be prepared to sign a rental agreement for the stay of the pet. It will state the amount of the "pet rent" to be paid every month, along with the amount of the pet deposit. Other things that I have found on pet addendums include:

1. Pets must be kept from disturbing the peace.
2. They must be kept from damaging property.
3. Any property that is damaged will immediately be fixed or restitution will be paid to the complex/landlord.
4. The pet must be under control at all times.
5. Pets cannot be restrained by tether or chain when outside the dwelling alone.
6. Pets are not to be left at home alone for long periods of time.
7. All pet deposits made by the pet in the lawn must be taken care of promptly.

8. Food or water should always be kept indoors for the pet.
9. All pets must be vaccinated and have their records available for inspection.

Remember that you are a guest in that dwelling for a period of time. Accidents can occur, but these are best cleaned up as quickly as possible. Always keep a can of good carpet cleaner with you at all times. They have spray cans now with the scrubber at the end that make excellent spot removers. In fact, I always kept a can of it around before I got my cat. There are also other commercial "sprinkles for pets" that can be put on the carpet before vacuuming to keep pet odors down.

Part of your pet maintenance also includes protecting your pets from fleas and worms. The only flea flicker in the apartment should be on the television during football season! You definitely don't want Rover doing the butt scootin' boogie on the carpet either. These can be controlled by regular use of flea collars, sprays, and special de-worming treats.

Although most of the time when we talk about traveling with animals people automatically think of dogs, more and more travelers are heading out with their feline friends. I remember one of the first times that I traveled with my rescue cat, Mila. The hotel clerk asked me what breed my dog was. I promptly answered, "Siamese." She said, "Oh, that is a cat. We don't see many people who travel with cats." They didn't even have cat treats, only doggie biscuits for a bedtime snack.

The rules are mostly the same for cats as they are for dogs, but some things are a little different, especially when starting out. It is much easier if you start out traveling when they are at a young age. We started training Mila on a leash the first time we went to the vet for her checkup. This is the second cat that I have had leash trained, but not all cats take to a leash. Be especially careful if you haven't tried leash training within the first year of life. I remember when I was a kid putting my older tomcat on a leash. Let's just say that I've never seen a cat go that ballistic.

Take them out on short rides at first, and then move to weekend trips. So far, we have made trips from Idaho to Oklahoma with our cat and from Idaho to Seattle with Mila. The second trip went a lot better, as I had looked online and found a car seat for her. It is a seat with a harness that will keep your pet secured while traveling. Once again, this takes some time to get used to, and I would hesitate to put an older feisty cat in it.

For other cats, I would definitely suggest a cat carrier. There are hard-sided and soft-sided ones available. If you are traveling by air, it is suggested to have a soft-sided one that will fit under the seat of the airplane. The hard-sided ones are better for car trips since they can be buckled in. You don't want your furry friend to go flying in case of an accident.

Like traveling with a dog, you will want to take along spill-proof water and food bowls/dishes. Traveling with a cat also requires a small travel-size litter box. We found a big plastic bowl at the thrift store that fits just right in between the front and back seats of the car that works out great for traveling. One thing I have learned by experience is not to take them to the pet area at the rest stops. Number one, they don't understand that they are supposed to potty outside (especially if you have an indoor cat). Number two, you will be buying some kind of flea and tick spray at the next truck stop. And I thought it would be a good idea to get her out of the car for a while…Nope, bad idea!

If your assignment calls for travel on an airplane there are more rules and regulations that go with that adventure. First of all, you want to go to the airline's website and see what their rules are for traveling with a pet. When you make your arrangements, you need to inform the airline that you will have a pet. It is very important to make arrangements for Rover, instead of just showing up with him. Airlines usually charge an extra $75 to $150 for the pet. When making your travel arrangements try to get non-stop flights.

For the airline websites that I visited, most of them required the pet to be in a carrier that can fit underneath the seat in front of you. This carrier is also counted as one of your carry-ons. While on the airplane or in the airport, the pet is not allowed out of that carrier; therefore, remember to take Rover to potty before entering the airport. Look for a pet relief area outside of the airport entrance. There is a list of airports and their pet relief areas at www.petfriendly.com.

One of the easier ways to travel with your pet is in a recreational vehicle (RV). The pet is always at home and doesn't have to get used to a new apartment every three to six months, just like their owners. You still have to make sure that the RV park you are staying in is pet friendly, but most of them that I have been in are pet friendly. There may be some breed restrictions, but the size restrictions are as strict as they are in an apartment. Keep in mind that most RV parks do not allow you to leave a dog unattended in the RVall day while you are at work related to the health risk of your pet.

Along with their leash and their favorite toy, you may want to get an exercise cage. There are all kinds of exercise cages, and most of them fold down. Of course, if you have a larger dog, you will want to take them for walks more often. I've seen a few traveling cats in my travels. Most of them are indoor cats, but I know a few who have cats that can be let outside and will come back to the RV. Most felines that I have been around though usually don't adjust to new places as well as a canine.

As with a new apartment, you want to make sure that there are no dangers for your pet. Make sure that cords can't be played with and cleaning materials are safely tucked under the cabinets, along with all the bug sprays. As with household furniture, you may also want to cover your furniture with a sheet or rug. I saw one RV where they had made seat covers out of rugs found at a thrift store.

If you have a bumper pull of 5th wheel, you would want your pet to ride in the truck with you. If you have a motorhome, the same rules apply for cars in that they either need to be crated or seat-belted/ harnessed in. Once again, in case of an accident, you don't want Rover to go flying.

~*~

Although I don't have much experience traveling with pets, and especially dogs, I asked my friend Wes Herdlein if they could answer some other questions for me.

The last dog that I owned was a Pomeranian/Chihuahua mix. She was a little dog with a big attitude. Any suggestions on reducing the amount of barking?

"I think small dogs tend to have more attitude." It's a common joke. It's funny to consider that small dogs have the Napoleon complex. Larger dogs seem to be much quieter and more secure than smaller breeds. They also seem to do less damage to property than small breed dogs can do. I think that owners let them get away with being loud or aggressive simply because they are so small. Everyone laughs at them and thinks it's "cute" when they get tough. People are never afraid of them. If a dog weighing 80 pounds acted the same way, they would be locked up, given up for adoption, or fenced all the time, etc. They would not enjoy the same freedom.

I have had several experiences training small dogs (when pet sitting for friends). It takes me about 4 days to break the barking habit. But, when they return to their owners, the habit starts again. This is usually because the owners put up with it. They think, "It's annoying, but not dangerous, so let's just ignore it." The problem is that when your dog constantly barks they are not at peace and are not well adjusted. They are anxious and nervous. Not happy campers!

The good news: it's very easy to break the habit (and who wants to travel alone? Don't you want your friend with you?) It only takes consistency. Every time he barks, give him a sharp and loud "no." You might be saying "no" every 12 seconds for a few days, but eventually he should understand. Don't let them bark when you enter the house. Don't let them bark when the doorbell rings. Don't let them bark at anything. If you start to let it slide and they get away with it a few times you are defeating the purpose.

Dogs are simple creatures; they don't understand "sometimes" or "maybe." They only understand absolute "yes" and "no." So be consistent, be in charge, be the pack leader, command respect. When you do this, your dog will feel more well-adjusted and will gain more freedom. Ceaser the "Dog Whisperer" has taught us more about dogs than we ever understood. But you must implement his ideas for them to be effective, not just listen to admire them.

By the way, I have traveled for 6 years with two dogs. They have learned to be flexible. I have never had a complaint. Never paid for pet damage. And the dogs are calm and relaxed. Hope it helps. Let me know how it goes.

Besides their usual yearly rabies shot, what other pet health needs do traveling pet owners need to be aware of?

In my opinion, heartworm, flea, and tick control are the most important preventative measures a pet owner can take. Fleas transmit tapeworm and cause flea allergy dermatitis. Ticks spread spotted fever, Lyme disease, and many other diseases. Heartworms, which are transmitted by mosquitoes, can cause liver failure, damage to the heart, lungs, and other organs, and many other serious health problems. Heartworm disease may even kill your pet. Heartworm, flea, and tick prevention is important, regardless of whether or not you are traveling. It can be even more important when you are on the road because you could be exposing your animal to different risk levels of these parasites in different areas of the country. It is so easy and inexpensive to have these preventative measures taken to protect your pet's health.

What do you do with your pets if you have to leave for a long period of time and are unable to take the pets?

When we travel for short vacations, we try our hardest to find accommodations for them to join us. However, when this is not possible, we find local resources for pet sitting. We usually start this process as soon as we arrive at a new location. We ask for local recommendations from co-workers that have pets, neighbors, or other dog owners that we meet. We also use Craigslist and Google to locate companies and individuals in our area that provide pet services. If we decide to use a pet sitter from Craigslist or Google, we always arrange to meet them ahead of time and we check their references. (We have always been lucky and found some great sitters from Craigslist.)

How do you find a reputable veterinarian once you get to your destination?

We usually will go to a veterinarian that is close to home. This way, if trouble arises with one of our dogs, we are close and can get them there as soon as possible. If you don't trust the vets close to your new home, I would get some recommendations from co-workers, neighbors, or friends. Yelp.com is also a great resource to find out what other pet owners are saying about your local vet clinics.

Any tips on reducing the anxiety of a move with pets?

Yes. First, make sure your pet can handle a long trip in the car. Condition the pets to small or short moves and they will accommodate the change over time. They actually adapt much faster than humans do. Simple minds only require simple things to make them happy, unlike most humans! Some animals have more anxiety than others in the car. It is best to address any anxiety disorders before you get on the road. Also, as soon as you move into your new place, set up a comfy and familiar bed and toy in a quiet area (if possible) for your dog or cat while you unload and unpack. Sometimes moving your stuff in and out of different homes can be stressful. This is a way to keep him calm by surrounding him with familiar scents in your new place.

How do I make sure my pet has enough, but not too much, food?

This is something that your veterinarian can help you determine.

Your pet's food intake can be determined by its weight, activity level, health conditions, etc. Unlike humans, pets usually cannot feed themselves. If they are over or underweight, it's almost always the owner's problem. Please be responsible and feed your pet in a healthy manner.

What helpful hints would have for owners of bigger dogs?

Sometimes larger dogs get a bad rap. Make sure that your larger dog is well adjusted. This means that he does not show aggressive behavior, does not bark uncontrollably, and is not easily stressed. You may need to address behavior issues with training before traveling. Housing is sometimes a little more challenging with larger animals, so if your dog can prove that it is well behaved, their size can be overlooked.

Chapter Fifteen

Traveling In An RV

Making The Decision To Travel In An RV

Whether I was in Oklahoma, Mississippi, California, or Iowa, I have always had the same accommodation—a twenty-nine foot travel trailer. Not exactly luxurious accommodations, but at least I didn't have to pack and unpack every three to six months. No, this lifestyle is not for everyone, but for me and my family it was just perfect.

It all started after my first assignment. Moving into the apartment in Phoenix was okay for the three of us, until we went to move out. Our home was two hundred miles away from the assignment and we found ourselves taking more and more stuff down each time we returned to the Phoenix apartment from our home in Lake Havasu City, Arizona.

After taking two trips with a U-Haul trailer to get everything back, we decided that we didn't adjust very well to keeping it downsized at the apartment. With the three of us, we needed to either buy a bigger permanent hauling trailer or look at a travel trailer.

Off to California I went, while my son and husband stayed back in Arizona to gather up some loose ends before joining me. I was by myself for one month, living in a motel room, since housing was scarce related to seasonal workers. After the family joined me, we moved into a larger motel suite, but that quickly became too close for comfort, hence the search for the alternative of a recreational vehicle (RV).

One thing that I'm frequently asked is, "Is there always a campground near the hospital?" Well, that it where planning takes effect. The first thing that I would check out when my recruiter mentioned an assignment to me was where the nearest RV park was located. The most

I've ever had to drive is 20 minutes to the hospital from the RV park. The most common places to look for a campground are www.woodalls.com and www.goodsamclub.com, and http://www.rvparkreviews.com/. With more and more nurses choosing the RV housing option, more and more travel companies housing departments and/or recruiters will assist you in finding a local campground.

What Type To Look For

What exactly people are looking for in an RV and their needs are so diverse that companies have been expanding their floor plans on a yearly basis. We started our hunt for an RV by visiting as many dealers as we could find in central California. When you go, be sure to also ask about any RV shows that might be coming up in the area.

After you have been to a few dealers, make a list of exactly what you want in an RV. Also, when you are out browsing, look at several different types of RVs. Most full-timers are either in a Class A Motorhome or 5th Wheel, but some prefer to travel in a travel trailer (bumper pull) or Class C Motorhome (a smaller vehicle like a Minnie Winnie).

The least expensive of these options is a travel trailer. A good one will average $15K to $30K, depending on size. If you are full-timing by yourself, you really need to consider one that is 25 ft. in length. If there are two of you, I would consider a 30 foot model. If you have children, look at one with a bunk system in the back. In my travels, I have seen families with four children traveling full time in a four-bunk travel trailer; therefore, this might be a perfect option instead of trying to find a larger apartment. We had a thirty-six footer that seemed to be just right for our family of three. It had two bedrooms so everyone could still have some sense of privacy.

Your next option, price-wise, would be a fifth wheel. These are generally priced from $30K to $80K on the new market. According to a friend of mind, those are much easier to handle than a bumper-pulled travel trailer and easier to hook/unhook from your vehicle.

In Arkansas I came across a travel nurse who was living in a Class C Motorhome. Those are the smaller Motorhomes that are usually easily recognized by the over-the-cab bed or storage. This traveler only had his wife and dog with him.

The cost of these run on average $60K to $100K. Being that they are smaller, they are most often looked at by a first-timer or female who isn't comfortable with the idea of owning or driving a larger "bus"-sized vehicle. They come in many variations now, including with slide-out and storage compartments instead of a bed over-the-cab.

This type of home might be looked at by a family of four, with the option of the over-cab-queen size bed for the parents and twin beds in the back for the children. I could definitely picture myself in one of these if I were a single female. Instead of having to get out for sleeping or using the restroom while on the road, you can just pull over and go to the back and leave the doors locked.

The largest and most expensive option would be a Class A Motorhome, which are the ones that are "bus"-sized. These range in price from $80K to over a million dollars.

Nice and spacious, they are definitely homes-away-from-home! Your gasoline Class As are the least expensive options, but they also have the lowest resale value. The diesel Class As are more expensive, but they hold more of their value when it comes time for a resale.

Coming in a wide variety, many are from 35 ft. to 40 ft. on the average; these babies come packed not only with a kitchen sink, but also a dishwasher as an option. After taking a tour of a factory in Iowa, I ventured into an RV that not only had a flat screen television, but also a complete entertainment system, including a fireplace. Now *that* is what I call entertainment!

Basic Buying Guide

Take a look at many floor plans. Where are the beds and the kitchen? We have found, in buying a travel trailer, that it is easier when stopping along the way if the bed is in the back. This way you can load up the kitchen/living area in the front of the trailer, with the bath in the middle. This way you can have all the extra weight in the front and you don't have to load and unload all the extras every time. All that is required is to open up the back door and crawl into the bed.

If you have a motorhome, make sure that you have a path from the front of the rig to the back where your bed is, or when on the road use the fold-out couch in the front of the coach and store all the extra stuff in the back. This, of course, will all depend on how many "extra" goodies you have along with you. We carried an extra outdoor table and chairs, plus at one time I had my outdoor barrel pond. The less you carry, the better off you are, but as any traveler can tell you, it is always easier said than done.

With any travel trailer or 5th wheel, the first thing you need to know is how much weight your tow vehicle can handle. In your operator's guide you will find the towing capacity. Tell the dealer, the first thing, what type of vehicle you are using for a tow vehicle, what type of tow package (extra transmission cooler and gauges), and any special items you might have on the vehicle that would affect its towing capacity. For example, our truck will pull 9500 lbs.; we have an external and internal transmission cooler, extra transmission gauges, and air suspension.

Once you know the amount that your vehicle can pull, you want to look for a trailer that is about 70% of that weight. Therefore, the trailer that I would be looking for would be approximately 6650 lbs. Once you have added all your living supplies, the trailer should weigh no more than 80% of your towing capacity. If, for some reason, you go over your 100% towing capacity and you get into an accident, you have a good chance of being liable due to the fact that your weight limit exceeds what your vehicle can handle.

Make sure that you have the proper hitch, also. You not only need the proper size ball hitch, but you need the appropriate weight distribution bar, anti-sway bar, and get the best brake control system that you can afford. Skimping on these details can make a big difference if you get into high winds, going up and down steep grades, or in case you need to make an emergency stop.

A big thing for full-timers is storage! Make sure that you have enough storage. This is where the motorhomes have a great advantage over a travel trailer. The "basement" storage is a great plus. There is also more closet space in the motorhomes than in a travel trailer on the average, although I have been in a few 5th wheels that have quite a bit of closet space. If you have a handyman around, an option for a travel trailer would be to convert a bunk system in a travel trailer to more closet space. One trailer I looked at last year in a home show had a small slide-out in the back where the kids had their own couch and entertainment center, along with fold up bunks. In my situation, it would be so easy to take out the bunks and make a closet out of that and use the small slide-out for an office space. When we were looking at toy-haulers once, a dealer told us about a full-timer who couldn't find exactly what she needed, so she took an empty trailer and put in her own furniture to make a home-on-wheels. In other words, use your imagination when you go shopping!

A few other things to consider when shopping are the bedroom and bathroom. Lie on the bed and see how it feels. Some aren't the most comfortable beds, but can be made more manageable by putting one of those space-age technology types of foam mattresses over it. In the last few years I have seen more and more motorhomes with the sleep number bed system as an option. You can also purchase a sleep number bed mattress system at your local camping supply store.

Sit on the commode and see if there is enough leg and arm space. The last few years I have seen more and more RVs with the optional shower on one side and the commode on the other side. What size shower and/or tub do you need? We were very lucky in the fact that we had a full-size tub. There wasn't too much difference between the tub size in my permanent home and my RV. Some have half-tubs and some just have the shower. This last year I even saw one that had a whirlpool tub in it, although that motorhome was a little more expensive than I could afford at $350K.

Also, look at what type of electrical system it has. The standard RV has either 30 amp or 50 amp, unless you get a gigantic motorhome, which may require 100 amp. With a 30 amp vehicle you might find yourself turning off the air conditioner while you run the microwave or blow-dry your hair. Usually, with a 50 amp, you don't have to worry about that. Also, it will make a big difference if you have one or two air conditioning units. With the RVs that have two air conditioning units, you will need a 50 amp or an upgraded electrical system that can handle all of the power needs.

What Options To Look For

In the beginning of the RV building world there were only two or three floor plans and styles that you could choose from, but now the options are almost endless.

In the travel trailer world you can find trailers with garages, trailers that have "toy boxes" for your motorcycles or golf cart, ones with slide-outs, and trailers with utility closets in the back.

In Arizona and Southern California, the toy haulers are quite common. Not only do people haul around their dune buggies and four wheelers, but golf carts and small electric cars. With gas prices soaring ever so high, I have often thought about getting a toy box and an electric car. You could probably even get a smart car in the back of a toy hauler!

The smaller garages at the back would also be nice for a full-timer. You could store things that you might use seasonally or keep your bikes locked up. The other day we saw an RV with a small storage area in the whole back of the trailer that opened up and you could hang items like your hoses, utility equipment, and miscellaneous hardware in there.

Other options that you may look for in the kitchen are a full-size or four-door refrigerator and freezer with an icemaker. These are great and can be found in a lot of the newer motorhomes. Also, in the kitchens of the newer motorhomes you might find a dishwasher or a trash compactor.

In many of the 5th wheels and motorhomes you might find a combination washer and dryer. Although these are very small, they are great to use for everyday clothes. You will probably still want to use the bigger machines at the laundromat for your bigger items, such as towels and linens.

In the living room area you can look for such options as an electric fireplace, entertainment center, computer center and satellite dish. Satellite dishes also come in many types, from just plain old television to ones that will also help you get onto the Internet and even track while moving (this will be discussed later on in more depth).

To make traveling and maneuvering easier you can find motorhomes with a navigational system and cameras in the back of the rig to assist you in backing up. After you have had either of these for very long you will wonder how you ever lived without them! I can't imagine going anywhere without my navigational system.

Motorhomes usually come with some kind of basement storage. This is the one major advantage to having a larger motorhome; there is a lot more storage for full-timers! There is even one company who not only makes a basement, but also has an upstairs. That's right, a set of stairs leads you to the top of the RV where there is a patio set up with grill, tables, chairs, and an umbrella. Of course you would want to take the umbrella down while you're going down the road. Ha!

There are many, many other options that you can have. What you have to decide is which options are worth the money for you and your family.

Internet Access While On The Road

Most RV parks now have wireless access. In fact, I searched all the campgrounds that we had stayed at and they all had wireless access. Some are free and some require an additional fee. All you need is a wireless card, which most computers come with now. You just look for a signal then type in your user name and password if needed. The most important thing you want to remember when hooking into an open wireless service is that you make sure that the type of connection you make is public. By choosing this option, discovery of other computers and devices on the network will be limited, and the use of the network by some programs might be restricted.

Another option is through your cell phone. For about $20, you can purchase a cable that will connect your cell phone to your computer through the USB port. After purchasing a dialup program for another $20, you can then use your phone. Check with your cell phone carrier about charges for this service. Some companies take air time out of your minutes, while others will let you use it unlimited for a set price.

Wireless cards are also an option. These cards are offered through cell phone companies and are like a wireless system that you plug into the network port on your laptop. In the bigger cities you can have up to broadband speeds with these systems, although the current price is about $60/month.

For your own personal broadband network you can also do the satellite Internet. There are three types that you can get. The first is a dish that is set up on a tripod. Every time you go to a new place, you set up the tripod and dish, aim the satellite, and you're off and running. The first couple of times you try it can be frustrating, but after much perseverance, you can do it! After my husband sets ours up, I can shoot it within five to ten minutes now.

Another system is on top of the rig, and you still have to manually adjust it every time. This really isn't too bad if you are moving only once every three to six months and can be easily figured out as with the tripod system. The disadvantage to this is that you have to make sure that your rig is perfectly level or you won't be able to find the satellite connection.

The least work that you will have to do is with an automatic satellite, but it is much more expensive than the first two. In fact, a few years ago I paid $1,500 for my system on the tripod, while a friend of mine paid $5,000 for her automatic one on top of the rig. It seems like she has more trouble with her system than I have with my system, and every time there is a problem she has to take her rig into the dealer to have the satellite worked on, where ours is much more easily repaired being that it is not connected to the rig. The system that you choose will depend on how computer savvy you are.

The drawback from having a system like mine is that you either have to be certified to aim the satellite or hire a certified installer to come out and aim the dish every time you move. I would recommend taking the class so you can aim your own dish.

In Conclusion

The mobile lifestyle is one that can be very rewarding if you hate packing and unpacking every few months. If you keep your traveling goodies to a minimum, your home can easily be unhooked from the park and moved in a just a few short hours.

When I first wrote this chapter we were in Iowa with our 35ft. Dutchman. Coming out of Iowa we had a semi-tractor/trailer pass us and we started fishtailing. Long story short, an hour later the trailer slid onto the tires and we closed down I-35 and I-70 for 30 minutes while they loaded us onto a wrecker.

We went back to traveling in apartments until our misadventures in a motel room in North Dakota (13 weeks with 2 cats and a hubby is a LONG time in one room!).

We now have a 29 ft. Coleman TT and absolutely love it with the duel slides in the living room! The cats love their new room to roam and are totally into the RV lifestyle! They can see out all the windows in the dining room, living room, and kitchen area.

Just this last year, I have started a Facebook group for traveling nurses who travel in an RV. We have nurses that are in travel trailers, 5thwheels, Class C motorhomes, and Class A motorhomes. Come on and join us! https://www.facebook.com/groups/245341118947585/

The one thing I hear the most is, “I wished I would have gotten an RV a lot sooner!”

Chapter Sixteen

Homeschooling While On The Road

For years I thought I couldn't do travel nursing because my son was in public school and I needed to give him a stable environment in which to live. I planned on going into travel nursing the minute he graduated. That was until April 2003.

My son's school informed me that my child had figured out that if he went to this in-school suspension program, he could do his schoolwork in another classroom without all the kids who called him names and picked on him unmercifully. Kids are just cruel in junior high school, especially if you don't conform to their idea of what a "cool" teenager is.

The counselor told me, "I just don't know what I'm going to do with your son next year." I looked at my husband, who shrugged, and then I turned to the school counselor and advised him that I didn't think that he was going to have to worry about my son next year.

My bachelor's degree actually is not in nursing; it's in secondary science education. After we went home, I informed my husband that I believed that it was time to hit the road. If they didn't know what to do with him, I didn't see where it would harm my child to be on the road fulltime in an "unstable" environment when he could learn things all over the United States.

I had a teacher's certificate at one time (lapsed when I went into nursing), and I didn't see where the school system was doing a better job than I could do at home. My suspicions were confirmed when I did his diagnostic testing and found that my 7th grader was actually functioning at a 3rd to 4th grade level. That made me a real believer in the Individual Educational Program (IEP) that schools have now set forth.

Okay, off of my soapbox and back into the real world of homeschooling. The decision was easy for me, since I had an educational degree background. After this chapter, you will have the knowledge to make an informed decision on whether or not homeschooling is right for you and your children, as well as what alternatives you have.

Exactly What Is Homeschooling?

Homeschooling is getting out the books every morning and doing lessons in math, science, history, grammar, and literature. Homeschooling is taking field trips. Homeschooling is running around in your pajamas doing algebra. Homeschooling is many different things that all surround the idea of teaching your children at home.

First is the traditional style of homeschooling. This follows the standard way of doing schoolwork. With this style, you find books that are geared towards the age and grade of your child and you have traditional reading, worksheets, and then tests. There are several curriculums that you can use for this style, including Alpha Omega Lifepacs (which use workbooks) or textbooks through Abeka Publishing or Bob Jones Publishing, which are Christian-based curriculums. There is a giant list of resources at www.homeschool.com/resources/. I am not familiar with all the companies or all the textbooks, but this is a great place to start your search for the best program that will fit your situation.

Another great source is to find out what the schools do with their old books. I found a gold mine of used schoolbooks in Oklahoma City. I also purchased a book with a plethora of resources called, "The Complete Home Learning Source Book." Check with your local Homeschool Association and find out when and where the next book fair is going to be. You can also get an idea of what other parents are using before you set out on your travel nursing adventure.

Computer learning is next on the list. Through one program called "Switched On Schoolhouse" or the "Robinson Curriculum," you install the program onto your computer and your child's computer and you have control over the student's curriculum. This is a great way to do things for some children and teachers alike. The lessons are automatically graded, and learning is on an interactive level.

Computer learning can also be accomplished with some programs online in which you enroll your child in a school, and they take classes online with teachers and tests through the Internet. This is a great option for the parent who is uneasy about attempting to teach their child at home. www.k12.com offers a directory of online public schools, online private schools, and individual courses.

Unit studies are very popular also. This is where you teach your children all subjects that are on one subject. This can be very useful as a traveling nurse, because you can do unit studies on the state in which you are traveling as well as the surrounding states. Children are taught math, as in how much is needed to purchase groceries, history through the state sites, biology through seeing what grows in that area and what type of energy is most common there, and are there any windmills or hydro plants? You can view guides for unit studies at www.homeschoollearning.com. By doing a search online you can find free unit study guides.

The new out-of-the-box type of homeschooling is called "unschooling." This is where the children learn from day-to-day events. No, this does not mean that they sit and watch television and play video games all day, but things are learned from experiences. Parents will often spend time going through the newspaper with their children and learning what is going on in the world and why things are happening the way they are. Math is learned from figuring out how much things cost, how to budget, and other word problems. Science is learned by exploring a park and checking out all the leaves and grasses and attempting to identify what kind of things are in the environment. No tests are done, but the children learn by experience. I think this is a great way of learning for travel nurses to incorporate, at least part-time, since we travel so much and see so many different things and live in so many different cultures.

All these curriculums can be found by doing a search online, contacting the publishing houses, and on eBay. If you are interested in looking at sources in your community, find your local homeschool association and ask for their help in finding homeschool materials. Materials can also be found at general bookstores. Even Borders, Barnes and Noble, and Hastings can special order books for you.

Personally, I buy my books online at PennywiseLearning.com or on eBay. After my son had completed all his material on another sheet of paper or in his notebook, I then sold the material as used on eBay and recovered at least half of the money that I had spent to get the books.

What About State Laws?

Laws are different in each state. As a traveling nurse, you primarily have to go by what your home state laws are, but there are certain situations when you will have to abide by the state laws to which you are assigned.

For instance, in Mississippi they have a law that states all recreational vehicle parks have to have documentation that your child, who is running around during the day, actually is homeschooled. For this, I just gave the park manager a copy of the affidavit that I had filled out for my home state, affirming that my child was homeschooled. This may also mean getting a letter from the school district in states that require you to keep in touch with the school district.

When we were in Tennessee, we didn't have to have a letter for the apartment complex, but we did need to have a letter for my 17-year-old's place of employment from the school board, stating that our son was enrolled in homeschool. To accomplish this, I wrote a letter of intent to the school board here and sent them verification of my qualifications to teach, and they sent me a letter for my son's employer that stated he was in homeschool. It was then I realized that in some states you must have a copy of your bachelor's degree in order to teach high school.

Why did I have to go through all of this? Because in different states you have different age requirements on how long your children must attend school. Although we were okay with our home state of Idaho, we still had to comply with some of the state requirements because of housing and employment. There are other states that we have been in (Oklahoma, Florida, California, and Iowa) where we were not required to do anything special related to our home residence, since it was not in those states. If there is a problem, someone will tell you; until that time it is usually best just to cruise through your assignment following your home state's rules.

Finding out the laws in each state is not as difficult as you would think; all you need to do is bookmark on your computer www.hslda.org. If you do not have a computer, the information can also be found through that state's department of education or local school district.

Some of the state laws are very restrictive and some are not so restrictive. For example, in Idaho the only rules are that if your child is between the ages of 7 years and 15 you must have some kind of alternative educational program. That means that once children are 16 they can "drop out" of school, although it is not necessarily advised. Other less restrictive states that I have been in are Texas and Oklahoma.

Medium restrictive states that I have been in include Arizona, California, and Mississippi. These states require such things as filing an annual affidavit or letter of intent, maintaining attendance records, and requiring basic subjects such as math, science, history, grammar, and literature. Tennessee also requires that you must have a college education to teach high school and that your child has to attend school until they are 18.

Other more restrictive states require you to have more extensive subjects, such as algebra, geometry, physics, and chemistry, along with documentation of the hours spent in school, days spent in school, maintaining accurate records, and taking state-wide standardized tests.

Other good resources for homeschool information include: www.homeschoolacademy.com, www.time4learning.com, www.saxonhomeschool.hmhco.com, and www.discoveryeducation.com.

Driving Me Crazy

Literally, for a homeschooled child of a traveling nurse, I was literally nuts by the time we wove our way through all the legal mumble jumble, but we made it.

Driver's education at our house was done by the "principal"—i.e. Dad! If you are located in a heavily populated area, I would suggest that you find a good driving school. If you are in a rural area, good old country roads that are unpopulated provide a good start. Talk to other nurses to see if someone has a place out in the country for a "feel" of what it is like to drive for the first time. Of course this is only done after your child has a learning permit.

Getting the learning permit—*that* was what drove me crazy with all these state rules. It is always best to have your child take the test in the state in which you are a resident, but if you are across the country and you think that your child is ready, then it can be done in some states. The key to this is that hopefully you are in a state in which your son/daughter can be a resident of that state, and you do not have to be. This is easily accomplished if your child has some kind of employment. For instance, at the time we still had the RV and my son worked for the campground part-time. It wasn't much, but it did give him a paycheck. We used a national bank, separate from our bank, and used his address as the assignment address. Sonny has a job and a bank account, now he can pass for a resident—well, at least in some states.

There are other states in which the parents also have to have a driver's license in that state. Although not advisable, if need be, your spouse can get a driver's license in the new state, but do not ever get your driver's license in another state, because then you are going to have trouble with the Internal Revenue Service in establishing a tax home.

It's not going to look good with your spouse being a resident of another state, but it is just one option to consider.

As previously stated, if at all possible find a local driving school for your child; if one can not be found, there are lots of driver's programs online, such as the one found at www.driversed.com. After completing the program, your child will receive a certificate of completion, which is approved by almost all the states (verify before you begin if you wish). It is a great course that I would recommend to anybody homeschooling their child.

Also, contact your insurance agency and see if they have programs available. We watched a movie and filled out a driving log to receive a discount on our insurance; you can also have your child take the SAT or ACT test and get a reduced "good student" rate. In fact, we kept a travel log for a while after my son completed his regular program in case we needed to prove how many hours he had behind the wheel.

One of the funniest experiences with this whole deal was that when we moved assignments, my son went to apply for his regular permit instead of a learner's permit and they wanted to know if he had any experience with a certified driving instructor. Of course he hadn't, but we had made a trip between assignments back home so he had driven most of the way from Iowa home to Idaho and to Florida. Over 3000 miles and none of it counted because he wasn't with a certified driving instructor.

What About Socialization?

You know what is funny about people who ask this question? They will also tell you about the terrible things that happened at Columbine High School, the Red Lake shootings, and all the teens that are arrested at school for having guns in their possession. Why did all these bad things happen at school? Because the majority of teens think that to be cool you have to knock someone else's "coolness" down. Unless your child is perfect, chances are they are being teased or bullied at school by someone. That is what I call "great socialization!"

At one of the RV parks we were in, the owner and manager said that the children were not allowed to use the recreational equipment on the weekends when other children were there, but they had found that the homeschooled children were much better behaved and they could go over there any time if it was just them. Several times I had people come to my trailer and ask if "the boy over there is your son?" After answering, "Yes," they would proceed to tell me what good things my son had done and then ask, "Is he homeschooled?" I don't know what other proof you need, but my personal experience is that people can tell by your child's behavior that they are homeschooled.

Yes, I believe our children need to be around other children of the same age, but with the proper influence. After getting settled into an area, we start the search for a church that has a good group of teenagers. I am a member of the Nazarene Church, and my husband was born and raised Baptist; therefore, we tend to stick to one of those two denominations. But there was one assignment in which we were Lutherans, related to the fact that that was where the best group of teenagers for our son to be social with.

Other than church groups, there are many other groups such as Boy Scouts, Girl Scouts, and Explorer Groups. Look for groups such as a bowling league, baseball league, basketball league, or the YMCA. The local Chamber of Commerce or Parks and Recreation Departments at the city should be able to help you in choosing a place for your child to interact with other children. Also, look for information through the local homeschool association.

From A Child

As a writing assignment, I asked Kalen what he would like to tell others about his life as the son of a fulltime traveling nurse, and this is what he had to say.

"I love traveling with my parents because I get to see so many exciting places. When I was in Arizona, I got to see the Grand Canyon, and I have been to an old gold mine. I got to go to the London Bridge on several occasions. In 2001, my family and I went several times to Chase Stadium, which was known back then as Bank One Ballpark, in Phoenix, to see the Diamondbacks play. This is also the year they won the World Series.

When I was in California I got to do several things, including learning a little Spanish, going to Monterey to go deep-sea fishing in the Pacific Ocean, and I even got to experience my first earthquake.

When we went to Iowa, I got my first job at a restaurant near the lake. Mom and I also got to go to see the scene of the crash where Buddy Holly, the Big Bopper, and Ritchie Valens passed away, which is now known as 'the day that the music died.'

When I went to Oklahoma, I was in Oklahoma City. I got to go to the Oklahoma Bombing site. Although I was living in Oklahoma at the time of the bombing, I don't remember much of it, so it was great to learn about something that happened while I was an Okie. In Tulsa we went to see the Tulsa Drillers, which is a AAA baseball team. I met a few friends there also. We also went to Tulsa to get my 16th birthday present, a 1985 Ford Mustang convertible, which my uncle painted for me.

Our fifth assignment was in Mississippi. I got to go to Corinth, where the north and south train route met with the east to west train at the crossroads. I got to visit several battlefields, but the most memorable one was the site of the Battle of Shiloh.

Next we went to Florida. While I was there, I worked for a local newspaper and then started my fast food career. Hurricane Wilma came to visit us, and that was a totally different experience for me! There was so much devastation in Florida that I can't imagine what it was like for those who were in Hurricane Katrina.

Unfortunately, my Mustang didn't make it out of Florida. When I was driving from Fort Lauderdale, Florida, to Nashville, Tennessee, the engine gave it up on the side of the road. I will just have to wait until the next assignment to think about another vehicle.

Right now I'm in Tennessee. I have made a great career choice here. I love my fast food job, and have even been recommended for a managerial position when I turn 18 years old. I have always wanted to be a police officer, but I am currently thinking about going into restaurant management instead.

Although I have had some great adventures over the last three years, there have been some drawbacks. Seems like every time that I get settled into a job and a new store, then it's time to move again. I have a long list of friends, but I don't see them. Most of my friends don't come from school, but from the church youth groups that I attend while on the road. I also miss my friends in my old hometown of Lake Havasu City, Arizona.

I also met my girlfriend on the road through the Internet. I haven't got to meet her yet, but my mom says that she is going to take an assignment in Washington this next year so that we can meet "in reality." This may seem strange to some teens, but hey, my mom and step-dad met that way! We have been chatting on the phone and computer for almost two years now. I have learned so much more traveling than I ever could learn in a classroom. I would definitely recommend nurses taking their children with them if at all possible. I love my life on the road! Thanks, Mom!"

Update 2012: Kalen has been living in Washington since my assignment there in 2006, and the girlfriend is now a fiancé and they plan on getting married in the summer of 2013.

In Conclusion

No, homeschooling is not for every parent on the road, but I have had several nurses ask me exactly how I homeschool my child, how I started out, and the benefits that I have found since we're on the road fulltime.

Yes, there are other ways to provide school for children while on the road, such as switching assignments in the middle of semesters, at Christmas break, or during summer break. You can get in three good assignments this way. Others that I know take a nine-month assignment during the school year, and then take a summer assignment somewhere in the cooler north or on the beach. Other parents choose to stay within a few hundred miles of their families, and their families stay at home. There is no *one* right or wrong way to school your child while on the road. You have to do what is most comfortable for you and your family.

For those of you who choose to homeschool, the freedom of learning live historical facts is worth "dragging" your children around the United States. I have absolutely no doubt that it makes them better students for the future, and I hope that this chapter will give you the motivation that you need to make that leap into the future of homeschooling.

Chapter Seventeen

Travel Company Fundamentals

This will be the first major decision that you will have to make after deciding to go on the road full time. There are quite a number of companies out there, and only by understanding the travel company itself, knowing what you want, and doing a lot of research will you be happy in your travel nursing career. There are quite a few that can get you a job, but only a handful that will give you exactly what *you* want. That is why the last five chapters of this book (almost half of the entire book) are dedicated to finding you the best travel nursing company for YOU.

One of the first things you need to understand is the structure of the agency that you are working for. You may only be in contact on a weekly basis with your recruiter, but people such as the staff supervisor, housing coordinator, payroll specialist, and quality review are some of the others that you will come in contact with.

Recruiter Basics

This is perhaps the most significant person in travel nursing. This is the individual in whom you will confide your every want for your livelihood, and who will attempt to give you everything you desire to make your life the fullest that it can be. This is the liaison between you and the hospital. It is their job to help select the appropriate assignment for you. This is the person who takes your profile for a company and submits it to the hospital.

The latest trend in staffing companies is to rename the recruiter as a "career consultant" or "talent manager." Behind the fancy new names, they are still people who are in the business of bringing nurses together with hospitals. Another trend is to have a recruiter assistant who helps with all the paperwork and finding jobs, but then you have a "staff supervisor" that is the connection between you and the hospital. Ultimately, you will come to rely on your recruiter or staff supervisor to locate the right obligation for you and ensure that all your needs are being met. This is also the person whom you contact if things are not the way you expected them to be.

One of the advantages of staying with the same company that I have found is that your staff supervisor and/or nursing recruiter will come to know your personality and nursing style. By getting to know you better, what you are, and where you are headed in your travel-nursing career, they can assist you in finding the right path. Remember that your recruiter should be there to assist you at any time. If not himself or herself, then someone should be on-call for the nursing company.

Your recruiter should be an asset to you and your choices, and not a deterrent to your nursing experience. Your recruiter should want you to feel contented in your new setting. They should be concerned about your safety by not putting you into precarious circumstances. Your recruiter should be a help to you by finding out what you like to do and where you want to go. Your recruiter should know your preferences for a small, moderate, large, or teaching hospital.

This last year I was having a terrible time finding a new assignment, and my recruiter that I have been with for quite a while called me and said, "I know that it is not the location that you really want, but it's close, and I think that you will love the area." Other times she would tell me of jobs, but tell me "I really don't think that you'll be interested in this assignment, but it is available and I just wanted you to know about it." And usually she is right on the money on what I like and where I want to go.

Your recruiter should know your strengths and weaknesses. They should know what areas of the hospital you can work in as a primary nurse and what areas you are able to float to.

The Used Car Salesman

Any recruiter, any person, can "sell" you, but do you really want a recruiter or a "used car salesman?" To prove my point, I did some research on what makes a successful car salesman. After visiting just a few websites on the characteristics of a good car salesman, I was astonished at how much the recruiters I have met had these same qualities.

A recruiter must be personable. What do I mean by "personable?" They must be pleasant in appearance and personality. No, you probably will never *see* your recruiter, but what about their telephone appearance? Good telephone skills are a must with any recruiter. They must have a pleasant voice, and be someone that you *want* to talk to, not someone that you *have* to talk to.

A recruiter must be knowledgeable. It is not a crime to not know the answer to your question, but your recruiter must know where to find the answer. In some research on travel nursing companies that I have done, several times I was referred to the human resources director, who promptly answered my questions about benefits.

How much does your recruiter know about the nursing field? He might be able to sell you a car, but does he know more about an oil change or a blood transfusion? I am a nurse because I care about people. I want to help others in their time of need and to help them feel better. Sure, I could give someone blood, but what kind of ethics would I have if I just gave the person any old blood without double checking the patient's blood type and double checking the name band before giving that patient the blood? It is a lot easier to replace the oil in your car than to fix a mistake with a blood transfusion.

I'm not saying that the recruiter has to be a nurse, just that they must have extended knowledge of the nursing field. How can a recruiter help you out when/if you get into a bind if they can't understand what is happening at the time? I just don't see how a recruiter can "go to bat" for you if they don't know what they are talking about. These hospitals are hiring travelers because they are short-staffed. Under these conditions, several things can go wrong. I would absolutely refuse to take a position if I didn't feel like I had support from my recruiter.

They must know their product, as well as that of the competition. In order to acquire new nurses, you have to offer the nurse something better than the other companies do. The only way you can do that is if you know what the other companies are offering. Little things, like just a few more dollars an hour or better insurance benefits, can make a big difference. So what if every assignment has a completion bonus if you are making only $20/hour? Attempt to find out what other companies are giving their employees at the same or a nearby location, and then make the deal just a little sweeter, which brings me to my next point of knowing your "customer."

The first thing out of a recruiter's mouth should be, "How can I help you?" So many times, what the recruiter says is translated into, "How can you help us?" These "headhunters" are out there to rope you in no matter what it takes. They *need* you. They don't have a company without the nurse, but so many think that the nurse needs them more. New cars look very nice on the lot, but a lot of good they are doing the salesperson if they stay on the lot.

The recruiter that is going to get my attention is the one that says, "How can I help you fulfill your needs in your nursing career?" Nurses travel for many reasons. The need for a nurse who is fighting bankruptcy is so much different from the nurse who just bought a new car and has a burning desire to see the world.

Above all, a recruiter must have a great personality. I have yet to see a rude, crude, and socially unacceptable nursing recruiter have very many nurses who work for them. Yes, there are some out there, and unfortunately, some of the nurses that I network with have had to work with them, but I have yet to meet a person who will stay with a recruiter who is always on the down and depressed side.

A great personality also means a nursing recruiter who is not only concerned about the benefits of having you work for them, but also what is in your best interest. Like the company that I work for presently—everyone shares the benefits of the nurses; there is no "fighting" for nurses because of that great commission.

A great personality also means that they will be there for you when you need someone to lean on. When the tough times come, you should be able to pick up the phone and discuss the problems you are having with your recruiter. We aren't going to get along with everyone, and not everything is going to be perfect. I want a recruiter whom I can call and tell that I really don't feel comfortable in my current situation because of even such a simple thing as a personality conflict. I want a recruiter who will weather the storm with me, not jump ship and let me feel like I have been stranded in the middle of the desert begging for water.

The Housing Coordinator

After you have selected an assignment, you will then work closely with the housing coordinator. Their job is to make some place your home away from home. Most travel companies have contracts with hotels, suites, and apartment complexes in which you get housing paid for by the company. Housing can include or exclude a roommate, selected by you and/or the company. Most companies pay for up to a one-bedroom apartment. A few of the companies even pay for bigger places for your entire family. And yes, the companies encourage your immediate family to travel with you. A happy traveler is a great worker! The company provides all of this for you, although sometimes you might have to ask for it.

If you already have a place to stay, most companies offer a housing stipend in which they give you a certain amount of money that you can use to provide your own housing. These housing stipends are usually tax-deductible, as long as you use the money for business housing. If you take the stipend as a "payroll addition," then it is taxed at the same rate as your paycheck. Many nurses take the stipend and either live with relatives or use it to live in a recreational vehicle.

Housing coordinators make every attempt to find the best housing available for the amount of money that they are budgeted for, according to the bill rate and the housing rate for the area. It frustrates them when something doesn't work out right or they just are not able to provide every stipulation the nurse wants, and then all the nurse wants to do is complain about the housing that they did find. Nurses need to realize that it is sometimes very hard to find exactly what the nurse wants at a price that he or she wants.

The Payroll Specialist

A payroll specialist is responsible to make sure that you are paid every pay period. Most companies make this easier by implementing direct deposit. The money is "zapped" from your travel nursing company right into your personal checking or savings account. Although it is your payroll's or the recruiter's job to put the data into the computer for you to be paid, the payroll specialist is the one responsible for making sure that you get your check at the appropriate time that you are scheduled to be paid. Check with your recruiter or staff supervisor to see whom you will turn to if there is a problem with payroll. Some companies prefer you to deal directly with the staff supervisor and some will have you deal directly with the payroll specialist.

Mike, a payroll controller states, "Payroll in the travel nursing industry is extremely complicated. Some have their housing paid, while others receive monthly housing stipends; travel pay is due on different dates; weekly pay includes taxed income, or some elect to receive a portion of their income tax free (tax advantage plan); reimbursements for nursing licenses, other applicable bonuses from time to time; hospitals observe different holidays and different hours to receive holiday pay; and notes on timesheets written from travelers are sometimes not legible. You also have to consider the nurse's request for paid time off days and vacation pay. It doesn't appear to be that complicated, but multiply that by several hundred travelers weekly and it becomes very complex!

With this type of complexity, mistakes can occur. It's what your travel company does about the situation and the response time to correct it that makes a difference. We, like everyone else, make mistakes. We create processes and modify processes each time mistakes occur in order to minimize them from reoccurring. We even go as far as to wire it into our traveler's bank accounts immediately, if it's our mistake, at no cost to the traveler. Some of these mistakes can be avoided by getting timesheets in on time. This permits our payroll department to ensure that your pay is correct before meeting the deadlines to be processed by payroll firms and entered into your direct deposit account in time for you to be paid on time."

Benefits Specialist

You might also come into contact with the benefits specialist. These wonderful people assist you with your benefits from 401K plans, insurance, incentive programs, completion bonuses, and reward programs. Don't be afraid to call them if you think you are not getting all the benefits that you are entitled to. They are very good resources for reliable answers. Unless your recruiter is getting the same benefits as you are, they may not know all the benefits that you are entitled to.

Shirley, a director of administrative services for a national travel nursing company, tells me, "Benefits were made to be used to offset skyrocketing healthcare costs when you need treatment. That is why our organization pays for our travelers' benefits in full each month. We research various insurance companies yearly to ensure that our travelers are receiving the maximum insurance coverage while containing the cost.

In addition, those who elect to join 401(k) programs need to take the time to read how to manipulate the 401(k) website that's assigned to those who join. You are able to track your investments and returns on a weekly basis, if you choose. Some travelers don't take the time to do their homework. The benefit is clearly to the traveler's advantage, but most don't recognize the value.

As long as our travelers understand that they have the right to ask and have the right to an answer in a timely manner, we're glad to help them in any way possible. Other free benefits including continuing education, online forms, online payroll stubs, vacation pay, earned paid time off days, and the like make being a traveler less complicated and risky. Make sure that you're able to use these things to your advantage! If you're not sure, feel free to ask. That's what we're here for!"

Quality Control Specialist

Some companies even use a quality control specialist, who is like a human resource department that helps you meet compliance criteria for each of your assignments. The quality control manager will help you in all aspects of getting ready for your assignment. I get a call on every assignment from the quality control manager, making sure that my needs are being taken care of by my staff supervisor. In my opinion, this is a *must* for every travel nursing company who wants to have a quality nursing staff. If the nurses are not happy, how can the patients be happy?

Quality Assurance

A few years ago, I spent a lovely morning with the quality assurance team for Trinity Healthcare Staffing and found the girls in the office to be quite pleasant. I sincerely hope that after this section of the book, nurses will have a better understanding of the functions of this department, and that they really aren't the "QA Nazis" that some nurses have them labeled as. Instead of being defined as "a person who fanatically seeks to control a specific activity or practice," they need to be thought of as a department that is dedicated to assuring that the quality of the nursing staff is well documented.

Their job is one of the toughest in the industry, due to the fact that it is their task is to keep up with what the hospitals have to have as far as immunizations, urine drug screens, medication testing, background checks, and other tests that are required, especially if the company is Joint Commission certified.

As I walked into the QA office, I faced a large board with the requirements for several vendor management and hospital associations, through which most travel nursing contracts are processed. Next to each vendor management name was a list of the particular requirements for that state or regional area. No two vendor management companies required the exact same things. Some require only one PPD, while others required two…others required titers for chicken pox, while others required just a statement that you have had the disease.

Before a job can be confirmed, all of the nurse's ducks have to be in a row in this river of paper. It is the quality assurance analyst's job to make sure that the nurse's paperwork is in line for the job that they are going to accept, and if it isn't, then it's their job to make sure that they get it. Therefore, they have to notify the recruiter of things needed to complete the file, and the recruiters have to "bug" the nurses until all the paperwork is in. Although this can be very annoying, nurses have to realize that this is required from the hospital to the nursing staff company.

Doing Your Shopping

There are plenty of travel companies out there. Do your shopping; do not just grab the first one that makes you an offer. Plan to start looking for a company about a month before planning on going into travel nursing if at all possible. This process will include finding out more about benefits, locations, and general operations of the travel company.

When shopping for a travel company, be aware that some are going to want you to fill out their application and send all of your personal records and qualifications before they will submit you to a hospital. At this point, be careful to give them just your basic information and let them know that you are just shopping for a travel company. Don't make the mistake of filling out applications and checklists for fifty different companies just to interview them.

Also, be careful about who you give your phone number to until you have done your homework. Once you give the travel company your phone number, you will receive phone calls every week, asking you about assignments. It doesn't take long to rack up the minutes on your cell phone. Plus it's a real inconvenience if you work night shift. You will have no other choice but to turn off your cell phone when you want to sleep.

After reading this chapter, you will be able to find the one company that is going to make you happy in the long run. You will be able to find the one company that goes where you want to go. But first, we need to begin the process of narrowing down your choices.

One thing that should be on that list is your wage requirements. In your staff job, you needed a certain amount per hour to live on. With travel nursing, the trend now is to know exactly how much you are going to bring home in a week. You need to know exactly what you need, and not necessarily what you want, to live your new lifestyle. What is the going rate for that area? Check out www.salary.com, you should be making about 10–20% more a week than the staff nurses. Remember now, that the company is taking 15–25%.

What kind of housing do you require? If you are single and fancy free? Is motel or extended-stay sufficient? The positives of staying in a motel is that they usually have laundry facilities, a pool, and of course, maid service! There are some very nice extended stays that will even allow you to have your four-legged family with you.

Most companies will provide a one-bedroom furnished apartment. You just bring clothes, linens, and personal items. Watch this option, though, because some companies will tell you that you have a "private" bedroom, when in reality you have a private bedroom with shared common areas with another traveler. This may be fine for a lonely traveler, but most of us like the privacy of our own apartment. This option definitely does not work out if you travel with your family.

Planning to take your family? Most companies will work with you on that. They will provide a two-bedroom apartment for you, although you may be expected to pay utilities or some of the rent. The most convenient way to travel with your family is in an RV.

What are your location requirements? Do you want to stay in your home state or the surrounding states? With the invention of compact states, you could decide just to travel in compact states. Favorite destinations seem to be Hawaii and Alaska on the west coast in the winter or Maine in the summer, with winter in Florida for the east coast. You might even choose to stay in the middle by going to North Dakota in the summer and to Texas in the winter. Love to ski? Then go snow skiing in Colorado in the winter and to the lakes of Tennessee for water skiing in the summer. The possibilities are endless.

What about other benefits that you should expect out of a travel nursing company? The biggest seems to be health insurance, 401K, continuing education requirements, longevity, and completion bonuses. These things all matter in your decision!

Find the one company who has the appropriate nursing retention program. What kinds of benefits are added on the longer that you are with them? Almost all companies have this, whether it is in lieu of money or fits into a reward program.

Don't settle for a company that does not provide a 401K program.

Not only should they allow you to put tax-free money in, but they should also be making some kind of vested contribution.

Make sure that the company is reliable. Once you get "out there" in the big world of travel nursing, there are going to be days where the only friend you have is your recruiter or staffing supervisor.

Keep your list handy in your planning stage. As we explore more about your career as a travel nurse, you may want to add more ideas. Don't forget to put on your list the places where you would like to travel. You will need that information because not all travel companies go to all areas of the United States and beyond.

Doing Your Research

Now that you have your list of benefit requirements, use the up-to-date graph, "The Ultimate List Of Travel Companies," on the website www.highwayhypodermics.com to get an idea of which companies offer the benefits that are most important to you. You will also want to read the chapter in this book entitled "Travel Company Profiles."

Do more research on the Internet by visiting discussion boards and travel nursing forums, and ask other nurses what they think of those travel companies. This is where you will find out the inside information on these companies. There are quite a few boards on Facebook including, "Traveling The Country, One Hospital At A Time," "Travel Nurse Network - The Gypsy Nurse," "Our Gypsy Nurse Caravan," and of course the Highway Hypodermics Page. We also sponsor an "RV Travelers" group and a "Homeschool" group.

Be aware that lurking recruiters may be on the discussion boards and travel nursing forums. Not that I would not talk to them, but just beware that the person who is telling you "Everything is great with this company" might just be working for that company; therefore, you will have a biased opinion. The only discussion board that I know of that doesn't have recruiters is "Traveling The Country, One Hospital At A Time."

The "Travel Nursing" group is full of jobs, "Travel Nursing Made Simple" and "Travel Nursing - Answers and Advice" are both recruiter administrated groups.

After narrowing your decision down to about five different companies that you would like to work for, submit a complete application for employment to these five companies.

Upon receiving your application, a recruiter will promptly contact you. Talk to the recruiter and find out what hospitals they have that you are interested in. Find out how many jobs they have available for your specialty. This is especially important if you have a specialty that is on the "hard to find" list, such as psychiatric, rehabilitation, or pediatric emergency care.

Not only should the recruiter interview you, but you should also interview the recruiter! This is easiest done if you get out a notebook to keep track of the questions that you have asked.

Each entry should list the company's name, address, phone number, and the person you talked to. The next entry should be the size of the company. The smaller companies may not have as great a selection of places to travel to, but the customer service is usually impeccable.

Next, you might want to know what kind of structure their recruiters work with. If the recruiters work on a commission basis, you will have a greater chance of a recruiter wanting to sign you up just to make money off of you. If the recruiter is on a shared commission basis you are more likely to find a company that will be based on a teamwork effort, which is always to the advantage of the travel nurse. This also leads to the fact that some companies cater to the hospital, whereas others cater to the nurse.

You will also want to know what the process is in case you decide to change recruiters. When problems arise, you want a recruiter that you feel you can work with. If you feel like the recruiter isn't working hard on your side, or if there are personality clashes, it is much easier to switch recruiters than to switch companies. You don't want to get attached to a company that is not going to work with you on problem solving. Along with this, you also need to find out if there is a recruiter supervisor and who it is. Sometimes this will be the owner in a small company or a regional supervisor in a larger company.

You will want to know from the recruiter if they can place you regionally, nationally, or internationally. Some companies only cover certain regions, or they have different offices for different regions. Some companies only cover certain states and there are some states that are only contracted with certain companies. If you are interested in traveling internationally, you will want to find a company that specializes in international travel. International travel brings into play a very different set of rules because of immunizations, passports, work visas, etc.

You will want to know how many assignments are available with the company. This is especially important if location is your number one priority. If this requirement isn't fulfilled, then you are going to find yourself hunting for a different company for each assignment.

You will need to find out what kinds of specialties are offered through the company. The most common specialty companies that I have found are companies who specialize only in providing hospital operating room personnel. A few companies out there specialize only in providing management personnel. If your specialty is Med/Surg, you will have quite a few companies to choose from, but if your specialty is psychiatric or rehabilitation, you might have trouble finding a company who provides those types of jobs.

You need to get out your list of priority benefits and ask about those. Your priority benefit list might include the type of insurance they provide, the name of the company their insurance is with, whether it's a PPO, HMO, or just a major medical plan. What are the deductibles and how much does the insurance cost the travel nurse? Yes, there are companies out there who provide free medical insurance for their travel nurses. This is a question that you have to ask yourself: are you willing to pay a small amount for your insurance?

You will want to know when you will be paid and how you will be paid. Most companies will send you a weekly check, but there are some out there that only pay bi-weekly or monthly. If you receive a housing stipend, find out if you will be paid the stipend on a weekly or monthly basis. Are monthly stipends paid at the first of the month or at the end of the month?

You will need to find out if the company writes guaranteed hours into their contracts. How many hours do you want to work? Some companies will give you a guarantee of thirty-six hours, while others will guarantee you forty-eight hours. Are those hours broken into eight-hour shifts, ten-hour shifts, or twelve-hour shifts?

What length of assignment does the company offer? In a fast response situation, you might find assignments lasting only four weeks. At other places, you might find companies that offer six to nine month contracts. For those nurses who are traveling with school-age children, maybe a nine-month contract during the school year would be preferred over a short-term contract.

If you take the housing, then you will want to know what type of housing is available. Are there are any additional costs to the traveler? Will you have to share housing with another traveler? If you take the subsidy, you will want to know if they pay just what your expenses are, or if you get to keep any of the extra money if there is any left over after paying your expenses. The housing subsidy should be equal to the cost of renting a one-bedroom apartment.

Another thing that you might want to know in the company interview is if airfare and rental car fees are provided. This is especially true if you plan to travel somewhere outside the continental forty-eight states, such as Hawaii, Alaska, or the Virgin Islands. Airfare is definitely needed for a trip to Hawaii, but some travel nurses opt out of the rental car fees and purchase a vehicle from other travel nurses who are leaving the island.

Submission Requirements

What is required before you can be submitted to a hospital? With most companies, all you need is an application for employment, a skills checklist, and a resume. Other travel companies will want all the ducks in a row before they will even submit you. If you are sure that you want to go with that company and location, then go for it, but be careful about filling out too many forms for too many companies. This can be very time consuming, and in effect, wasting time if you are not serious about working for that company.

After the interview, if you feel comfortable in continuing a relationship with those companies, then fill out other required forms. One mistake I made when I started out was to fill out the checklist and an application with about 30 different companies. Not only did it take several days to do all of those applications and checklists, but my phone wouldn't stop ringing until I actually went on assignment and my home phone number was disconnected.

Personally, I never give out the phone number of my current place of employment. Some recruiters don't care how busy you are; they are out to secure you—"their" travel nurse—and you have the problem of too many phone calls at your current place of business. And yes, whatever company you are looking at, they do have recruiters that work in the evening and at night!

Once you have decided on a travel company you will need to pick a place for them to submit your profile. Be very careful to keep track of what company has sent your profile to which hospital. Your chances at that hospital can be ruined if two different travel companies submit your profile.

Chapter Eighteen

Questions About Contracts

The travel nursing contract is the piece of paper that has all the rules about the next 13 weeks of your life. This is a very important piece of paper that may take years to fully understand. There are all kinds of situations that can come up in 13 weeks. Hopefully after reading this chapter, you will have a better understanding about what a contract really means and what happens if things don't turn out as planned. These are questions are from novice and experienced travelers all over the United States. Hopefully, they can answer your questions for the future!

I verbally agreed to a contract in New York, but there is a new job assignment in Oklahoma that I'm in interested related to the fact that it is near my parents. Just wondering what the penalties are if I can cancel my New York contract and go with the Oklahoma contract?

Or as the old verbiage says, a man's word is good as a contract. You really need to go with your verbal contract unless you have significant factors that will affect the verbal contract. One of the first things you will need to do is to discuss the consequences of you declining the first contract. The biggest problem is going to be if your travel company has already secured housing at first assignment. If housing arrangements have already been made you could be responsible for a three-month lease at the new apartment complex. Other than housing responsibilities, it is your choice whether to stand by your commitment or to change to another commitment. Just remember that this is greatly frowned upon by the travel industry, and you may have trouble getting a next assignment with them.

anted September 23rd and 24th off to attend the travel nursing ence. My manager scheduled me for the 22nd. I work night shift. This put me ending on the 23rd at 7:00 AM. Therefore, there is no way I can make my flight that leave on September 22nd at 7:00 PM.

As night shift workers, we have to remember that we are always a day ahead. If you wanted to be at the conference at 8:00 AM on the 23rd you should have realized that there was no way you could work the night of the 22nd. Therefore it is your responsibility to request off starting the 21st. There are two conclusions in this scenario. Either you are going to have to work something out with the manager, or you will have to attend the conference one day late, which will mean that you will have to reschedule your flight.

I need an assignment that starts right after the traveler's conference (the first of October). I found one with another travel company and they submitted me. Problem is, my current recruiter saw the job and also submitted me. The pay is the same. I have heard great things about the first company, and I'm really excited about the switch, but on the other hand, I feel loyal to my first travel company; although, I'm not too thrilled about them putting me in for a job that I didn't verbally agree to them submitting me to.

This is a very touchy subject. The biggest question is why did your primary company submit you without your consent? Next we can look at which company is better to go with. You need to take a close look at the benefits that you are receiving from both companies. You also need to take a look at which recruiter you trust the most. Because that's what it all boils down to, your recruiter can make or break an assignment.

My biggest question here would be why the recruiter automatically submitted you for this assignment. Did you have an agreement with this recruiter that would allow him or her to submit you without your direct verbal okey-dokey?

This is one of the downfalls to having several companies work with you. It has always been my rule of law, to have only one primary recruiter with several others working for me if I cannot find an assignment with my primary recruiter. If you are working with several companies, it is imperative that you keep track of which companies have submitted you for what assignments.

In the end, I would go with your original company, unless, you have a legitimate reason to change companies. The most common legitimate reason would be if the pay rate was extremely higher with the different company.

When you are finishing one contract about how far in advance do you sign your next?

About four weeks before the end of my contract, I start looking for another. The truth of the matter is, hospitals are usually looking for start dates of as soon as possible to up to four weeks out. That is not to say that some assignments can be arranged for a start date further out, but most are between two to six weeks out.

I signed a contract over a month ago, but just received notification that I needed an up-to-date physical and urine drug screen (UDS). I am on the road and don't have a clue where I can stop and get these things done.

This situation just happened to me on my current assignment. I was traveling from Iowa to California and they wanted me to stop and get a physical and UDS. My first the action was to inform them that if they could find a place for me to park a 29ft. trailer, I would be more than happy to get their physical and UDS done. It just happened to be that I was stopping in Arizona for a week and my travel company arranged for my tests to be done along the road. If there is any way possible to stop at a place on the road, then get the tests done, but if it is not convenient for you continue onto the assignment location and get it done once you get to your assignment location. As the old saying goes, a failure of planning on their part, does not constitute an emergency on my part!

Is the contract that you sign with your travel agency a different document than the hospital signs with the agency?

Unfortunately, new travelers do not understand that the contract with the travel agency to the hospital is different from the contract with the travel agency to the travel nurse. This should not be a problem, unless there are specifics in your contract about the floors that you will work or the days off that you would like that are not communicated in the contract between the agency and the hospital. This is why communication is so important between you and your recruiter. All specifics of a contract should be discussed with your recruiter before the official document is penned.

I'm thinking about going out on my own and taking a seasonal contract. Are there any seasonal positions for the winter?

Yes there are plenty of seasonal contracts! The most are in Florida, Texas, Colorado, and Arizona for the winter. Some of them include:

Florida: Lee Health System in Florida, Baycare Health, Community Hospital,and Physicians Regionia in Naples, FL; Health First Hospital, Punta Gorda, Holy Corss in Fort Lauderdale; and Tenet Healthcare in various locations. Texas: Heart Hospital and David's Healthcare in Austin plus Good Shephard of Longview. Colorado: Centura, University of Colorado, and Aspen Valley Hospital. Arizona: Yuma Regional Medical Center and Banner Healthcare.

Is it normal to do annual competencies for a new assignment???

Unfortunately yes, you end up doing competencies for each new travel hospital and every new travel company if you switch companies. If you stay long enough at the hospital, you may have to also participate in their annual skills day! That is one of the "bad" things about travel nursing.

To text, or not to text! Should your communications with your travel nursing recruiter be through text, email, phone, or a combination?

I have found that a combination is best. A lot of the time I now communicate with my recruiter through Facebook messaging. That way she knows when I'm up and awake. If there is something urgent, then I will call her and vice versa. When dealing with contracts, I have found that email is best. This way you have a record of every negotiation that you make.

What happens if I miss a shift? I saw on a forum the other day that a nurse had to pay her company back for a missed day.

This depends on a few things. Did you have an opportunity to make up the day? How many hours do you have in? To complete a contract 100%, you must have been there all your contracted hours. Your contracted hours should be 468 if you work 36 hours a week for 13 weeks. If you are under this amount, then some companies require you to pay them back for the money that they lost on your contracted hours. One company I know charges $18/hour for the hours that you don't work. This also hinges on the factor of whether or not you have taken company housing, or the stipend. With the stipend, you just don't get the stipend or your regular hourly rate for the hours that you didn't work.

Do all contracts come with a 36-hour guarantee? And what about holidays?

Unfortunately, no...not all of them automatically come with a 36-hour guarantee, but that can be negotiated in your contract. This will need to be discussed with your recruiter, if the hospital doesn't already have a policy. Some companies will have exceptions, for example: "Traveler can be called off once every 2 weeks." Banner Health has a policy in which travelers can be called off one day. This is more like a 24-hour guarantee. One year in November, I worked 3 days but got paid for 8 days, plus my housing was not affected.

Holidays are also negotiable, if the hospital doesn't already have a policy. For instance, the hospital that I'm at now doesn't allow travelers to work the holidays related to the fact that the workers are all union. If they don't have travelers, then they can cancel regular employees and save on the Holiday pay rate.

What are the perks of renewing a contract?

The first perk is that you do not have to do a mountain of paperwork. You already know the staff, which reduces the stress of starting a new assignment, and you don't have to pack up and move again! Other perks that are optional or can be negotiated, as in an increase in pay; they don't have to pay you for traveling from point A to point B again, so ask for that cash!

Also, ask yourself if there is going to be a change in the living conditions? If you are in Alaska or Florida, this could be a big deal! In my last renewal, I asked for an "air-conditioning stipend." Therefore, my pay rate has increased a little related to the costs to turn on the a/c in a travel trailer during the summer in Southern California.

So nothing is official until a contract is signed even if I have a verbal on accepting a position already, correct?

This is a sticky situation. In fact, this is why a lot of companies have gone with the agreement that you have to sign the contract within 24 hours of accepting the assignment. Now, that doesn't mean that you can't negotiate a contract. I have a wonderful travel company and recruiter, but I have yet to accept the first contract that was sent to me!

Can I cancel a contract at any time for any reason? What are the penalties to do that?

A lot of this depends on why you are cancelling or quitting a contract early. I had one assignment that was cut 2 weeks short related to the fact my father came down with Guillian-Barre Syndrome. Although I was willing to come back and work my two weeks, the hospital wrote down, "11-week contract completed in good standing."

If you have an assignment in which you don't get along with someone and your life is a living hell that may or may not be a reason to quit an assignment. Just this last year, I had an assignment in which the nursing supervisor always found something that I was doing wrong. It came down to the point where she even yelled at me in front of patients in the middle of shift change. Although there were personality conflicts, at no time did I feel like my nursing skills were in question, and also I did have the backing of the director of nursing; therefore, I stuck it out until the end.

The closest that I have come to having a dangerous assignment was in Myrtle Beach, SC. In fact, this was the end of my floor career. I was working day shift, and it was busy, but we all pitched in together, and it was survivable. I actually renewed my contract and moved to night shift (my personal preferred shift). I didn't realize that I was stepping into hell. Most of the night shift was all new graduates who knew everything. Never in my life have I been told that I'm not needed in the middle of a code, that the newbies can handle it. I had up to eight patients all by myself, and the nursing assistants were all busy helping out the regular staff. Needless to say, as a result of having no help, my back gave out, and the last 6 weeks of my contract was cancelled. I worked out a deal with my travel company, paid my own housing, and got lucky with no penalty. This is the difference between a great small/medium company to one of larger ones who would have charged me an arm and leg for everything that went wrong in that contract!

I have never had it happen to me, personally, but I know of a hospital where three traveling nurses walked off the job (not while they were doing patient care though). They were not allowed to call the physicians at night, they were asked just to write orders. I can see doing this with things you might have standing orders for—over the counter medications (Milk of Mag, Tylenol, Ibuprofen)—but not for prescription medications. This is an example of a situation in which, if you went in front of the nursing board, you would be practicing way over your level. This would most definitely be putting your license in danger; therefore, I would be contacting my recruiter and my travel company to get me out of there. Once again, a great company would stand beside you and not charge you.

That being said, the biggest charge companies are most concerned with is the 3-month lease that they are liable for. Expect to be charged for this. Some companies will even charge you for their portion of the bill rate that they are missing out on. One company I worked with had a flat fee, that if a contract was cancelled, I owed them $3000 in penalties.

Remember also, that everything is negotiable!

Does anyone wait until the last possible moment to sign their contract in case something comes up? If so what do you tell your recruiter that is pestering you?

More and more I'm seeing where companies want you to sign the contract within 24 hours. If you don't know for sure if you are all in on the contract, then you really need to make up your mind before you even interview. This is also true if you have other places that you have been submitted. Some hospitals will wait, but some want an answer that day. During the interview ask when you can expect an answer back from them, and also you need to tell them when you will be answering back, usually within two to three days. Any recruiter who "pushes" you into a job within the first few hours is not a recruiter, but a used car salesman. With that being said, your recruiter also expects you to touch base with him/her after the interview, and for you to give them an answer within the next few days. If it's been more than 3 days, yeah, the recruiter is going to start pestering you for a decision. Also, you have to remember you are not the only one applying for that job.

I have a month left on my contract, and related to snowbird season being over, they are closing down the ER Hold unit, in which I was contracted for. Now they want me to be a hospital float for the rest of my contract. Can they do this to me?

One thing about snowbirds is that they always arrive and leave at different times and it's very hard to predict when it is actually going to be over. This is the part that we mentioned in chapter two where a traveler has to be flexible and adaptable. Somewhere in your contract you probably have a phrase that you will float to like units. Unfortunately, you are going to be floated 100% of the time now, related to the fact that there are no patients in your unit. Keep in mind, though, they only need to float you to areas of competence. You could cancel the contract, but chances are you will have to pay a penalty.

I'm a month into my contract and the hospital is already asking me to stay for a year. Is this usual for a hospital?

If the hospital likes you and you like the hospital and the need is there, then yes, it is very likely that the hospital will want to renew you. Renewing you for up to a year is very rare. I could see this though if the hospital is always short staffed, and they know they are going to need someone still in one year. Most likely the hospital will renew you for another 13 weeks. I've also had contracts renewed for 6 weeks and 8 weeks.

When it comes to being at a hospital for up to a year, you have to remember that once you sign that contract stating that you will be there 365 days your tax home automatically switches to your assignment location; therefore, all your subsides will immediately become taxable. This includes all housing, meals, incidentals, and entertainment monies that you have received.

The hospital that I'm currently at has three difference ICU units (Medical, Surgical, and Cardiac). I am extending my contract for another 13 weeks, but they want to move me from Surgical ICU to Medical ICU. Can they make me change units?

Hospitals can't make you do anything that you don't want! On the other hand, this may be an excellent opportunity for you to broaden your horizons. The biggest question is, "What are the differences between SICU and MICU? Do you feel that you are competent to make the switch?" From what I know about SICU/MICU this type of switch would be very similar. You would be a great fit if you had started out on a medical/surgical type of unit. Then you have a little bit of experience on the surgical side of things.

On the other hand, CCU would be the biggest change. You would most definitely have arterial lines, balloon pumps, and a whole different plethora of medications. Once again, I would invite you to take a deep long look at your experience. Do you have telemetry or step-down experience?

Don't let your recruiter push you into an assignment that you aren't qualified for also! When I went from telemetry to step-down in

2004, it was with the encouragement of the recruiter that "You can do anything." Well, related to a misunderstanding of "taking care of post cardiac cath patients," it landed me in a peculiar situation as I learned the different between a patient coming back with a sheath that hasn't been pulled and a patient coming back with an angioseal. Oh, I learned how to remove sheaths from helping out the other nurses, but the staff was none too happy that I didn't get post cath patients!

I have been with "Happy Camper Nurse Staffing" for 5 years and really love them, but "Innovative Travelers" has a job that I really want. I know I can switch, but why do I feel so guilty about switching? What is my recruiter going to think of me?

Longevity with one company is something that travelers usually aspire for, but is rarely attained unless you are with one of the larger companies. If you want the freedom to visit all parts of the United States, then there is a chance that you will have to switch companies at some point in your career.

What you have to learn is, even though we get "attached" to a great recruiter, this is a business, and you have to do what is best for you. A great recruiter will be happy for you, in that you are going where you really want to be, even though the assignment didn't come through him/her. If the recruiter pressures you to stay with him/her and makes you feel guilty for leaving them, that recruiter just sees you as a dollar sign, and unfortunately, you have been "pimped out" for the last 5 years!

I was talking to a recruiter on Facebook, and they have a job that I really want. I sent "Sandy" a resume, skills checklist, and 2 references for them to submit me to Albuquerque, NM. My now recruiter, "Peter", saw the online post that I was interested in Albuquerque and he submitted me also. As we are talking about opportunities 2 hours later, Peter tells me, "Oh, I saw on Facebook where you were interested in the Albuquerque job, so I submitted you. Whatever Sandy was going to pay you, I will pay you $5 more an hour!"

This is wrong on so many levels! First of all, unless you have given expressed written consent for a recruiter to submit you, then no recruiter should be submitting you to anything without you expressed interest. The ONLY time it is okay is when you have only one recruiter working for you and you have given her written permission, usually through email, to submit you. This usually only happens if you have a trusting relationship with your recruiter and you have a hard to find specialty, as in House Supervisor. Related to the fact that I sleep during the day, I don't want to wake up at 10 PM and know that a job came up, but now a day has been wasted because I was asleep. So, I will give my recruiter permission to submit me without waking me up. This is a very rare thing to occur though!

Unfortunately, this travel nurse lost out on the Albuquerque assignment related to the fact that she was submitted by two different agencies. This also presented a problem in that she no longer trust Peter and felt like she was being pimped out, so she had to go through the long process of finding a new travel company and new recruiter.

This is my second assignment with Great States Staffing and my contract ends in two weeks. I was getting a little nervous about not having a job, so I verbally accepted a high paying contract in South Dakota that starts in 4 weeks. I have just been advised by a recruiter at Favorite Staffing that a job in Hawaii has just come up; therefore, I had them go ahead and send my profile. To my surprise, I just interviewed with the hospital in Hawaii and they want me there in 3 weeks, which is just perfect. Now what do I do?

First of all, as much as you would love to go to Hawaii, I would not have allowed anyone to submit me since I already had agreed to go to South Dakota. On the other hand, related to the fact that it is Hawaii, I can understand why you went for it.

First you need to realize that a verbal agreement is your word. If you have verbally agreed then it is usually just a matter of time that the written contract is signed. Also, if you answered yes to your recruiter in an email, then this can be evidence of a legal and binding written contract.

Truth of the matter is that a company will probably not come after you for any monetary penalties unless the lease has been purchased on your housing in South Dakota. Just remember, that you may be held responsible for any costs that the first company has incurred related to you taking the South Dakota assignment.

On the other hand, you are correct in that you have not signed anything. So, legally there is no signed contract that you can be held accountable for.

The truth of this situation is that you can go ahead and take the Hawaii assignment, but be prepared to pay the price of a being a

"DNR" (do not return) from the company who submitted you to South Dakota. This may also affect any references that will be needed from that company.

I recently signed a contract with a hospital in Virginia. It was on my drive from Texas to Virginia that I got the news that the hospital hired someone else and they were terminating my contract.

In this case, we have to look at both the contract with the hospital to the travel company and the contract between you and the company. You have no idea what the contract with the hospital said, but somewhere there had to be a clause about cancelling a contract.

Your contract with the company probably has a clause in there that you are an "at will" employee. Therefore, your chances of you getting payment for the entire contract are probably not going to happen.

In reality the hospital should be liable for all expenses that have occurred by the travel company to get it to that point, but holding them accountable probably isn't going to happen. The company will probably just not use that hospital for contracts any longer.

The chances of you getting what is owed to you for expenses of this assignment is probably not going to happen either. Back to reality, you will probably have to cut your losses and carry on to the next assignment.

Is this fair to the nurse and the travel company? Of course not! But there is little that can be done to "make" the hospital pay for the expenses. This is another reason why it is important for a nurse to have a month's worse of expenses saved up so that you can financially float for a few weeks.

What is going to happen here is that you will return home and the travel company will make every effort to find you a new contract as soon as possible. This again is where the great companies are different than the average companies. A great company would make sure that you make it back home safe and sound. An average company will send you greetings and good luck in making it back home.

The unfortunate thing about this business is that sometimes we have to suck it up and take our losses. Some things are just out of our control.

My contract with Cedars Sinai ends May 15th, but I'm not on the schedule for the last week. My contract states that I do have a 36-hour guarantee. Is the hospital liable for that last week?

First thing that I would do is discuss this with your nursing manager. I would take your contract to her and ask her to be put on the schedule for the next week. In today's world, I would approach this with an email, that way you would have some kind of written account of the communication between you and the manager.

After you have informed the manager of the mistake, it is the manager's place to add on that extra week. If they do not add an extra week, then according to the contract, yes, you are entitled to 36 hours worth of pay.

Now the reality of the situation, is the hospital going to actually pay for the extra week? Don't really know. On the other hand, your contract is with the travel company and not with the hospital. Therefore, legally, the travel company is liable for the extra week's worth of pay related to the written contract.

Will the company pay? Depends on whether or not they are a great company or an average company and will depend on whether they can get payment from the hospital. If you are a great travel nurse and the travel company wants to retain you, then yes, usually they do pay. But, if the hospital doesn't pay them and they are all about the money, chances are you are not going to get paid. Then you will have to make the decision on whether or not you want to go with the same company for your next assignment.

I was cancelled on Monday. Now it is Friday and I have a girls' night out planned, but the hospital called and wants me to come in. They are stating that I have to come in related to the fact that my contract states that I have to be available for any other shifts in that week.

Unfortunately, this phrase is in many travel nursing contracts. It all has to do with that 36-hour guarantee. The hospital sees it as a need that you must work 3 days a week. If you get called off for one of those days, they expect you to be available for another shift in that week. The travel company wants you to work this shift related to the fact that if you don't work, they don't get paid. Therefore, the reality of the situation is that if you don't go in for the third shift then your 36-hour guarantee is going to be null and void. If you can go in, then I highly recommend it. This lends to your credibility of being adaptable. If you have had a warming up for the party, then absolutely do not go in, but I would not be expecting my 36-hour guarantee either.

I just received my new contract for my assignment in Arizona. In this contract it states that I will make $20/hour for the first 36 hours of orientation. Huh? Can they really get away with this?

If you sign that contract then yes, they can get away with this! Remember, as a travel nurse it is your first duty to read your contract over with a fine-tooth comb. I would shoot this back to my recruiter and tell them that I did not agree to the ridiculous orientation rate.

Then the ball is in their court. They can talk to the hospital, but ultimately it's their decision on what rate you should be paid. Remember that your contract is with the travel company and not with the hospital.

A contract is a legal and binding agreement between two parties. If you do not agree to the lower rate for orientation, then we do not have an agreement between two parties.

I would really try to work this out with your travel company, but if it means that much to you, then no, you are under no obligation to accept the contract as written, and the whole 13 weeks is out, not just the first week.

I just accepted an assignment in Texas and after my first week of orientation I'm scared to death. I'm horrified by what I have seen from patient safety issues, to safety of the staff, to putting your nursing license on the line. I'm just not sure that I'm willing to put my life or license on the line, but what is my recourse?

First of all, I totally believe that the only reason to walk out on a contract is when you feel you nursing license is on the line. When it comes down to it, the charge nurse and the director/manager are not going to be with you when you are standing in front of the state nursing board defending your license.

If for any reason you feel that your nursing license is on the line… RUN, and don't look back. Of course, while you are running you will need to notify your recruiter of why you are running. Any great travel company will totally stand by you on this, or you don't need that travel company.

I was working the telemetry unit and my back "seized" up on me. It felt like someone was tugging on my spinal cord and the pain was extreme. When I went to the ER, they classified it as a repetitious injury. Can I get cancelled from my contract by the hospital if I was injured?

What usually happens in this case is that your contract is cancelled related to a workman's compensation injury. Unfortunately, I know about this first hand. In 2007, the day shift had given a patient Lasix at 6:00 PM. By the time I came on at 7:00 PM, the medication was effective and I spent the night getting a patient up and down to use the restroom. By the end of the night, my back as seized up and I couldn't move without severe pain. It was like someone had grabbed my spine and squeezed every time I moved. I ended up in the ER an hour after work. After an MRI, I was diagnosed with a herniated L4/L5, which ended my contract.

Related to the fact that I could no longer work, my contract ended on that day. The only expense to my travel company was my housing. I ended up paying for my housing for the next month and staying in South Carolina for physical therapy.

At any time that you are injured, workman's compensation should take effect. Therefore, the company is liable for any compensation that you are owed. In my case, my travel company was liable for my damages and not the hospital. This is why travel companies have to have workman's compensation insurance on you.

This pretty much ended my career as a telemetry nurse and I had to make the transition back to ER and then to House Supervisor. Every injury is different and depending on the final outcome, you may or may not be able to return to the floor. As for your contract, if you are not able to complete the contract related to an injury then workman's compensation should be liable for the difference. Talk to your travel company! A resolution can be worked out.

No chapter can answer all the questions that a traveling nurse has about contracts, but it is my sincere belief that we have touched on the most common problems that arise in travel nursing. If you have some other situation that you need help with, please don't hesitate to contact me at highwayhypo@yahoo.com.

Chapter Nineteen

On The Road Again With the Gang

~*~

Denise from South Carolina

Denise is an adult ICU, CCU, and Trauma nurse who values money, benefits, location and a great recruiter. She prefers two bedroom housing and doesn't mind paying a little. She has been traveling for 10 years and looking for only the top pay. She prefers to make over $40/hour and loves a company with longevity and education benefits. Her least favorite hospitals have been Kaisers, Seton Medical Center, and Alta Bates Summit. Her favorite cities have been Santa Rosa and Pleasanton. Her least favorite have been San Jose, and Oakland in California. She prefers to work 12-hour days with alternating weekends off. She also prefers teaching hospitals with support and transporters. She would like to tell a first timer that, "You are a visitor. Do not try to change things. Always smile and help your co-workers."

~*~

Jennifer from Colorado

Jennifer is a Critical Care nurse who prefers a great salary and great location. She has been traveling for under a year with Aya Healthcare. Get it all in writing, if it's not, it never happened. Don't let your recruiter fast-talk you. Go in with a positive attitude (and chocolate). Expect to be floated, and take the crappy assignments. Enjoy where you are!!!!

~*~

Carol from Texas

Carol is a perioperative and circulating nurse for the OR. She places recruiter and salary on the top of her list! She has been traveling for 4 years with several different companies. Her only disaster was with Cross Country. Her favorite city has been Dover, NH, with her least being Frisco, CO.

About her first assignment she writes, "It was fun and a learning experience. My first assignment was a small, 2 OR hospital in Colorado during ski season. I love ortho, so I got a lot of that, that season. Of course there were some negatives, but I would rather remember the good experience and the great people I met and worked with there, instead of the few "bad apples." It does take a special person to travel and it isn't for everyone."

And she would like other travel nurses to, "Be open, friendly, and remember there is more than one way to do something. Some things even change in different parts of the country. Be open to new experiences and don't prejudge what people will be like. I have met some wonderful friends in an area of the country I was told was not very friendly. Enjoy yourself, make the best of any situation, and explore. You may never be there again."

~*~

Kim from Missouri

Kim is an ICU/PACU nurse from Missouri that has been traveling for 3 years. She was not impressed with the staff at American Mobile, but liked her recruiter. She is in between assignment now. She prefers to take the two bedroom and pay a little, and she travels on the basis of location and the recruiter. Her favorite city has been Eugene, OR with her least favorite being New Haven, CT.

She stated that her first assignment was crap. She didn't know what she really wanted and took whatever was available. She would like to remind travelers to,"Figure out what is most important to you. Is it money, location, whether you have to float and to where etc. and make sure you are fully aware of expectations before you arrive."

~*~

Anna from Alabama

Anna is an ER nurse who travels for the great benefits and prefers a totally awesome recruiter! She takes the one bedroom apartment that is paid for by the company. Her disaster company was Stat Staffing Solutions-Farmington Hills, MI. Her least favorite city was Detroit, MI.

About her first assignment she writes, "The hospital was great, you know it's always one person you will run into that tries to damper your situation. She was rude, and didn't offer help. But, she needed me to help her. The company did not give me my end of assignment bonus due to the nurse manager giving me a bogus review, I think they work together so the end of assignment bonuses are kept and pocketed for themselves."

She would like to tell a nurse to get everything in writing! Research the travel company and the area, and especially check the reviews of the hospital.

~*~

Shannon from Wyoming

Shannon is an OR nurse from Wyoming that takes the housing stipend and finds her own housing. She has traveled two years with Premier Healthcare Professionals. Her only disaster company was Medical Solutions. Her least favorite was CRMC in Cheyenne, WY, with her least favorite city also being Cheyenne. Her favorite city has been Denver.

About her first travel assignment she states, "I had a great first experience; Melissa with PHP treated me like family. I never felt like I was a workhorse with PHP. I made the mistake of working with Medical Solutions on my second assignment...Never Again...! My best advice is be specific on what you want and need. Do not assume anything until it is in writing, some reps will promise you the moon and come through on nothing. Stick with a company and one rep if you find a good one. Don't let companies tell you that no one offers first day paid medical, PHP does."

This is what she would like to tell a first timer, "Just always remember no matter what happens during your contract at a facility it's temporary...you can do anything for 13 weeks."

~*~

Renee from Colorado

Renee is an OR nurse from Colorado. She has been with Bridge

Staffing for 5 years. American Mobile was a disaster company for her. She travels for the excellent salary and prefers a stupendous recruiter! Her non-friendly hospitals have been: Holy Cross Taos, Espanola NM, UNM University, and Eastern New Mexico Regional Hospital. Her favorite city has been Denver, while her least favorites have been Roswell, Espanola, El Paso, and Albuquerque.

Her first assignment was a mess, "I had an unfriendly manager who manipulated everyone. If you went along with her unsafe practices and unfairness you might survive. It was a ridiculous place to work, but definitely eye opening experience. Thank goodness I had a good recruiter at the time to talk to."

She would like to tell a first timer, "Get everything in writing. Compare several companies. Do not go with a pushy recruiter; choose someone you feel comfortable with. Check highway hypodermics top ten-travel companies list. PHP and Bridge have 1st day insurance and it is excellent. Make sure to keep accurate record of your time and make sure your company honors your contract on all issues. If they try to screw you—move on to another company. There are good ones out there and please note in all these reviews some of the same companies keep coming up as disasters. Pay attention and do not sign with them."

~*~

Barb from Ohio

Barb is a Critical Care nurse from Ohio who has been traveling under a year with Innovative Placements. Her priorities include an excellent salary followed by location, recruiter, and benefits. She takes the housing stipends and finds her own accommodations. Her disaster assignment was with Nightingale Nurses at Kindred Long Term Acute Care.

Her first assignment was awful! "I was told I was hired for ICU, only to find out it was an LTAC! Recruiter was stunned when I told her I hated it!! I will never, never recommend Nightingale nurses to my worst enemy! What a bunch of cheating liars and thieves. Thank God my assignment was only 8 weeks—I wouldn't have lasted any longer. Very unsafe working conditions, both for the nurses and patients—what a shame! I would rather beg for money on a street corner than return to a Kindred facility!"

She would like to tell a first timer, "Learn to be flexible and remember, "it's only temporary" unless you choose to extend. Get everything in writing and review it carefully before you sign. Get information about the area you're staying—go and explore! Enjoy yourself and see the world!"

~*~

Rhonda from Ohio

Rhonda is an ER nurse from Ohio who travels for the great salaries and locations. She has been traveling off and on for the last 16 years. She is currently with Cross Country, and has had a bad experience with Strategic.

About her first assignment she states, "First assignment small hospital in Templeton, Ca. I was very nervous going across country to work but staff was awesome!"

She also states, "I have traveled off and on since '98 and have had pretty positive assignments. Be flexible, remember you're there to help but don't be a pushover. I have always been offered a full time position at every facility, which makes me feel good. As everyone says get everything in writing, pay attention to pay stubs and don't be afraid to ask questions. Be aware of "smooth operators"—my recruiter at CCTC is amazing and doesn't hesitate to tell me if a place wouldn't be in my best interest. Had a bad experience with Strategic—was put up in a known crack house that ran its own prostitution ring then had to pay for hotel out of my pocket while other housing was arranged. Have always been pleased with CCTC. Good luck! Travel is wonderful, see the country, meet new people. It gives back as much as you put into it."

~*~

Bea from Colorado

Bea is a PACU nurse from Colorado who is all about the benefits, great location, and an excellent recruiter. She prefers a one bedroom paid for and has been with American Mobile for 5 years. Her only disaster company was with Nightingale who were never available when you needed to speak with them. She has enjoyed most of the cities that she has traveled in but didn't really care for Taos, NM.

About her first experience she writes, "Went from the west coast to the east coast. Wonderful drive, wonderful city I lived in. However the hospital was a disaster. It never put me off traveling, however."

She would like to tell a first timer, "Be friendly, flexible, help you fellow nurses as much as possible. Don't get involved in hospital politics and don't share too much about your company, pay, or anything else you don't want spread around. Every time and every assignment, do extensive research on the companies and facilities. Traveling is not for the faint of heart."

~*~

Carmen from Louisiana

Carmen is a CCU nurse from Louisiana. Location and salary and most important to her followed by a great recruiter and benefits. She has been traveling for over 10 years and takes the one bedroom housing provided by the company. She is currently traveling with Fastaff and doesn't plan on switching any time soon! Her least favorite hospitals were in California at Long Beach and Riverside County. Her favorite has been Oahu, HI.

About her first contract she states, "My first experience was with Cross County TravCorps. Paige Sawtell was my recruiter. She really took care of me. I went to Hawaii. It was awesome. I stayed 3 years!"

She would like to tell other nurses, "Don't let fear stop you from doing anything! Medicine is the same everywhere. The only thing that is different is paperwork. Jump in!"

~*~

Doris from Pennsylania

Doris is from Pennsylvania and works in the ICU. When she picks a travel company, she looks for one with the best benefits and locations. She has been traveling for 2 years and takes the housing stipend. She is currently with Gifted Nurses, and does not plan to switch anytime soon! Her favorite hospital has been Williamsport Medical Center with Madison, WI, as her favorite town.

About her first assignment she writes, "The hospital was horrible. ICU nurses unhappy due to continuing mandating of overtime, and managers not caring if nurses tired. Also some dangerous practices went there. She was glad to get out."

She would like to tell other nurses, "Don't complain or have a bad attitude. Don't be lazy, and offer to help fellow nurses. Don't try and change things in the unit."

~*~

Shannon from MO

Shannon is from St. Louis and works in the OR. She travels for the great salary, but also prefers to have an excellent recruiter. She takes the one bedroom housing from the travel company. She is currently with Trustaff and does not plan on changing companies any time soon. Her least favorite hospital has been Rideout Memorial in Marysville, CA.

About her first contract she writes, "The surgeons were insulting, called nurses names, purposely tried to set you up for failure, screamed at you, all with no repercussions. I was contracted for days when I got there I was mid-shift. Half the hospital consists of travel nurses, felt like my license was on the line every day I worked. Hospital was listed as level 3 it was more of a level 1. Been a nurse for 11 years in OR, right now I don't want to be a nurse anymore. I don't even make what the full time staff nurses there do. My call pay is less than the scrub tech's who work there. SAD!"

She would like to tell a first timer, "Make sure your recruiter explains in full every aspect of your contract. If your gut instinct tells you something trust it, there are lots of travel companies out there. Find a recruiter you feel completely comfortable with. Research the place you are going to (how big city, demographics, hospital reviews on Google, etc.) and choose wisely."

~*~

Elaina from South Carolina

Elaina is a dialysis nurse from South Carolina that travels and places top priority on salary and location. She has been traveling with Quik Travel Staffing for almost a year now and loved Palm Springs, CA.

About her first travel assignment she writes, "My first assignment was in San Antonio where I had one week of orientation and then working with a very grateful and appreciative staff. Worked 60 hours my first week, and many more to follow! Felt like I was truly helping the team and enjoyed Texas immensely! It is such a wonderful state."

She would like to tell first timers, "Stay organized and always have a smile on your face! Don't give anyone a reason to dislike you. Don't be afraid to tell someone you won't do something until you're properly trained. Do a lot of research before you begin, research the area, hospital, agency, etc., and it's okay to do a few interviews to decide! Don't travel for money, because honestly, it's not as much as much as everyone seems to think. Go on day trips! Buy a camera! Be open minded because you're going to have surprises!"

~*~

Kerry from OH

Kerry is an ER nurse who travels with Trustaff. He prefers a great location and salary. His favorite city has been Westminster, MD, with his least favorite being Columbus, OH. He currently takes the housing stipend and finds his own pad.

About his first assignment he writes, "My first travel experience was in a small town, Westminster, Maryland, just outside Baltimore. It was a nice town and the people friendly. The staff were gracious and treated me like one of the permanent staffers. Was offered an extension but declined as the travel each week from Maryland to Ohio became tiring."

He would like to tell a first timer, "Anyone can do anything for 13 weeks. I know now I can never be a regular staffer in a hospital. If you are single, or even have family, traveling is the best way to go. You can negotiate with your agency for more money with each assignment. Also, you want to start looking for the next assignment at least 5 weeks prior to the current one ending. Sometimes unforeseen things happen where jobs are cancelled."

~*~

Kim from Virginia

Kim is a labor and delivery nurse from Virginia who travels for the money, location, and has to have a great recruiter! She has been traveling for 5 years and is currently traveling with Talemed. Her least favorite hospitals have been Pitt County Memorial (Vidant Health), Greenville, NC and South Fulton Medical Center, East Point, GA. Her favorite places have been Pineville, NC and Fredericksburg, VA.

About her first assignment she writes, "My first experience was in Nashville at a hospital that did 7,000 deliveries/year. I came from a small hospital that did 20 deliveries/month. The staff was awesome and treated me like I was one of them. It was a great learning experience."

She would like to tell a first timer, "First, you can do anything for 13 weeks. Second, just because something is done differently doesn't mean it's wrong. Remember, you're there to help, not change the unit. Don't let anyone (recruiters or staff at hospitals) run over you. Most of all, have fun and try to learn something new at every assignment."

~*~

Virgie from New Mexico

Virgie is a PACU and ER nurse who travels the United States in an RV. She is currently with Accountable Staffing in Tulsa, OK. She has been traveling for 5 years with her favorite hospital being in Culpepper, VA. Her least favorite hospitals have been Physicians Hospital Keno in Tucson, AZ and Memorial in Las Cruces, NM. Her favorite city was Culpepper, VA.

About her first assignment she writes, "It was a disastrous one with American Mobile. I told them I don't do Psych/L&D/or Peds. My first day in orientation at Keno hospital in Tucson, I was informed that this was a Level I psych Center, "Didn't anyone tell you?" NO! American wouldn't allow me to get out of the contract. We spent the whole first week learning self-defense against patients because a nurse recently had been hit over the head with a chair by a patient and was paralyzed. Nice FYI's I think. They kept this information from me. Memorial hospital in Las Cruces is filled to the brim with nurse-eating piranhas. I wouldn't recommend going there!"

She would like to tell a first timer to,"Remember that you are a guest in the facility that you are working in. Be easy going and go with their flow. Don't compare their hospital with others that you have worked in. Don't try to change their way of doing things, just do it. You're there to help, so help. Don't participate in gossip and certainly don't start it about your fellow workers. Do not participate in heelbiting of nurses. Stay clear of all the 'politic'-ing of the hospital. Show up on time and don't complain. Do your job and do it well."

~*~

Cherie from New York

Cherie is from New York and finds that a great recruiter along with a great salary is what she is aiming for! She has been traveling 4 years with LRS Healthcare and doesn't plan to switch companies. Her least favorite place was Kern Medical Center in Bakersfield, CA, with her favorite being at Vidant Medical Center in Greenville, NC.

About her first assignment she writes, “My first experience was some in Greenville, NC. The staff welcomed me with open arms and treated me like family. I went there for a 13-week assignment and stayed a whole year!! I have been on the road close to 5 years now, most have been good, a few bad, but I try not to let the bad ones discourage me. I have a great company and a recruiter who is wonderful. I am in this for the long haul.”

She would like to tell a first timer, “Work HARD, be organized, be flexible, and do not get caught up in hospital politics, gossip, chit chat... stay focused on your job.”

~*~

Tamara from South Dakota

Tamara is a NICU nurse from South Dakota who chooses her assignments related to location and salary. She has been traveling for 2 years now with RN Network and has no plans of switching companies. Currently she resides in an RV. Her least favorite cities have been El Paso (not much to do and very dusty) and Houston (roads are horrible and everything rusts quickly). Her favorite cities have been Tiki Island, TX and Galveston, TX, related to the fact that there is a lot to do at these places.

About her first travel experience she writes, “It was at Fairview Southdale in Edina, MN. Staff was very receptive, grateful, helpful, and of course “Minnesota Nice”. I could not have asked for a better 1st assignment experience. They were all professional, and I never heard a negative comment about anything or anybody.”

She would like to tell a first timer, “If you do not have a “tax home” you cannot participate in the Tax Advantage plan. Google this and do your research. Your tax home is not simply what is on your driver’s license as most recruiters will tell you (usually because they themselves are unaware of the requirements used to declare a tax home. In practice, the courts and the IRS rely on a 3-factor safe-harbor that the IRS created in Rev. Rul. 73-529. Here are the 3 factors: (1) Does the taxpayer, in fact, have a tax home and use it for business while living there? (2) Does the taxpayer have duplicate living expenses when traveling out of town? (3) What is his or her personal attachment to the claimed home? (Has the person ever lived there? Does his or her spouse or child(ren) live there (the family member must be “lineal”)? Does the person frequently use the claimed abode for lodging?) Those who meet two factors lose the safe-harbor and are at the mercy of "facts and circumstances" analysis. Those who meet only one factor are deemed itinerants—that is, they have no permanent personal residence so they cannot have a tax home and thus cannot have or deduct travel expenses. FYI if you are a fulltime RVer and have no duplicate expenses (pay rent via a legal lease or a mortgage, etc.) you do not have a tax home. If you do not have a tax home, declare you do, and the IRS audits you, then you will find yourself in a heap of trouble. Back taxes and penalties and fines, are outrageous!!!

I was aware of this on my 2nd assignment, but have run into nurses who know about this and do it anyways; taking the chance they will never get caught. Mostly, though, I have run into nurses who have no idea there are requirements to get the tax-free stipends. Always, always, always, research the hospitals they want to send you to. Do not get pressured into signing right away or loose the assignment. Allow one day to review your contract, and go over it several times and with another set of eyes. Have another read it to you aloud. Become buddies with the other travelers, swap stories, and compare the hospitals you have been to (not at work; keep all discussions on personal time and out of earshot of staff nurses). Funny how you run into familiar faces after a year or so."

~*~

Frieda from California

Frieda is an ER nurse from California who travels for the money and the location. She takes the one bedroom housing from the travel company. She has been traveling for more than 10 years and currently is with Trustaff. Her favorite cities have been San Diego and Upstate New York. Her least favorite cities have been Riverside, CA and Sacramento, CA.

About her first assignment she writes, "First job was fantastic. I made more, had housing paid for. Staff nurse pay in Los Angeles, CA was $19.00 an hour. Travel pay was $20.00 plus free housing. The hospital was great, offered a raise and extension. Pay is now less than staff, and many travel companies lie about the salary, say they cannot put it in writing. Then, no matter what they say or write they help themselves to your paycheck. I am meeting more and more travelers that are not travelers: Tired of having the company take their money."

This is what she would like to tell a first timer, "Do not use the companies that are getting bad reviews. Look at the facts. I traveled a long time and hospitals and travel companies are as different as people. We can stop this fraud and abuse of nurses by travel companies, together we can. Report to the Better Business Bureau (free report) the Labor Board (free report), the Joint Commission (free report). And get an attorney that works on payment for case won. Keep records, save emails. Do not let them avoid putting it in writing and then take your money. When they do this, take them to task outside of the organization. They will try to protect each other. Avoid recruiters, become a principal to a hospital. As a traveler of over 15 years, can say staff is now a much better proposition. It was not when I was a newer nurse. I am proud to have survived. I have two more degrees now as well accomplished while traveling locally and nationwide with accredited programs! I am working on my second master's. Don't fall for these profit-seeking companies that exploit you and figure you will forget about it because you are a traveler. You are not an object. You are a worthy person and a nurse."

~*~

Amanda from Virginia

Amanda is an ICU nurse who looks for a company with great benefits. She takes the housing stipend and finds her own housing. She has been traveling a year with Travel Nurse Across America and has no plans to switch companies. Her favorite city has been Roanoke, VA and her least favorite has been Lynchburg, VA.

About her first experience she writes, "Interviewed over the phone and accepted the position. Started less than 3 weeks later. Orientation was short (3 days, with two days in the classroom, one day of tour, and a four hour orientation to one of the units). Worked in the resource pool. It was difficult because every unit is different (obviously). Not only was I new to the hospital/staff/equipment/people/policies and procedures... It was like starting over every shift. Constantly looking for stuff!

What she would like to tell first timers is, "Do your research. Is the hospital Magnet? What is the nurse-to-patient ratio? How is the collaboration between nurses and other staff? These are all great questions to ask during the interview. Remember they need you. You have a right to know what your next 13 (or more) weeks is going to be like. It can be a miserable time, or a wonderful time! For me, I enjoyed going to work every day. Carillion in Roanoke, VA is a great hospital. If they paid what Travel Nurse Across America paid, I would stay! Oh, also—do NOT accept the housing. If you must accept the housing, only stay for the first month. Then ask your agency for the stipend/housing allowance. Chances are, the money they give you could pay for two apartments! Take advantage of it :)"

~*~

Missy from Alabama

Missy is an ER nurse from Alabama who has been traveling for four years. She is currently with LRS Staffing, related to a bad experience with Onward Healthcare. Georgetown was great assignment on day shift, but awful on nights. Her favorite city has been Elkins, WV, with her least favorite being Rosebud, SD.

She would like to tell a first timer, "My first travel job started out in a very unique manner. My Grandpa passed away the morning that I was leaving. I had to stay and handle his affairs. Being a new traveler, I did not know I could have requested for my start date to be postponed. So I left Sunday afternoon and arrived at 2 AM for orientation at 8 AM. I was so nervous and scared. The staff at the hospital took me under their wing and made me feel as if I was part of their family. I loved it so much I didn't want to leave and extended till the snow started. (I am allergic to white stuff…lol). I still have friends there that I stay in touch with. I will always be grateful for that wonderful first experience and how it has shaped my experience in a positive manner!"

She would like to tell a first timer, "Just breathe, after the first week or two you will settle in, just remember you only have to learn their ways…You already know how to be a nurse!"

~*~

Glenece from Arkansas

Glenece is a dialysis nurse from Arkansas who travels for the great salary. She has been traveling for 8 years and is currently with Fresenius Medical. Her favorite city has been St. Thomas, VI, with her least favorite being El Paso, TX.

About her first assignment she writes, "My first travel assignment was at a unit close to my birth town. I was around familiar faces/places. I was a little nervous since this was a new adventure for me. My unit manager picked up on this immediately and made my new life as a traveler miserable. Good thing I had family/friends to ease the stress."

She would like to tell a first timer, "1) pick assignment close to home. 2) make sure you ask unit manager about orientation. 3) make sure you are familiar with the charting system/machines/equipment 4) put on your big girl/boy underwear and do what you know to do...when in doubt...don't be afraid/ashamed to ask."

~*~

Amber from Mississippi

Amber is a labor and delivery nurse who travels with American Mobile. She travels with her family and takes the two bedroom housing. Her favorite cities have been Austin, TX, Portland, OR, and Santa Clara, CA, with Abilene, TX and Washington DC her least favorite.

About her first assignment she writes, "I was in a tiny town at a new LD unit. It was awesome. They treated me like I was one of their own staff. The only thing was they double and sometimes triple checked everything I did. Apparently, I was paying for the sins of travelers past."

She would like to tell a first timer, "Sometimes assignments get off to a bad start. Keep smiling and communicating. Remember, every place has "the" way of doing things. You can't change it. Remember your best practice and do your best. Sometimes your preceptor is trying to establish dominance, just let them. They are trying to show you how smart they are because sometimes you make them a little insecure. Last, not everyone will agree with your lifestyle choice. I travel with my two kids and I'm told frequently how traumatic it must be for my kids. I just smile and say no and walk away. You won't win, walk away! Have fun most of all! Live life and love every moment. This is your great adventure!"

~*~

Teri from New Hampshire

Teri is an ICU and ER nurse who travels for the great salary. She has been traveling for 5 years and takes the housing stipend. She is currently with PPR Healthcare. Her favorite city has been San Francisco with her least favorite being Plymouth, NH, related to the fact that it was just too rural for her although the people were very nice there.

About her first assignment she writes, "It was at Charity Hospital in New Orleans. That hospital needed to be condemned before Katrina.

I don't need to say more to anyone that ever worked there. I worked in the ER."

She would like to tell a first timer, "Remember you are a visitor. Don't get too bent about things that you can't change. Practice safe nursing."

~*~

Leslie from Illinois

Leslie is a PACU nurse who places a great recruiter as her top priority in an assignment. She travels alone and doesn't mind taking corporate housing. She has been traveling for 9 years and is currently with Sunbelt. Her favorite city has been Washington DC, with Fredericksburg, VA being her least favorite.

About her first assignment she writes, "I did local travel in the DC area. Money was great. Walter Reed was great. It was very rewarding assignment, above and beyond the pay. I also worked at Washington Hospital Center and they use the travelers as their float pool. Floating you at a moment's notice to areas you are not familiar with, out of your area of expertise."

What she would like to tell a first timer, "I have had great experiences with Trinity Healthcare Staffing Group. Even if the hospital sucked (and many do), they were always professional and kept their promises."

~*~

Mickey from North Carolina

Mickey is an RN who travels for the great locations. She takes the housing stipend and finds her own. She has been traveling for a year. Her least favorite city was Cape Fear, NC.

About her first assignment she writes, "My experience was wonderful while working on the unit. When an internist came to work either inebriated or hung-over, I should have kept my mouth shut! Fulfilling the contract from that point on was difficult to say the least."

She would like to tell a first timer, "SMILE! Look for the good in every position and remember that there is always someone there who has something to prove or something to hide...but there will always be wonderful nurses with whom you get to spend your contracted time. You can make friends for Life!"

~*~

Mandy from Florida

Mandy is an CCU/ICU nurse who places an excellent salary and great locations as her top priorities in finding an assignment. She takes the housing stipend and finds her own place to stay. She has been with Flexcare and doesn't have desire to switch companies.

About her first assignment she writes, "I registered with 7 companies! I chose FlexCare Staffing; they're upfront/honest about money/packages. Ashley, my recruiter, made me feel like I was her ONLY client. She was remarkably patient and dedicated through my indecision, lack of knowledge, worked with me to get exactly what I wanted. Organized, friendly, efficient, kind, even when she had to call me at night, from home and on weekends...way above and beyond. She was on it immediately and contacted the hospitals. They are able to get contracts with all of the areas I am interested in. Ashley made me look my best and impressed the hospital recruiter. I feel very lucky to have the experience I did and to have found the perfect company and recruiter. I am getting life insurance, 401k, and partial reimbursement for medical insurance (about 1/2 for the plan I chose). The stipend is the highest allowed, so I can put that money toward what I see fit."

She would like to tell a first timer, "I went overboard and registered with 7 companies, because I wanted to see what they all had to offer. It seems that all companies have access to the same lists of jobs available. Some companies work more often with certain areas/hospitals. Some work mainly within their state or surrounding states. All have access to the same maximum stipend, but depending on the company, they have different overhead or take a different percentage. Most of what the benefits are come out of that maximum stipend. It's up to you to figure out what is the maximum stipend you can get, then see if the benefits offered compare to benefits you could get on your own with the stipend. This website is a great place to start (www.highwayhypodermics.com), to look at the possible benefits and what to ask the recruiters to get an idea of what kind of service/benefits you will get. Take your time choosing an area you like, be aware of the cost of living and the commute time. But also know that if you do find something you really like, jump on it because with so many recruiters out there, it will be gone in a day. Have all of your ID, vaccinations, certifications, and licenses in order and be prepared to take competency tests. There will also be a lot of docs to fill out for the hospital you choose. The docs seem never ending on your fist assignment. Can't think of anything else to say, exce sure your recruiter gives you personal attention and doesn't k waiting, or you will be very frustrated and feel as though you a... dark. Have someone on your side and it all just works out!"

~*~

Lynnette from Tennessee

Lynnette is an ICU and Psychiatric nurse who places a great location and great recruiter as her top priorities in finding an assignment. She takes the one bedroom housing and has traveled for 5 years. She is currently traveling with TotalMed Staffing and doesn't plan on changing anytime soon. Her favorite hospital has been Flagstaff with her least favorite being Clinton, MO.

About her first assignment she writes, "My very first was a disaster because the hospital was very unfriendly to travelers and the girl I was hired to relieve on a small geropsych unit had an unhealthy obsession with the unit (she was mentally unbalanced and had not had a day off in over 6 months).She followed me around obsessing with every move and the hospital was reluctant to pay 2 nurses. This experience was not fun, but the girl was so unbalanced that I couldn't take it personally. I found a new company and my next job I renewed for a year."

She would like to tell a first timer, "Read this site (www.highwayhypodermics.com) and join the Gypsy Nurses group on Facebook. Study for this as you would anything in nursing. Have some money set aside just in case. And don't "dial it in". Give the job your best, and you will be rewarded with a great experience."

~*~

Tammy from North Carolina

Tammy is a telemetry and step-down nurse who places an excellent salary and benefits as her top priorities. She takes the two bedroom housing and doesn't mind paying some. She has been traveling for 2 years with Supplemental and doesn't plan on changing companies soon. So far, all of her assignment hospitals have been great. Her favorite city has been Dallas, TX, with her least favorite being Fayetteville, NC.

About her first assignment she writes, "My first travel assignment was ok. Well, I was very open-minded. The hospital was very friendly.

I was offered a permanent position. It was a good experience. My recruiter made the process simple. The initial paperwork was a bit nerve wrecking but it was good."

She would like to tell a first timer, "Save money along the way. I had an experience where I was called off for weeks. Hours were not guaranteed. I was a thousand miles from home. I had spent most of my savings just trying to maintain bills and to just eat. My recruiter found me a new assignment finally. I would advise anyone to save enough money to maintain for at least 3 months or more if possible. Just make it part of the travel routine."

~*~

Teri from Pennsylvania

Teri is an OR nurse who places a great salary and benefits as her top priorities. She has been traveling for 5 years and takes the two bedroom housing. Her favorite city has been Sitka, AK, with Tuba City, AZ being her least favorite.

About her first assignment she writes, "Went to Oklahoma University Medical Center in Oklahoma City, OK. Great learning experience as it was my first time at a level I trauma center. I also got to scrub quite a bit, which I feel makes me a better circulator. The housing was great. I extended 3 times."

She would like to tell a first timer, "Flexibility is important. I am frequently asked to change shifts. It is also very important to be professional and not get involved in the politics or to try and change their way of doing things."

~*~

Danny from Kentucky

Danny is an OR nurse who travels for the great salary, benefits, locations, and recruiters. He takes the stipend and travels in an RV. He has been traveling for 14 years and is currently with OR Nurses Inc. His favorite town has been Charleston, SC, with Miami, FL being his least favorite.

About his first assignment he writes, "Until I started traveling the biggest hospital that I worked at had 4 OR rooms. I went to Hershey, PA to Hershey Medical Center. Thought I was going to get swallowed and spit out. The place was huge, and they do a massive amount of everything. They are awesome there. It was a great learning experience in a great town and they were just great professionals."

He would like to tell a first timer, "If you find a recruiter that you have relationship with that you feel you are being treated fairly and you are understood and the recruiter knows your family's names and your interest. Stay with that recruiter. If they happen to change companies, go with them. These types are hard to find!"

~*~

Martha from Georgia

Martha is an OR nurse who travels for the great locations and recruiters. She takes the one bedroom housing that is paid for by the company. She has been traveling 5 years with Fastaff after a disaster with Cross Country. Her lease favorite city has been Detroit, MI, with Lebanon, NH being her favorite.

About her first experience she writes, "The first hospital I went to was in my home state, just so I could see if this was for me. And while I didn't like working nights, I did enjoy the flexibility of being a travel nurse, because if I didn't like where I was then at the end of the assignment I could just leave. I caught on to the fact that this hospital was desperate for help."

She would like to tell a first timer to go for it! You are going to have so much fun.

~*~

Jeffrey from Texas

Jeffrey is a critical care nurse whose top priority is a great recruiter. He has been traveling for 3 years. He favorite city has been Las Vegas, NV, with Fort Defiance, AZ his least favorite. About Fort Defiance he writes, "They were very prejudicial to Caucasian race, especially male. If any issue arises regarding you as a person, or professional standards it will be misconstrued as your cultural deficit. From experience, the Navajo are very corrupt materialistically and spiritually, who will lash out against the "white man" when they have the opportunity. They cannot be trusted. Not worth your Nursing License."

About his first assignment he writes, "Worked with AMS Healthcare. Steve Lawrence was my Recruiter. Compared to other recruiters he would be a 9/10. He called me frequently and even came out for a visit. He was very supportive, and never thought twice about my concerns."

He would like to tell a first timer, "A lot of travel agencies are in it only for the money and not in your best interest. Most of them are simply "Used Car Salesman." You know, they're your dearest best friend, and they're looking after your best interest, and a great bargain/opportunity, etc. Well, if you think that they're not..."there's a sucker born every minute." The best advice is not necessarily what type of questions to ask, but the amount of questions, to the point of annoyance. See how they field the questions. If they don't have answers; they don't respond exactly to the questions; they try to be upbeat even though they don't know the answers; they don't take you seriously, they don't have time to talk to you (like Faststaff, when the recruiter didn't want to discuss definitive concerns, just wanted me to hurry with my application). Questions, questions, questions. Even if a recruiter reads this, they cannot evade the assessment on the other end of their false attitude and condescension. Go with your gut feeling. The thing that is true is that they feel you're beneath them as a person and that nurses don't deserve the income and perks that they do deserve. They have no clue of the scope of practice, responsibilities, qualifications, certifications, or the stress that nurses are under. So, just to have another person add to that stress is unacceptable. Just remember, the recruiter works for you, you don't work for the recruiter."

~*~

MaryBeth from Illinois

MaryBeth is an OR nurse who travels for the money and great recruiter. She takes the one bedroom housing that is paid for by the company. She has been traveling for 2 years with American Mobile Nursing. Her favorite hospital has been Medstar Washington Hospital Center with her favorite city being Rapid City, SD, and her least favorite city being Washington, DC.

About her first assignment she writes, "My first travel experience was as a CVOR RN in Rapid City, SD. I worked with 4 RNs and 4 surgical techs for 2 cardiac surgeons. I also was utilized in their general surgery cases when the CV schedule was light. The people were really great. They were a considerate group of hard working people. The upper administration is clueless. The staff is overworked, way too much call but when the staff is that small, there is no alternative."

She would like to tell a first timer, "I do not recommend taking an assignment at Medstar Washington Hospital Center. It is a filthy hospital and the permanent staff from top to bottom is LAZY and incapable of getting things done correctly—from cleaning the floors and walls to spelling you last name correctly so you can log into the computer system. It was the WORST hospital I have ever worked in. There were some wonderful, hard-working RNs in the Main OR, but they were in the minority. My recommendation is do not work with American Mobile Nursing or take an assignment at Washington Hospital Center."

~*~

Mandy from Florida

Mandy is an ICU nurse who travels for the great salaries and locations. She takes the housing stipend and finds her own. She is currently traveling with FlexCare and does not plan on changing soon. About finding a travel company she writes, "I signed up with 7 agencies to see the difference. 2 met my expectations, of those 2, my FlexCare recruiter was the best. I will stick with them."

About her first assignment she writes, "My experience was good because I have a great recruiter who is detail oriented, friendly and available. I held out for the location I wanted, passed up some so-so locations, and it worked out great. I ended up at a huge teaching hospital in Oregon. The people are nice and the hospital is state of the art. I took the stipend because I haven't found an agency that has 'special housing' that would be any different than what I could get on my own. They will help you find a place or provide it, which is essentially the same thing."

She would like to remind a first timer to make sure you have an honest and available recruiter.

~*~

Susan from Tennessee

Susan is an ER nurse who travels for the excellent salary and benefits. She has been traveling for a year and takes the one bedroom housing. She travels with RTG. Her favorite city has been Juneau, AK.

About her first experience she writes, "My first travel experience was wonderful!! I was placed in a small town with a small emergency department, but very welcoming to travelers. They offered a week of orientation, which is not the norm. The manager made sure to call and keep in touch to make sure that we didn't need anything or have any questions throughout the assignment."

She would like to tell a first timer, “Don’t just settle your first time out on the road. Do your research and make sure you state clearly in your contract like: whether or not you will float.”

~*~

Chris from California

Chris is an ICU nurse who places location and a great recruiter as his top priorities. He takes the money and finds his own housing. He travels with Cross Country.

About his first assignment he writes, “I accepted a last minute position at Loma Linda Murrieta in Murrieta, CA to help Cross Country out. On day one I was paired with someone who was having a bad day and rather than focus on my training she was on her cell all day and not present. Thus, I had to be my own advocate and followed other folks around. The hospital is new and the staff green and still finding their way in regards to policies and such. I had more years than all the nurses on my floor combined. They all did things differently. I got 1 day of “orientation” and was expected to work immediately. After my one day I got a call that they terminated my contract. The reason provided was fair communication and the fact that I refused to work OT that very day—I was tired and new. The rep for Cross Country was ice cold when I asked her what I could do to keep my reputation clean from this. Not caring at all that I now had a “fire” on my record for one day of work. We are nothing but money for the agencies. I will never try traveling again.”

What he would like to tell a first timer, “There is a chance your stellar reputation you built over many years will be ruined for no reason and you could move your entire life around for a job only to be left jobless.”

~*~

Diane from Ohio

Diane is an OR nurse from Ohio who places a great location and recruiter as her top priorities. She takes the one bedroom housing from the company that is paid for. She has been traveling for 5 years and is currently with Medical Staffing Options after a disaster assignment with On Assignment. Her favorite city has been Langehorne, PA, with Howard University Medical Center being her least favorite hospital.

About her first assignment she writes, “My first day started out rather shaky as I overheard the RN orienting me refusing to have a traveler in her room. Once I had a grip on where things were kept it was more comfortable for me. I loved the city and had weekends to explore. I found that the travelers would hang together and meet for lunch and go out together on weekends and evenings. Was excited when I found they wanted to renew the contract."

About her first time she writes, "Ask a lot of questions of your recruiter and the facility. Do not be afraid to complain about housing and ask for changes from your company. Check out multiple companies before choosing your company for travel, asking questions about housing, etc. and keep notes of your conversations to check against your contract."

~*~

Jayne from Wisconsin

Jayne is a Labor and Delivery nurse who also takes care of Mother and Baby. She travels for great locations and will take corporate housing. She has been traveling for under a year and is currently with Aya Healthcare.

About her first assignment she writes, "Great. My first contract put me back in my hometown so I was very comfortable. I knew the staff, docs and, department. My 2nd contract has been more challenging because the average number of deliveries is 4/mo. I was told I may have to "back up MS" but instead I have basically been working MS and have had very little work in OB. I have had 1 vaginal delivery and 3 C-sections in 13 weeks. Not what I was told in my interview and not at all what I expected."

What she would like to tell a first timer, "Ask a lot of questions and don't leave anything as a verbal "yes." Get it in writing in your contract, including if you want specific days off."

~*~

Erik from South Carolina

Erik is an ER nurse who places a great salary and location as top priorities and who takes the one bedroom housing that is provided by Aureus Medical staffing. His favorite city has been Stamford, CT.

About his first experience he writes, "My first experience was very exciting and very stressful. I knew that I was getting into something

I had never done before but I was ready for it. I arrived the weekend before I started so I could "explore the city" and my new neighborhood. The hospital was great. 90% of people there I loved but the other 10% I could care less if I ever see them again. The orientation was quick, and then I hit the ground running. It was totally worth it."

About his first time he writes, "I would say make sure things are in writing. If you have a question about something, don't be afraid to ask. If they are discussing things with you before submitting you to a hospital, and you don't like it, speak up. They can usually get what you are requesting. Also, when I first started I signed up with 3 different companies so I had multiple options. And I still look at other companies now to get me where I want to go which is NYC. Good luck and you will enjoy it."

~*~

Dianne from California

Dianne is an ER nurse who travels for the great salary, benefits, and location. She has been traveling for 2 years and will take corporate housing. She is currently traveling with Trustaff. Her least favorite city has been Yuba City, CA, with Ukiah, CA being her favorite.

About her first assignment she writes, "It was a disaster. I was sent to a hospital that had at least 50% travelers. There was not one nurse in the ER that had more than 1 year of experience. 25 actual beds and 20 hall beds; cardiac, stroke, and seizure patients in the hall; no cardiac monitoring capabilities. Every day I worried that my license would be suspended. Stay away from Yuba City."

She would like to tell a first timer, "You can do anything for 13 weeks. Present yourself as competent and work hard."

~*~

Elaine from Florida

Elaine is an ICU nurse who travels for the great salary and location. She has been traveling for almost 2 years and travels in an RV. She has been traveling for 2 years with Premier Healthcare Professionals. Her favorite city has been Ocala, FL; her least favorite has been Riverside, CA.

About her first assignment she writes, "Bought an RV headed to Ocala Florida and if you like scenery this is the place to be!! The hospital welcomed me with open arms and always treated me like one of the gang!! I am currently on my second assignment in this location. Would like to return once a year!! The girls on SICU were loads of fun although you do work hard. Lots of traumas, so I learned quite a bit. This is not for you if you're a city person but if you like to fish, kayak, hike, and enjoy more wildlife than I've ever seen. It even has wild monkeys!! The work was difficult, but the pay was decent for Florida and the scenery to die for. I would highly recommend for all those travelers with a thick skin, willing to work hard and play hard."

To first timers she writes, "Go in do your job, smile, let them know you are always available to help and you will have no problems. I've enjoyed every assignment with maybe the exception of Riverside Community Hospital and they even grew on me over time. If you work on the floors stay away from Riverside but if you do ED or ICU they were just wonderful...again you work hard!! Fort Bragg California were some of the most laid back people I've ever met, great assignment if you're self-motivated!! Good Luck to all you new travelers. I wouldn't work full time ever again."

~*~

Carol from South Carolina

Carol is a Home Health nurse who travels for great locations, salary, and a great recruiter. She takes the housing stipend and finds her own place. She has been traveling for 5 years with Sunbelt Healthcare. Her favorite cities have been Gaffney, SC and Charleston, SC, with her least favorite being Anderson, SC.

About her first assignment she writes, "My first travel assignment was with Gentiva in Gaffney, SC. The staff there was friendly and helpful. Even the patients there were also friendly. I had orientation to my caseload for one week and was eased into the assignment. I could call anytime if a problem come up and not feel like I was a bother."

She would tell a first timer, "Pray! Make sure everything is in writing: amount of pay, completion bonus, requested days off, and length of assignment. Remember you're only there for a short time, so don't try to change their policies and stay out their politics."

~*~

Wendy from Wisconsin

Wendy is a med/surg/tele nurse who travels for the great locations and salary. She has been traveling for 2 years with Trustaff. Her favorite city has been Ashland, KY with Ottumwa, IA being her least favorite.

About her first assignment she writes, "Amazing!!! The hospital was beautiful, the staff were wonderful, the patient ratio was 4:1 with CNA staff. My recruiter and my Trustaff team (as with all of my assignments) would call and or email checking in with me to see how I was doing. I couldn't have asked for a better experience!"

She would like to tell a first timer, "Be organized. Keep files and copies of everything! Be open minded, willing, and polite; we are guests in other's hospitals, be respectful of that! Let your healing ways shine forth; you will meet thousands of amazing and wonderful people!! God Bless."

~*~

Judith from Maryland

Judith is a certified OR nurse who places a great recruiter and benefits as her priorities. She has been traveling for a year and takes the one bedroom paid for by Trustaff. Her favorite city has been Dallas, TX.

About her first assignment she writes, "I was accepted at this hospital with open arms. I was able to learn more about specialties that I had little experience in. I have great hours and am able to pick up overtime with ease. I do volunteer to take call, which is more money. I enjoy every day what I do for a living now."

What she would like to tell a first timer, "Find yourself a really good recruiter. I found one in Brendan Peterman with TruStaff. He was able to walk me through the whole transition step by step with ease. As long as you get your part of the deal done, i.e. paperwork, you should also have a seamless crossover. Brendan checks in with me every week and during the holidays, twice a week. He makes sure that there are no mistakes when it comes to my paycheck. I trust this recruiter because he has proven himself to be a hard worker and trustworthy. I am sure that he would love to get a call from you and help you just as much as he has helped me. But I'm not giving him up!!"

~*~

Kerri from Texas

Kerri is an ICU nurse who loves to travel related to the salary, benefits, location, and recruiter. She has been traveling for almost 5 years and takes the one bedroom housing that is paid for. She is currently with TruStaff and has no plans in changing companies. Her favorite city has been Fort Worth, TX with San Antonio, TX being her least favorite.

About her first assignment she writes, "Paid every two weeks meaning that I didn't receive a paycheck for three weeks and the first was paper! I like the facility, but it was a definite learning experience. I spoke with my recruiter once in three months. Needless to say, I only did one assignment with American Traveler. Hopefully it isn't the same."

She would like to tell a first timer, "Avoid a recruiter that sounds like a used car salesman or is pushy. Don't agency-hop unless there is a legitimate reason. Longevity/extension bonuses are really nice and you can get max pay, not just the posted amount after the first assignment. Give them the vibe that you are there to stay. They will increase the pay. Jase Simpson at TruStaff has been there for me without being annoying or pushy and knows my needs. I have been with 3 agencies over 4 years and TruStaff will be my last!"

Chapter Twenty

Recruiter Responses

Finding the right recruiter for you can be even trickier than finding the right travel nursing company. What kind of recruiter to do you want? How exactly will they react when the times get tough? Well, recently I asked recruiters about some situations. These exact situations have happened in reality, but for obvious reasons, the names have been changed.

Hospital Situations

In a large metropolitan area, Nurse Floating Flo contracts to float between three hospitals within a 10-mile radius of her housing. Starting in the 6th week, the company asks her to float to a hospital 15 miles away, the 7th week she goes to one on the other side of the city, that is 30 miles away, plus one that is 17 miles away. The nurse is willing to take the first few, but after the behavior continues, she has had enough and voices this to her recruiter.

Baby Nurse Betty is a skilled labor and delivery nurse, who also can float to postpartum care after the delivery as well as the well-newborn nursery. At 7:30 PM, the staffing company hotline gets a call stating that they want her to float to the NICU, which is beyond her competency level. What is your company's response?

Nurse Roach is all excited about her first travel nursing assignment. She drives 750 miles to her new assignment housing. After getting the keys from management, she opens the door and three cockroaches scurry across the floor. After further investigation, she also finds a ring of mold in the shower. She can't stand it and immediately texts you with pictures. How do you respond?

You have worked with Nurse Asthmatic for 3 years now and she has done a great job for you, when she takes an assignment in Southeast Colorado. She envisions magic mountains that reach to the sky, only to find that she has landed in wheat country. Not wanting to cause problems she continues to work and everything is fine, until harvest. She has an asthma attack, ends up in the hospital, and is told that she is going to miss at least 2 weeks of work related to asthma induced pneumonia. How do you work things out?

You have worked hard to find Nurse Roulette a job in Las Vegas. You send the nurse a contract that she readily accepts, signs, and sends back. The next morning the bags are packed and Nurse Roulette is on the way to the assignment of her dreams. At 0800 she is out the door and to the hospital. Checking in with HR, they inform her that there is no contract between the hospital and the company, related to the fact that it has not been approved by HR. About the same time, the recruiting manager comes to you and tells you not to send Nurse Roulette on the assignment. This shouldn't have happened, but unfortunately it does happen. What do you do?

What would you like travel nurses to know about being a great traveling nurse and making your job easier?

Phil from Critical Nursing Solutions, Inc.

Phil has been a recruiter for Critical Nursing Solutions, Inc. for 5 years. The following is his answers to the situations above.

Floating Flo: You won't be in this situation with our company. If it were to happen the first time, I would hope you would communicate this with me before the situation gets out of hand and "We" would work together with hospital to correct situation. If the situation is exactly how the question reads, we would make sure you were working where you want to work/the hospital you were contracted with and our company would still assist with the hospital's needs.

Baby Betty: We would call the nurse and ask them first if they were capable in assisting the hospitals demand if the nurse completed competency testing prior to assignment. If the nurse says they are unable to work that unit or doesn't feel comfortable, we would just tell the hospital no but depending on the hospital's location we just might have a per diem (local) nurse of that specialty to assist with hospital's needs.

Nurse Roach: I would ask the nurse what he/she would like to be done. A new room? A new place to stay? CNS would call management/leasing office and arrange another room to assist with the nurse's needs or arrange another for the nurse to stay.

Nurse Asthmatic: We would arrange him/her absence with the hospital. And ask how we can help assist with the nurse and facility.

Nurse Roulette: This has never happened but if this were to happen, I would call the nurse and explain what happened, and strategize with nurse on the next course of action.

If you were impressed with Phil's answers, you can read Phil by email: phil@cnsnursing.com

~*~

Michelle from PRCS

Michelle has been a recruiter for 14 years with PRCS Healthcare. Here are her answers to the above questions.

Floating Flo: I would stop the nonsense:)! I would reach out to the facility and point out (in a positive way) Nurse Floating Flo's dedication and willingness, and a reminder of the agreement of her floating 10 miles. I would back our Nurse but resolve it positively with the facility. If the facility is adamant about it, I would either reassign the nurse or build in a mileage reimbursement.

Baby Betty: Our response would be to stand firm on our policy that travelers can only float to areas in which they are both clinically trained and oriented. Any variance in that policy jeopardizes the nurse and his/her practice safety. Not something we would be willing to do!

Nurse Roach: First, we apologize profusely and put Nurse Roach up somewhere temporarily that night after a long drive. Then, we secure some choices in alternate housing for her to go by (since she is already there and local) and look at. We are very particular that our Nurses be comfortable and safe in lodging.

Nurse Asthmatic: We relieve Nurse Asthmatic of her commitments during her absence and support her in any way we can. It is not her issue or fault for becoming ill, and it is up to PRCS to support her through that. We also thank her for her willingness to stick that assignment out!

Nurse Roulette: We apologize for the last minute cancellation and lack of planning and communication. Then, we reimburse the Nurse for her travel expenses and get her another assignment, possibly another facility in the area where she wanted to be.

If you would like to work with Michelle's answers, you can email her at: mwilliams@prcshealthcare.com

~*~

Madison from Randstad Healthcare

Madison has been a recruiter for Randstad Healthcare for a year now. The following is her answers to the questions above.

Floating Flo: I would thank her for being so flexible up to this point and would immediately address her concerns with the client to get it resolved, being sure to share feedback and communication with her along the way.

Baby Betty: Our nurses are absolutely not allowed to float to units beyond their competency level. It is a risk to the patient, the nurse's license, and a liability to the agency. We would reach out to the facility and address this immediately with our client.

Nurse Roach: I would immediately have the housing coordinator get in touch with the landlord to have the apartment cleaned and treated for bugs, as well as arrange for temporary housing while the situation was being resolved.

Nurse Asthmatic: First, I would make sure that Nurse Asthmatic is getting plenty of rest and feels confident that I will be looking out for her in this situation. Second, obviously the nurse's health is the primary concern, so I would need to talk to her to find out if she feels that with downtime she would be able to return to work or if we need to find a replacement for her at the facility and pick back up after she is well. For future assignments we will be mindful of areas that have the potential to cause an asthma attack.

Nurse Roulette: First, the likelihood of something like this happening is very slim because Randstad Healthcare would not confirm her to this job without an official contract with the facility. In the unlikely event that something like this did happen, I would see to it that we put the nurse in housing until we can get the contract figured out. I would ensure that we do everything possible to correct the situation as quickly as possible.

If you are interested in working with Madison, you can email her at: madison.hampton@randstadusa.com

~*~

Amanda from Randstad Healthcare

Amanda has been a recruiter with Randstad for 13 years now. The following is her answers to the questions above.

Floating Flo: I would address this situation with the Account Manager of the hospital who would, in turn, contact the facility to advocate on behalf of Nurse Floating Flo. We would remind the facility about the original terms of the contract, and request to stop the floating to areas outside of a 10-mile radius. If the hospital pleads with us to continue having Nurse Floating Flo float to further areas, then I would ask my Account Manager if we can offer Nurse Floating Flo a mileage reimbursement. If Nurse Floating Flo is still not agreeable, then we would let the hospital know that we would need to end the assignment (with an adequate notice) if they cannot agree to the original terms of the contract.

Baby Betty: We would alert the hospital that Nurse Betty is unable to care for NICU patients, and as her contract states, she is only required to float to units that are within her scope of practice. We would advise the hospital to use her in another area (L/D, Post Partum or Newborn Well-Baby Nursery) or send her home.

Nurse Roach: We would immediately arrange for a hotel-stay for Nurse Roach while other options are researched.

Nurse Asthmatic: We would supply a doctor's note to the facility advising them of Nurse Asthmatic's condition. If her doctor felt that she was able to stay in the area, then we would arrange for an extension on the end of the assignment to make-up the hours. If Nurse Asthmatic was advised to leave the area due to her health, then we would cancel the assignment.

Nurse Roulette: This situation wouldn't occur with Randstad Healthcare. We always ensure that we have received signed confirmations/contracts from both the hospital and the nurse before the nurse arrives at the hospital. Hypothetically though, in this situation, I would immediately let Nurse Roulette know of the situation, and apologize profusely. I would try to get to the bottom of what happened, and explain as much as possible to Nurse Roulette. I work diligently to find out when Nurse Roulette is actually able to start the assignment, in order to figure out our next step. If it turns out that the hospital will not get approval for her to start, then I would do everything in my power to get her into another position elsewhere as soon as possible.

Amanda can be reached by email at: amanda.belloff@randstadusa.com.

~*~

Emily from Randstad Healthcare

Emily has been a recruiter for 3 years with Randstad Healthcare. The following is her answers to the questions above.

Floating Flo: The first thing that I always tell an RN is to speak to her manager and let her know in a professional manner what her concerns are to give them a chance to make it right. If there is no resolution from that conversation, we can definitely step in and speak to our contact and let them know that this was not part of what had been agreed on and see if it is possible to keep the RN at the original agreed upon hospitals. If that is not possible, we can look at trying to get additional mileage compensation. Communication with the manager and the hospital is important. Often times these issues can be resolved with a single conversation before drastic action needs to take place. We always support our RNs and have their best interest in mind while trying to work through any conflict or surprise that may pop up on an assignment.

Baby Betty: First and foremost, we NEVER want an RN to be put in a situation where they feel they are practicing outside the scope of their specialty or skill level. I would tell her to immediately voice her concern to the Charge Nurse, manager, or house supervisor on duty at the time. I would ask her detailed questions, such as, what is the acuity of the patients assigned to you? Often times they will take a newborn RN and assign her patients in the NICU that are very low acuity, no vents, no drips etc.…or have her monitor a patient that is being ready to be moved etc.…or have her on the unit to assist the other RNs with no patients personally assigned to her. I would tell her to make sure she has all the details of the assignment before panicking when hearing the word NICU. If there was no resolution and she were in fact scheduled to work on the NICU and assigned patients that she is not trained to care for, a member of the Randstad Healthcare team would call the manager and speak on her behalf regarding the decision and request to be placed on a unit where she is more qualified to work. There is nothing more important to an RN than her license to practice nursing and we take that very seriously and will support and protect our nurses to the fullest.

Nurse Roach: I would immediately apologize. Our goal is to find comfortable, clean, and safe housing at all times, within 10 miles from the hospital. We do our best to research every apartment that we use. I would have our housing coordinator immediately get involved. There are options to try to take care of the problems. We could have her moved to another unit and request that they spray for insects and make sure there are no other issues with the new unit. If the entire apartment is not clean or free of insects, we could definitely try to set her up in a hotel for the night and move her to another complex. We cannot however move to a new complex because the complex is older or not "fancy" enough. There are some cities, i.e. Baltimore and Boston, where all housing that is available in the city is primarily older. We do our best to set expectations accordingly so that travel nurse would know what to expect. If they are looking for certain amenities or a new apartment complex, we can try to find something accordingly, letting them know that they may have a longer commute. Our housing coordinator is very involved, sends pictures, and tries to give every RN a few choices to pick from and also takes personal requests for certain housing as long as it is within the housing budget.

Nurse Asthmatic: My first concern would be the health of the RN. Is she ok? What does she want to do? Does she want to go back to work once she is feeling better after the two weeks or does she want to go home? Is she cleared to return to work by her doctor? If she wants to go back to work, we would have been in communication with the unit manager and found out if that was a possibility from their end. We could extend her contract those two weeks if necessary. If she just wanted to leave the assignment due to her health concerns, I would do everything in my power to help her find her next assignment. To preface this, we to try to prepare our RNs in advance for their assignment. We let them know what the local weather and topography might look like. Will there be snow, will you be isolated, is it a small town, will it be extremely hot, is there a beach? Communication is the most important part of traveling. Often, situations similar to this one can be avoided with great communication on the front end when discussing jobs.

Nurse Roulette: I want to start out by saying, that there is such a precise onboarding process with our company, where all contracts are checked and double checked that this would have been picked up on long before it got to this stage. We would try to resolve the contract issue directly with the hospital and have our legal team get involved to try to save the contract. That being said, I would immediately help the RN either find another job immediately in Vegas or as close to as possible. If that were not a possibility I would help the RN to get home and begin trying to find her another position anywhere that she was willing to go.

If you are interested in working with Emily, you can contact her by email at: emily.matteson@RandstadUSA.com

~*~

Lindsay from Randstad Healthcare

Lindsay has been a recruiter with Randstad Healthcare for 5 years. The following is her answers the questions posted above.

Floating Flo: As an agency we will reach out to the hospital or staffing contact and see what the contract originally stated. If the original contract states only float to 3 hospitals within a 10-mile radius then we would ask the hospital to honor the contractual agreement. If they state the job has changed and they won't honor their side of the original contract then we will give the RN the choice of sticking it out or moving on to another contract. We also would offer mileage reimbursement to help supplement the cost of driving so far. As an agency, there is only so much that we can do to control the hospital, however we are a business that prides ourselves on sticking to our word and would gladly do whatever we needed to in order to help our traveler.

Baby Betty: We would immediately call the hospital and express to them that it's unacceptable to float an RN to a unit they are not qualified to work on as it may jeopardize the RN's license and patient's safety. If the problem continues, we would have our Director of Nursing contact an Executive level employee at the hospital to express our concerns and the fact they are going against Joint Commission regulations. We would provide suggestions to the hospital to float one of their own nurses with experience in that area, or call one of their Per Diem agencies to help supplement their staff. If they are unwilling to work with us and they continued to want to float the RN after multiple attempts to resolve the situation we would ask the RN if they wanted to move on to another contract.

Nurse Roach: We would contact the apartment to see if they could move her to another unit that is better maintained and clean. If there were no other units available we would ask for the apartment to hire a professional cleaning and pest control company to disinfect the apartment and spray for bugs/roaches. If they refused, we would hire a company on our own to come in and perform the necessary duties to make the apartment cleaner and more comfortable for the traveler. If the problem continues after professional cleaning and pest control we would eventually move them to an apartment that doesn't have the infestation.

Nurse Asthmatic: We would first ask the hospital if they are willing to wait at least 2 weeks or more for the RN to be discharged. If in fact the hospital is not willing to wait we would immediately look for another contract that would be a conducive to someone who has severe allergies. We would suggest a doctor's release form showing they're able to return to work and ensure the RN feels comfortable moving forward. We would cover the housing fees for breaking the lease if the RN was in our housing.

Nurse Roulette: We would first call the hospital and the hiring manager (who interviewed and offered the assignment) to see if there was anything we could do to get things resolved considering the RN has already traveled across country to get there and has arrived promptly to the assignment. We would then communicate to the hospital proof of the contractual agreement and signatures that we received to move forward in the process of confirmation. If the hospital continued to be difficult, we would immediately call every hospital we work with in Vegas to beg, plead, and borrow to ensure the traveler has another job in a timely manner. If nothing is available we would then search for other locations within a commutable distance to Vegas.

If you are interested in working with Lindsay, you can email her at: lindsay.manes@RandstadUSA.com.

~*~

Diane from Atlas Medstaff

Diane has been a recruiter for a total of 9 years, with the last two at Atlas Medstaff. The following is her answers to the questions above.

Floating Flo: First, I would listen to my nurse and get an understanding of her frustration and see what she feels would be an agreeable solution. Ideally this would have been clarified prior to the start of the contract but it is important for the recruiter to communicate these concerns to the hospital and work on an agreeable solution for the nurse.

Baby Betty: As a recruiter, I would listen to the Nurse's concerns and work with the client manager to make sure we all have an understanding of what this hospital's NICU demands will be. If we need to push back on the hospital and deny this we will.

Nurse Roach: Immediately let her know we are here to help her. She is probably exhausted after driving 750 miles. Find her a place to stay tonight and then work on a long-term solution. Clarify the situation and if necessary, add the bad housing to a do-not-use list.

Nurse Asthmatic: Communication first. Make sure she is OK. Talk to the hospital. See what would be acceptable to them. Work with everyone to see when she can get back on the schedule and see if we can find a replacement. Make note of this to be sure not to send her to another assignment that could hurt her health.

Nurse Roulette: Compensate Nurse Roulette for her travel; see if there is another position for her in Las Vegas. Pay for her housing for a few days while you look then send her home. Learn from this mistake and make sure you always have a clear contract with the hospital before sending a nurse there.

If you are interested in traveling with Diane, you can contact her at: dernatt@atlasmedstaff.com

~*~

Jan from The Right Solutions

Jan has been a recruiter for 8 years with The Right Solutions. The following is her answers the questions asked above.

Floating Flo: When a nurse is asked to function outside of the terms of their contract, it must be addressed. It's challenging for a traveler to orient to one facility. Orienting to three would be especially stressful. Extra driving would add extra stress for this traveler.

First, it's important to assess the traveler's situation. Specifically, how is the additional distance when floating affecting them? I would find out how often the situation is occurring, whether the nurse is being required to change shifts, and whether there is a negative impact on the traveler's finances due to the extra mileage. After I have obtained that information, our company would then work with the facility to assure the terms of the contract are met, or if necessary, provide additional resources and support as necessary to accommodate our traveler.

Baby Betty: Every traveler's contract at The Right Solutions states, "The healthcare professional agrees to float only to units where they are experienced and proficient." The Right Solutions has a manager on-call during after hours, so there is someone available 24/7 for our travelers. Nurses are instructed to call TRS immediately if they are floated to a unit that is out of their scope of practice. Our company would immediately address the issue with the facility's acting supervisor at the time to address the situation.

Nurse Roach: It is important that a traveler feels their housing is safe, clean, and comfortable. In the rare case that a traveler arrives at their assignment location and finds housing conditions unacceptable, the issue is addressed immediately. Our housing department works together with the landlord to correct any issues such as insects or uncleanliness. If the housing conditions are still unacceptable to the traveler, or if the negative conditions cannot be fixed, we offer to find alternative housing for our traveler. Fortunately, this is a rare occurrence at The Right Solutions. We encourage our travelers, if at all possible, to arrive on assignment a day early so that they can inspect each housing option that has been given to them. Housing preferences are different with each individual, and this process allows the nurse to choose the housing option that best meets their needs.

Nurse Asthmatic: TRS is RN owned and operated, so it's only natural that the health of our travelers is a company priority.

Most often, if a nurse has an accident or is ill, the facility is willing to work with the nurse as long as they can return to work in a reasonable amount of time. This particular situation is unique, because the illness was caused by an environmental factor that most likely will not change. A physician would be needed to determine the likelihood of the asthma reoccurring once the nurse is released to work. Due to the severity of the traveler's reaction to the wheat, it is possible the nurse would need to be put on a different assignment unless medications could be taken to keep the asthma under control.

Nurse Roulette: This nurse becomes a top priority, for myself as well as the rest of the TRS team. My first action is always to check to see if other assignments are available in the same approximate location. If not, we would evaluate what support and resources this traveler needs until their next assignment is found. This traveler is part of the TRS family, and will have our support.

If you would like to work with Jan, you can email her at: jsteele@therightsolutions.com.

~*~

Liz from Talemed

Liz has been a recruiter for 3 years now with Talemed. The following is her answers to the questions posted above.

Floating Flo: Contact the facility and see if we can switch the shifts to better suit her needs. Also see if housing is in a more desirable location.

Baby Betty: She cannot float to a unit that she is not proficient in. We only send our RNs to areas that they are comfortable and competent in. We always test our RNs in any unit that they are going to be working.

Nurse Roach: I call the housing department to put her in a hotel that is safe and clean! Sometimes the housing that is provided to Travel Companies can be misleading...and we do not want anyone to be put into an unfit living situation. I have had nurses call me late at night and we tell them to just leave. We put them up into a nice hotel while we find a more suitable apartment.

Nurse Asthmatic: I would first off make sure that she is being taken care of and does not need anything further from us. Then I would contact the facility and let them know the situation. We would need to get her out of that part of the country if the allergies will still be affected. The health of our travelers is very important to us. Without them being healthy...they cannot care for patient's health.

Nurse Roulette: We would first see if there are any other facilities in need of an RN. If there are not any other positions coming available we would make sure that she makes it home safely. As a recruiter I would make sure the hotel and travel is paid for. This is a rare occurrence but when it does happen the nurse is not at fault, therefore we don't want this situation to cause any financial burden.

What can a traveler do to make your job easier? I think that this is the toughest question! I know as a recruiter if you are up front and honest with me I can make the best of our working relationship. Always tell your recruiter your expectations and fears! If we know where you want to, what type of facility, what you expect to make we can find a great fit. Obviously it would be great to have every traveler be totally open to any position...But we understand that you each have you own needs. Some travel for money, some for adventure. If you and I are on the same page then we can make sure you are somewhere you love making the money you want!

If you were impressed with Liz's answers, you can email her at: liz.maffey@talemed.com.

~*~

Joe from Talemed

Joe has been a recruiter with Talemed for 6 years. The following is his answers to my questions above.

Floating Flo: In the first place, the hospitals which this RN would have been specifically mentioned in the contract as opposed to just a vague "10 mile radius." This bit of information alone would have then been brought to the RN's attention and she/he would have known about the potential of floating to these facilities going into the contract. Secondly, if the entity offering this position was unable to provide the specific names of the hospitals that the RN could be floated to I would make the RN aware of this fact and then would have stated that due to the vague details of this contract, if this RN accepts the contract, they should be ready to be extremely flexible to these facilities needs which could possibly include floating to other facilities in the area, floating to other units they are qualified to work in, and potentially even having their shift changed on them. If the RN still wants to accept this contract under these circumstances then the RN will be responsible for accommodating whatever is asked of her/him. At this point the RN can still decide whether or not to accept this contract. By asking the above questions and getting specific information pertaining to the position, a good recruiter should never have the above situation occur.

Baby Betty: TaleMed's response would be to contact the hospital immediately and let them know that this RN has not completed the Joint Commission required testing to work in this unit, nor has this RN ever had experience working in this unit, nor is this RN in anyway qualified to work in this unit. Due to these reasons this RN would only be putting tiny defenseless Neonates in harm's way and is unable contractually to fulfill this request. If the hospitals insists then TaleMed would politely let them know that we will unfortunately need to pull our RN from this contract as we cannot possibly allow her/him to put patients or their career at risk. We would of course also wish them the best of luck in finding the nursing help they need.

Nurse Roach: Again, a good recruiter will prep the RN in regards to how to properly assume residence for an apartment which would include inspecting the unit in its entirety with the leasing agent and/or landlord before ever even holding a single key for this establishment in their hands. By law taking the keys is accepting the premises as is. However, with proper documentation of the premises (photos, emailed details, etc.) under either situation TaleMed would immediately begin finding other accommodations for this RN. This RN may be asked to stay in a hotel or extended stay for a few days (potentially even one full week) until a proper apartment, etc. can be found.

Nurse Asthmatic: Again, a good recruiter will have informed this RN to research the area and hospital in great detail before accepting this position. Also the recruiter should know their traveler and know that their traveler is wanting to go where the "magic mountains reach the sky" and then will have informed this RN that it is going to be a bit of a drive to said mountains and that what she/he is going to actually encounter is a whole lot of farm lands/wheat. The harvest and the wheat should not be any kind a surprise. However, apparently this RN still took this assignment. This being said, TaleMed would have to see if the contracted hospital is able to go two weeks without this contract worker or not. The hospital may choose to end the contract early and ask the staffing company to find a replacement. If this were to happen (which I doubt it would) TaleMed would begin immediately putting ALL recruiters on the task of finding this one Travel RN another position she/he can accommodate to begin ASAP which does not mass produce wheat.

Nurse Roulette: No. This does not happen. If an offer in writing comes from the contracted hospital to TaleMed this means that this contract has been approved by HR/Upper management. Only if an offer in writing is received by TaleMed would the contract have been sent. However, again IF this were to ever happen we would again put ALL recruiters at TaleMed on finding this RN another assignment which is agreeable to them.

What can a nurse do to make your job easier? Just to never be afraid to ask questions. We are here to answer them. Also RNs should be more concerned with weekly bring home after taxes as opposed to hourly rate. I find many companies which offer these high hourly rates end up disappointing and misleading these RNs more often than naught. If a company says "you will make $43/hr. and housing provided" then ask them what your hourly amount will be if you do not take housing provided. This hourly amount should go up. If a company says that "your weekly bring home will be X and housing provided" ask them what your weekly bring home will be if you do not take their housing. This weekly amount should then be X+ a logical amount for you to provide your own housing. If not, then this should be a red flag.

If you are interested in finding out more from Joe, you can email him at: joe.bartoszek@talemed.com.

~*~

Crystal from Expedient MedStaff

Crystal has been a recruiter for 14 years with the last year at Expedient MedStaff. The following is her answers to the questions above.

Floating Flo: I would have our VP of Clinical Services reach out to the facility to discuss the issues. We would work with both the traveler and facility in an effort to resolve the concerns. Freedom is known for strongly advocating for our nurses. We would make every effort to get the facility to stay within the realms of the agreement and if the facility refuses we would work with the nurse to accommodate the fact that the facility is staying within the terms of the contract.

Baby Betty: I personally carry the emergency cell and would receive such a call. I advise the RN to refuse to accept report for patients on the unit she/he is not qualified to work. I speak directly with the Charge RN, Nurse Manager and/or House Supervisor advising that our RN has been told not to accept patient reports. I advise that it is not within the realms of the contract that our nurse be floated to areas in which she/he is not qualified to work. I advise that if they chose to float the RN to such a unit, the RN may work only as a helper to other RNs and will not be accepting report on any patients. I advise that the RN has been instructed to choose to clock out and end her/his shift if told that they must accept patient load. As a rule, that approach resolves the issue and the RN is not floated. There has only been one time in which I have actually had to have a RN clock out. Most facilities will agree not to float and/or give patient assignments once I've spoken to them.

Nurse Roach: I advise RNs to inspect immediately upon arrival, preferably with the apartment manager if possible. I advise that any concerns should be immediately reported to me. If housing is unacceptable I advise the RN to not move in and then proceed in making arrangements for a hotel for the night/weekend. I then have our housing department work with the complex and RN to either make the apartment suitable and/or for housing to find another option for the traveler.

Nurse Asthmatic: The answer would vary depending upon the RNs needs/wishes and what the hospital is willing to negotiate. If the RN felt that after 2 weeks he/she would be able to complete the assignment we would advise the hospital of the issue and ask they not cancel the contract. If there was concern that there may be ongoing issues after the 2 weeks have passed we would look to place the RN into another assignment.

Nurse Roulette: This should never happen. A RN should never be given a contract until the hospital has confirmed the RN. First Day information and housing information should not be given to the RN until the hospital has cleared them through QA. The only way for this scenario to occur is if the agency is not communicating well enough with the hospital and the nurse.

What would you like nurses to know? Though we are all aware that the mounds of paperwork and QA documents required are a pain, it is unfortunately a necessary evil. Being prompt at completing requirements and providing medical docs and certs prevents last minute QA issues. If a document is not acceptable by the hospital and/or is missing it is best to know that sooner rather than later. Providing QA documents last minute can cause issues with starting the contract on time.

If you would like to visit more with Crystal, you can email her at: crystal@expedientmedstaff.com.

~*~

Danielle from Valley Healthcare Systems

Danielle has been a recruiter for a year at Valley Healthcare Systems; the following is her answers to the situations above.

Floating Flo: According to Nurse Flo's Contract, it should state the hospitals that she is required to float to. If the hospitals aren't listed on her contract, then she's not required to work there, period.

Baby Betty: She is not to float to NICU; it's out of her scope.

Nurse Roach: Let's find you new housing right away! I wouldn't want to live in those conditions, why should my nurse Roach?

Nurse Asthmatic: I would get her on a new assignment. She obviously can't stay in wheat country because of her asthma. She would need to get a Dr.'s note or try to see if there's any remedy from the Dr. to control her asthma.

Nurse Roulette: Call Nurse Roulette ASAP and HALT her at the airport. Call the airport if I can't get a hold of Nurse Roulette because her phone is off as she is boarding the plane. I would need to reroute her in Vegas as soon as I find a replacement position for her.

Is there anything else you would like to add? Be upfront and honest. I'm sure you are working with other recruiters/companies and I hope you are. But, I need to know where and when you've been submitted to hospitals from other recruiters so I don't submit you too and it causes you not to get the position at all.

Another pet peeve is when nurses "go dark". I speak to them letting them know the details to the position, i.e. pay, hospital, number of beds, etc. It sounds great to the nurse, they say YES, submit me. I submit, they are offered the position, and BOOM... the nurse goes dark after I send the contract. I call a million times, I text and email, the nurse is MIA. I treat my nurses the way I want to be treated. My nurses are people—not just a number that I'm trying to push through.

If you were impressed with Danielle's answers, you can email her at: dsawtelle@vhcsystems.com.

~*~

Spencer from RTG Medical

Spencer has been a recruiter for a year with RTG Medical. The following is his answers to the questions above.

Floating Flo: First of all, I encourage all of my nurses to voice these concerns as soon as they are evident so they can be addressed promptly. If it was agreed that you would be floating to three different hospitals, then you could expect to possibly float to three different hospitals. These details would be worked out between RTG and the three hospitals that were included in the initial contact. If additional hospitals beyond the three contracted were needing services, RTG could negotiate with them to provide this. Ultimately, no nurse will be required to work in hospitals that they are not contracted/oriented with. I am thorough and upfront with what is expected for each assignment, and I would not expect something like this to arise.

Baby Betty: Under no circumstances should a nurse have to work in an unsafe environment, put their license on the line, or be forced to perform duties that were not reasonably agreed upon in the first place.

If there would ever be an issue where a nurse was not comfortable in a given situation, that nurse would get my full support. The entire reason that competency tests/skills checklists are completed is to assure that situations such as these do not arise. This would be communicated to the hospital in a very direct manner.

Nurse Roach: As my nurses have access to my personal contact information at all times, she would likely be on the phone with me where I would be advising her to find a suitable hotel room in which to set up temporarily. I would then apologize profusely and get to making it up to her. My company has many different resources for finding housing in any given location. These resources are built from nurse referrals, accounts of past experiences, and diligent research over the course of time. So, we have been able to weed out bad apples over the years. However, it is my job to make sure that my nurses have a satisfactory experience. As I intend to develop relationships work with my nurses for long periods of time, and finding housing is something that can leave an impression, this issue would certainly receive my immediate time and attention!

Nurse Asthmatic: As mentioned before, the health and safety of my nurses is my greatest concern, and I would respond to the situation having this in mind. I would immediately inform the facility of the situation and figure out the best approach to moving forward. If this would be a one-time incident and the ailment could be treated and controlled, then continuing the assignment may be an option. If working there would continue to be an issue, I would be in discussions with my nurse to see where the best location would be for the next assignment. While hospitals are concerned about their staffing, they are typically reasonable about working with agencies/nurses in situations such as these where health is a concern, and I would see to it that the nurse's reputation/eligibility would be intact.

Nurse Roulette: First of all, it is not good practice to leave any nurse high and dry in any situation. The first thing I would do is take care of any needs that the nurse would have immediately (housing, food, relocation funds, etc.). Then, I would address how we would find work for the nurse. Whether that is figuring out if the hospital in fact did have needs, finding other facilities in the area, or relocating to another assignment, it would be figured out. Again, I can't emphasize enough that it is my intention to build long term working relationships with my nurses. In doing so, I plan to be proactive in avoiding these types of situations. However, if they do come about, by no means would my nurse be expected to deal with the situation alone.

What else would you like nurses to know? If you don't know, ASK!!! I am a recruiter, yes, but I am more importantly a valuable resource that you need to be using! I could recruit people all day to work, but ultimately it does neither of us any good if we aren't developing a better understanding of one another. Some nurses see recruiters as simply a means to an end, an aid to a financial transaction, a sales person. And some recruiters are salespeople, but I just don't see it like that.

If you would like to contact Spencer, he can be reached by email at: Spencer.Goracke@RTGMedical.com.

~*~

Michele from Onward Healthcare

Michele has been a recruiter for 13 years, with the last year with Onward Healthcare. The following is her answers to the situations above.

Floating Flo: The first thing that I always tell an RN is to speak to her manager and let her know in a professional manner what her concerns are to give them a chance to make it right. If there is no resolution from that conversation, we can definitely step in and speak to our contact and let them know that this was not part of what had been agreed on and see if it is possible to keep the RN at the original agreed upon hospitals. If that is not possible, we can look at trying to get additional mileage compensation. Communication with the manager and the hospital is important. Often times these issues can be resolved with a single conversation before drastic action needs to take place. We always support our RNs and have their best interest in mind while trying to work through any conflict or surprise that may pop up on an assignment.

Baby Betty: Onward will only have her float in her area of specialty that she is has been doing for the last year. It is a huge liability to float to areas that RN is not trained in. We wouldn't jeopardize an RN license!

Nurse Roach: I would respond immediately. I take housing issues very personally. I want my RNs to live in acceptable and nice housing just like I would. I would tell her to leave and check into a hotel and save the receipt so we can reimburse. I would have our housing get in touch with apartment complex and move her either to another unit or find her something else.

Nurse Asthmatic: I would talk to her about her situation. This may not be a good fit for her. I would see if we can get her a doctor note to release her from her assignment. I wouldn't want my RN to be sick the whole assignment!

Nurse Roulette: I find her another assignment in the area. I have experience with other competitors doing that to RNs. Onward doesn't send ANYONE on an assignment until it is confirmed with client. Why would we send a RN to an assignment if we don't have a contract? We want to get paid as well as RN!

Is there anything else you would like nurses to know? Having open communication to a key between recruiter and RN. I have been in the industry for 13 years. I love working for Onward because they are honest and treat RNs great. I have worked in the past for shady companies and was not happy. I am very honest and upfront with my travelers and hope in return they are with me!

If you are interested in working with Michele, you may contact her at: msimon@onwardheathcare.com.

~*~

Grace from Stat Staff Professionals

Grace has been a recruiter for 7 years, with the last year spent with Stat Staff Professionals. The following is her answers to situations above.

Floating Flo: We would never want a nurse traveling further than he or she is comfortable. I would thank her for being so accommodating and confirm exactly how far the nurse was willing to travel. I would then inform the account manager immediately. We would then contact the company to address the situation and work to an amicable resolution.

Baby Betty: At Stat Staff Professionals, patient safety is of the utmost importance. We would never want a nurse to be working in an area where he or she is not comfortable or properly trained. I would first contact the nurse to explain the situation so she is aware. We would then contact the facility to notify them that the RN is not qualified to float into that department.

Nurse Roach: I would tell him or her to immediately return the keys to management and inform them of the conditions of the housing. I would then contact the housing company myself to work to coordinate clean and safe accommodations. If they are able to offer alternatives, I would ask the nurse to inspect them to ensure they are satisfactory. If not, we would provide the nurse temporary housing in a local hotel until proper accommodations could be arranged.

Nurse Asthmatic: I would first confirm that the nurse is being taken care of. I would then contact the facility on her behalf to let them know of the issue and our best estimate of how many shifts will be missed. If they are willing to continue the contract, we would keep up communication with the nurse to be able to notify the hospital of a return date. If they are not able to and end up cancelling the remaining portion of the contract, we would immediately begin working on finding another contract for the nurse, doing our best to be mindful that the area have less of a risk of asthmatic triggers.

Nurse Roulette: With Stat Staff Professionals, this has never happened. In the unlikely event of this situation, I would immediately inform the nurse of the error and immediately work to fix the problem. Since the nurse is already at the facility, our account manager would work diligently to try to establish an immediate contract. In the event that it is not an option, I would immediately work with my team to find the nurse another position.

What would you like nurses to know? Communication and honesty are the key to a successful contract. If you can be upfront and honest with us, we will do the same to you. If you are having an issue, let us know. If I offer you a position that you are not interested in, just tell me. I would never want to put anyone in a situation where they will not be satisfied. Happy nurses make happy patients!

If you would like to contact Grace for more information, you can email her at: gfreer@statstaffpro.com.

~*~

Monica from Millenia Medical Staffing

Monica has been a recruiter for 10 years with the last year at Millenia Medical Staffing. The following is her answers to the situations described above.

Floating Flo: First, I would listen to her concerns. In my years of recruiting I know nurses want to be heard. I would then ask if she would like for me to address this to stop, or perhaps we could increase her pay package to compensate for her time. Whichever way the nurse decides is how I will address it with my hospital Account Manager and make sure resolution is reached. I would let him know that this nurse agreed to float within a certain specific radius, but now she is being taken advantage of by the facility. She was willing to help some, but not on a consistent bases. So either it stops or her pay needs to be increased. I will then reach back out to the nurse and keep her in the loop as to what is being done about this situation for her. After the resolution is resolved, I will then continue to follow up with her to make sure the resolution has not faltered.

Baby Betty: First, we tell the hospital that we need to see if Betty is willing to float since it is outside of her competency level. Some nurses want to float and have a chance to learn or expand their skills. If Betty says no, then we will speak with the nurse and explain to the hospital that we do not allow our nurses to work in areas outside their competency level and the nurse is un-willing to go. This can lead to errors and of course problems for our nurse, which nobody would like to have happen. It is more important to me to have safe practices for our nurses then to always have to appease a hospital.

Nurse Roach: I have had this situation happen before and I can say that I have the nurse leave the housing and go to a hotel room...which our company pays for of course. The nurse will stay at the hotel until we resolve this situation and obtain acceptable accommodations for her. We also have the nurse go see the new accommodations herself before she moves in. That way she is familiar and comfortable.

Nurse Asthmatic: I have had nurses that have had medical issues arise at times. You unfortunately cannot predict when these things will happen and it is not fair to penalize the nurse for them. Our company sticks by the nurse and sees to it that she gets well, and NOT charge her in any way for missed work or housing and will provide some money to her while out on medical leave. While the nurse is recovering in the hospital I will discuss with her what she wants to do next. Stay and finish while probably taking some medications or would she like for me to find her another assignment.

Nurse Roulette: I can honestly say that I take several precautions and a step to ensure this does not happen. I am constantly in touch with the Account Manager about orientation and what the facility needs from my traveler. However, if this did happen, then I would make sure that first our company pays all traveling expenses for this nurse to return home and compensate time lost working. Second, I would be doing everything I can to find her another assignment as quickly as possible...all the while profusely apologizing. This has not happened to me with my nurses and I pray that it never does.

How can a nurse make your job easier? Being a travel nurse is an adventure that only a few in the whole nursing community get to enjoy. I love talking to nurses and hearing about their adventures and sites they have seen; it's like I get to live vicariously through them. My job is to be here to help and assist you anyway I can. I am constantly available 24hrs a day to help (and yes nurses have called me late at night for help) for any situation or questions that might be asked. What makes a great travel nurse to me...just developing a long term lasting relationship and that hopefully you enjoy me as a recruiter enough to recommend me to your friends.

If you were impressed with Monica's answers, you can email her at: mhamilton@milleniamedical.com.

~*~

Wendy from Dzeel Clinical

Wendy has been a recruiter for 14 years with the last year at Dzeel Clinical. The following is her answers to the situations above.

Floating Flo: First things first I'd have to investigate with the client. Why did they begin to float her to facilities outside of the original 3 would be the question. If the facility intended to do this all along I'd have to step in and put a stop to it if the nurse wished. If the nurse is OK with the float, I'd ask them to compensate the nurse for the travel outside of the original parameters. If the nurse didn't want to float I'd defend her right to refuse! If the facility started floating her because of census that they couldn't predict, that's a little different. I'd still insist they compensate the nurse for her travels, but I'd have to ask the nurse to be understanding with the facility. Everyone is at the mercy of census, good or bad and sometimes sister facilities have to help each other out. I would insist on stipulations to make it fair to my nurse. I'd ask for floating to ONLY occur once a week and ONLY as a last resort and the nurse would have to be agreeable to floating to the area of the other facility. Safety is paramount and everyone must feel comfortable and secure.

Baby Betty: NO! L&D, Post Partum even Nursery are nowhere in the scope of NICU and I would never allow it! Not happening...If my nurse agreed to float knowing it was outside of her scope, I'd have her on the carpet faster than she could turn her head left. ALL of my nurses are expected to practice within their skill settings and they all know I will back them up. I'll move them to a new assignment if I have to before I risk a patient, a nurse's license, or my liability.

Nurse Roach: Ummm, after I've apologized about 100 times, she gets to spend a few nights in a nice hotel at my expense while I find her a new apartment. I even toss in a nice dinner and maybe a bottle of wine to say thank you for allowing me to address the problem.

Nurse Asthmatic: My first thought would be, is she OK? If she's OK now, will she be OK if she continues the assignment? If she were only a couple of weeks in the assignment I'd start looking for a replacement nurse and this nurse a new assignment. If she was at the end of her contract I'd have to ask the hard questions...can she continue, should she continue, and does the facility need her to continue? In a lot of instances when medical related situations arise the facility can be very agreeable to allow the nurse to end early so they can go home and recover. IF they absolutely needed her, I'd let the nurse decide. Nothing is worth one's health…so if she truly felt she couldn't continue I'd let her out of her contract without penalty, but I would ask that she commit to another one fairly quickly so I could try to recoup some of the loss from the previous assignment. I'd deal with the facility.

Nurse Roulette: I truly have to guess on this one as I've never had this happen. I don't send a contract out the door to the nurse until I have one in hand and signed by the facility, BUT if it were to happen...I'd ask the Recruiting Manager to fire whoever let this happen and then scramble and see if the original contract can be salvaged. If the contract is in HR, how close to sign are we. If it were salvageable I'd put the nurse up in my housing at no cost to her and pay her a flat wage for hours missed due to our negligence until she was able to start. IF it were not salvageable, I'd immediately start looking for another assignment within 100 miles of the previous. The nurse would be allowed to stay in the apartment for up to one week OR she could opt to head home in which I'd cover ALL of her travel costs and pay 40 hours of wages out at a flat hourly rate for hours missed.

What would you like nurses to know? Be Honest! We know you are shopping around...we expect it and a great recruiter should encourage it. Just be straight with us about it. Don't play one on the other and never let more than one submit you to the same job. It puts the client in an awkward spot, it makes us look like boobs and leaves a bad taste in the mouth of the recruiter who you eventually have to say no to because every recruiter feels like they worked the hardest for you and was the most deserving of the contract.

If you would like to work with Wendy, you can contact her at: wendy@dzeelclinical.com.

~*~

Tricia from Advantage RN

Tricia has been a recruiter for 3 ½ years with the last year at Advantage RN. This following is what she would do in the circumstances mentioned above.

Floating Flo: Well I would have to know about this right away, as I stay in constant contact with my nurses—I'm their life line, their advocate! I would tell her, I'm reaching out to our hospital contact as this was not in your contract. Also, I would advise her to mention to her direct manager that she is not contracted to float like this. If a resolution she is not happy with then we give notice and fine a better fit.

Baby Betty: If she is night nurse: Nurse Betty should tell the person who calls her she is not a NICU nurse and then call me ASAP. If she is Dayshift: she again can tell them she is not comfortable working NICU as it's not her skill set. Further, that her shift is over and by floating to this new unit she would be in OT. I NEVER encourage my nurse to work or float to a unit that they are not comfortable in. Yes you are there to help the hospital but only within your own skill set.

Nurse Roach: I call her back and tell her hang tight. I will forward the pictures to my on call housing department—which is a ARN employee phone 24/7—and get her a new place within a short time. I would give her the option of speaking to the manager of the property herself. If she would rather call herself I will remind her of the on call number. Either way I will reach back out to her within 20–30 minutes to verify on-call has stepped in to assist.

Nurse Asthmatic: First off, if I had worked with her 3 years I would know about her allergies and make sure this was a good match before sending her. Next I would go over her options with her—stay, by extending, moving on, making up hours, etc. I also would have my HR department looking to what medical benefits she was entitled too—or short-term disability.

Nurse Roulette: OMG I had a real similar thing happen 2 years ago. 1st off I go to my CEO/and director to find out the details of who dropped the ball. I would also ask if the hospital and their HR can work out this contract. If an advance of funds is needed I will get approval for that—while we get you set on a new assignment. At the next moment I would work with all account manager as back up to market your profile and see if we can get you an assignment at another hospital.

What can nurses do to make your job easier? Well I get it! Having a conversation and putting your trusting into someone is not easy. Packing up and driving hundreds of miles away based on a phone call from someone you barley know is SCARY! I try to put myself in your shoes...I make myself available to you 24/7. Even if you never travel with me I can be your resource. Some of my favorite nurses didn't travel with me right away because we didn't have the right location. But they referred nurses to me:). And now they travel with me!!!

If you would like to work with Tricia, she can be reached at tricia@ advantagern.com.

~*~

Keith from Medical Staffing Solutions, Inc.

Keith has been a recruiter for 20 years with the last 2 years being a Medical Staffing Solutions Inc. (MSSI).

Floating Flo: First, I would thank the nurse for letting me know what her situation is. Honesty is always the best policy. Second, I would contact our account manager that is directly responsible for our contract with this facility and request that the facility stays within the context of the signed agreement.

Baby Betty: I would let the facility know that Nurse Betty is not to float to NICU and that it is beyond her competency level. I would hope to find common ground with the facility and then call my nurse to let them know all is well. Our contracts are very specific as to where each nurse is allowed to float so this just does not happen at MSSI.

Nurse Roach: If this ever happened I would first thank the nurse for sending me pictures and calling, then apologize and immediately make arrangement for a hotel for the night. Depending upon all the circumstances I may have the nurse move into a different apartment. All of our apartments are inspected and cleaned prior to move in. A huge difference with MSSI vs. most other agencies is that our housing is "suitcase ready." All you have to bring is your personal belongings. This is why about 95% of our travelers let us arrange the housing for them. They LOVE this level of service, which is why most of our travelers check with us first.

Nurse Asthmatic: I have not had this happen to us however if it did I would for sure suggest that the nurse listens to her doctor first and follow their advice. Depending upon the doctor's recommendation we would then proceed with a plan that works best for the nurse and hospital.

Nurse Roulette: I really can't comment as this would never happen at MSSI. Sending a nurse without a contract with the facility makes no sense at all. Our nurses are not sent to a facility unless contracts are signed.

What would you like nurses to know? It's truly a partnership. Honesty is always the best policy and both nurse and recruiter working together as a team usually ends with very happy outcomes!

If you would like to contact Keith, he can be reached at: keith@medicalstaffingsolutionsinc.com.

~*~

Annette from Freedom Healthcare Staffing

Annette has been a recruiter for 10 years with the last 1½ years at Freedom Healthcare Staffing. The following is what she would do in the above situations.

Floating Flo: Freedom Healthcare is a very strong Nurse Advocate and we would immediately involve our Client Services Manager in this issue. If the contract states that the radius is within 10 miles then we would expect that the nurse would only be required to float within a 10-mile radius.

Baby Betty: The nurse would need to reach out to me immediately. We ask our nurses to only care for patients that they are qualified to care for and if they are asked to care for patients that they are not qualified to care for then they are to refuse to accept those patients. Our Client Services Manager would immediately reach out to the Nurse Manager or Charge Nurse and let them know we have advised our RN to only care for patients they are qualified to care for.

Nurse Roach: I would tell my nurse to not move into the apartment and we would immediately put them in a hotel until the situation can be resolved. Our housing manager would then find acceptable housing for the nurse. These things do happen as we are not always able to inspect the housing before we place someone there so when it does we act quickly to remedy the situation.

Nurse Asthmatic: This really depends on what the nurse wants to do. If they want to continue with the assignment we can see if they can make up the time at the end. If the nurse just cannot physically stay then we need to give notice to the hospital and find another assignment.

Nurse Roulette: This should never happen. We have a contract that the facility has signed as well just like the contract between the nurse and the company. If it does happen we would of course take care of the nurse either by hoteling or providing monies for the nurse to return home until we can find another contract.

She would like nurses to know: The best thing to do is to tell your Recruiter exactly what you want and not settle on an assignment. Be upfront about shift, location, and if you are going to need any time off during the contract. Your recruiter should always have your best interest at heart and if they do not then find another recruiter.

If you were impressed with Annette's answers, she can be reached at: abolster@freedomhcs.com.

~*~

David with PRCS Healthcare

David has been a recruiter for a little over 5 years with the last 4 at PRCS Healthcare. The following is his answers to the questions above.

Floating Flo: I would compensate the nurse accordingly. If the nurse was willing to do the traveling to each hospital, I could re-word her contract and get her some extra gas money. If she was sick and tired of the extensive traveling, I would reach out to the facility and work out an action plan and let them know that the contract we signed was only having her float between the initial 3 facilities. In the end, I would make sure the nurse was happy with the results.

Baby Betty: I would notify the facility that my nurse is not competent in that area and that we cannot have her float to the NICU. This not only jeopardizes my nurse's license, but it also puts the patient at risk. Both of which, we cannot allow.

Nurse Roach: If the conditions were unlivable, I would book her a hotel (ON US) until we came up with a plan. I would see if there was potential to fix the current conditions, but if not, we would get her a new apartment elsewhere.

Nurse Asthmatic: I immediately notify the hospital, and let them know that my nurse has become severely ill.We are all human, people get sick. Then, I would see if the nurse is physically able to continue the contract after she FULLY recovers. If she ends up missing two full weeks, perhaps we could simply add those two weeks to the end of her contract to make up for lost time. Ultimately, it is up to the nurse and how she feels about continuing.

Nurse Roulette: Exhaust every option to see if the nurse is able to work the assignment. If not, immediately try to relocate her to a different assignment in the same area. If we are unable to find her an assignment in Vegas, we could reimburse her for all of the travel expenses that she incurred. Ultimately, we would find her something new.

He would like nurses to know: Our job is never "easy." We see all different sides of this business (the good, the bad, and the ugly). I feel that open communication and honesty is best way to make our job better. Allowing us to be open with one another and simply communicating with me in a timely manner could make a world of a difference.

If you are interested in contacting David, you can reach him at: david.blaha@prcshealthcare.com.

~*~

April from PRCS Healthcare

April has been with PRCS for 10 years, but only as a recruiter for the last year. The following is her answers to the situations above.

Floating Flo: I would place the traveler back at the original three facilities she agreed to float. Explain to traveler we were asking her to float to other facilities to gain exposure to those. See if she would possibly be interested in working those locations as well. Explain to traveler we did not intend to upset her by traveling outside radius.

Baby Betty: We explain to the facility this is outside of Betty's skill set level. Ask the facility if they would set up a shadow shift for Betty and we will speak with Betty and get her opinion if this is an area she would like to receive training for future shifts.

Nurse Roach: Immediately put her in Extended Stay until we can find another unit. Our agency has 24-hour phone service.

Nurse Asthmatic: Contact facility immediately and notify them of traveler in hospital. Speak with traveler and ask what she would like to do as in end assignment and relocate to another location or finish assignment. If she decides to end assignment place her in an environment that would not cause her harm.

Nurse Roulette: I call Nurse Roulette immediately and explain the situation. I speak with my manager and fellow recruiters and place her as a Hot RN needing assignment ASAP. My Manager will in turn contact HR and see when they will have the signed contract to our agency. Contact other facilities in Vegas we have contracts with and try and get Roulette into one of those facilities. See if I can park Roulette in another short assignment until the Vegas contract is signed.

How can travel nurses make your job easier? I would ask that Travel Nurses work on their resumes as in making them travel nurse's resumes. Listing facilities they have worked with month, date, year and if it was a staff position or travel position. If it is a travel position, list the agency and contact phone number. List all certifications with expiration dates and company.

Thank you so much for every recruiter who stopped by the website and filled out the interview. As many of you know, one of my main goals in life is to bring great companies and great recruiters together with some totally awesome and educated nurses!

Chapter Twenty-One

Travel Company Profiles

Advantage Nursing Services

Advantage Nursing Services provides assignments for registered nurses, licensed nurses, respiratory therapists, and surgical technologists. They are a large company who primarily staffs the states of Louisiana, Texas, and New Mexico.

They feel that their southern hospitality along with professionalism and respect for their nurses are priority. Not only do they have someone on call 24/7, but they also have a clinical nurse liaison that is available. They pride themselves in doing the best to accommodate their nurses. If the nurse isn't happy with their recruiter, they are happy to place them with another recruiter.

Advantage Nursing Services is a Joint Commission Certified company that offers blue cross insurance along with direct deposit and many other company discounts.

Part of their philosophy at Advantage Nursing Services is that they believe in treating their nurses like family. That's why they give the same great service to their nurses as they give to their clients. They have been in the business since 1984 and have a great reputation. They love their nurses!

For more information contact them at: Advantage Nursing Services, 340 Severn Ave. suite 320, Metairie, LA 70008. Call them at: 800-749-1122Or visit their website at: www.advantagenursing.com.

~*~

Alliant Healthcare Staffing

Alliant Healthcare Staffing is a medium-sized, Joint Commission

Certified company that has nationwide RN, CST, ST, Rad Tech, Respiratory Therapist, Sterile Processor positions.

They guarantee personal service by getting to know their employees, their skills sets, and their specific preferences as a top priority. They know that the key to a successful and ongoing relationship with their travelers is communication. Learning their must-haves and, just as importantly, what "will not work" for them is a must. They will go above and beyond to assist their traveler in getting placed at a work assignment that is a great fit and to ensure that they have a positive and rewarding experience working with Alliant.

Alliant Healthcare Staffing's customer support team is available to you 24/7, 365 days a year, with live telephone and email support. Alliant has representatives available to help address your questions/needs. They also have a Clinical Nurse Liaison that is available during normal business hours.

Members of the Alliant Healthcare Staffing office are trained and they understand the reality of the healthcare profession. Alliant emphasizes the support it provides to its employees. In keeping with its philosophy of employee as client, every effort is made by the staffing coordinator to accommodate its employees' professional needs and areas of interest. Alliant fosters the attitude in its employees that their positions are not "temporary assignments," but full-time, professional opportunities. Alliant's high retention rate confirms the success of this policy.

They provide for their travelers Carefirst Blue Cross Blue Shield PPO Health Insurance that includes Davis Vision. Alliant also offers dental insurance. Their IRA is a simple plan with a 1% company match. Other benefits include: travel reimbursements, a tax-free housing stipend, and referral bonuses.

Alliant Healthcare Staffing considers its employees as valued clients. According to this philosophy, each person is treated as an individual asset, and his or her needs are considered and met to the best of their ability for each assignment. They take steps to ensure that each employee is professionally challenged and satisfied with their assignment, and if not, Alliant makes every effort to resolve the issue or change the employee to another, more suitable assignment as quickly as possible Alliant has found that an employee's performance often reflects the employer's attitude towards the employee. If employees are satisfied with their employer and feel that they are being treated with respect and consideration, they will perform professionally and have no desire to change employers or "agency hop." Finally, in order to deliver the highest quality performance to each of Alliant's clients, any problem or concern of their employees, no matter how slight, is treated promptly and fairly.

For more information contact them at: Alliant Healthcare Staffing, 7201 Wisconsin Ave., STE 705, Bethesda, MD 20814. Call them at: 301-654-1002 Or find them on the web: www.alliantstaffing.com.

~*~

Atlas Medstaff

Atlas Medstaff is a small veteran owned company that specializes in placing RNs, LPNs, and Allied Health travelers, including Lab, PT, and OT. Assignments usually range from 6 to 13 weeks and sometimes even longer! Each traveler has a recruiter specially assignment to them. Unlike some of the other companies, their recruiters handle no more than 20 travelers at a time.

Atlas Medstaff is a Joint Commission certified company that has a Clinical Liaison during business from 8:00 AM to 5:00 PM central time. The travelers drive the boat at Altas. They are flexible enough to allow this type of open communication between recruiters and their nurses.

They offer a very high quality insurance plan through BC/BS of Nebraska for health. They also offer a very nice Dental and Vision Insurance through Guardian. They also have a 401K plan through Edward Jones and Mass Mutual. Company match of 3% starts at 7000hrs of work. Other promotion and benefits include their "Dream Job. Dream Vacation." benefit after the completion of your first travel assignment with Atlas. They will give the nurse a free round-trip ticket to anywhere in the Continental USA plus $250 in spending money or you can get an iPad2...nurse's choice!

Their family mentality and their experience make them different than other companies. Nurses are not another number with Atlas MedStaff...they are actually a part of the atlas family!

Atlas MedStaff believes in family values and the power of friendship. They support you with their team that has over three decades of experience. The nurse is their top priority. That's why they build lifelong friendships and create a culture of family. They understand the stresses of today's healthcare industry can overwhelm you, let them be there for you every step of the way. Whether you've never traveled as a nurse before or you're a travel nursing veteran, you'll get their utmost attention and support, no matter what. They commit themselves to finding your ideal travel assignment because that is what a good friend does. Their dedication places you in the best position.

For more information on Atlas Medstaff, you can find them at: 11840 Nicholas St., Suite #215, Omaha, NE 68154. You can phone them at: 855-884-2360, or visit their website: www.atlasmedstaff.com.

~*~

Aya Healthcare

At Aya Healthcare, they offer numerous opportunities for healthcare professionals. They are experts in travel nursing and local contract placements. Aya Healthcare staffs nationwide and have territory managers who diligently work to help secure you a job in an ideal location. They also have strong client relationships and often get jobs not seen by their competitors.

They are a large company broken down into several specialized teams allowing them to focus on each individual healthcare provider throughout the cycle of their assignment. They are a privately held company that holds itself accountable to it its nurses.

Aya Healthcare understands that each healthcare provider makes a difference to their patients and they want to make that same positive difference in the lives of their employees. They have specialized recruiters and customer service representatives to ensure that healthcare providers working with Aya have a positive experience doing that they love. They understand that the way they care for you makes a difference in your life and they strive to go above and beyond to provide a remarkable employment experience. They have customer service representatives who specialize in each step of the travel experience. From on-boarding to certifications and licensing, to benefits and payroll, you can always be confident that you will have a knowledgeable representative available to answer any of your questions or concerns. In addition, to ensure timeliness and personal service, each healthcare provider is assigned a dedicated Customer Service Representative. They want to get to know you and they feel the best way to do so, is making sure that you always have access to a friendly, familiar representative, who knows your unique travel history which allows them to serve you in the best way possible.

Aya Healthcare has been Joint Commission certified since 2006.

They belong to NATHO. They also have a Clinical Nurse Liaison who is available after hours and on the weekends who can provide advice on clinical issues and offer assistance from a clinical viewpoint.

They strive to hire the best professionals in the industry and put them through a rigorous recruiter training program to ensure that they are a fit for most nurses. Additionally, they have hands-on managers who are available to assess the recruiters' relationships with the nurses. They are happy to accommodate any special requests when it comes to finding the right recruiter. Just let them know what you are looking for and they will connect you with the right recruiter today!

Aya provides Blue Shield health insurance with several options available. Their Dental, Life and Vision provider is Guardian. They also provide a company match 401k for all nurse employees.

They are happy to pick up nurses coming into Sacramento to get their license and give them rides to the California Board of nursing. They love to send pizzas on your birthday and do special treats at the holidays. They even have a "Happiness" team to welcome you aboard and check in throughout your assignment to make sure you have the best experience possible!

Aya Healthcare knows that healthcare providers are looking for two key things. First, they need to get a good job that they love. Second, they need to have a fun employment experience that they love. Here's why they are the best at those two things. First, they work with lots of great facilities nationwide. They have great relationships with the facilities because of their number of years in business and their history of providing them with ideal healthcare professionals. Thus, they are able to get their healthcare providers a great job that they love. Because they understand the needs of their healthcare providers, they work diligently to deliver them a great employment experience. They have the foresight to secure the right employment experience and if anything goes awry, they work tirelessly to ensure positive resolution and a continued positive employment experience. Their "happiness" team makes sure each and every nurse is happy and feels taken care of!

Because they have happy healthcare professionals, at Aya Healthcare, their healthcare providers continue working with them time and time again. They also tell their friends and family how happy they are with the job that they do for them. They invite you to get in touch with them to see how they can help you get you a job that you love and see how much fun you have working with them.

For more information on Aya Healthcare, you can visit them at: 5930 Cornerstone Court West, Suite 300, San Diego, CA 92121. You can phone them at: 866-687-7390, or visit their website: www.ayatravelnursingjobs.com.

~*~

Cirrus Medical Staffing

Cirrus Medical Staffing provides travel nurses and therapists in all specialties including OR, CVOR, ICU, CVICU, ER, L&D, Dialysis, and even management positions. They place nurses in all 50 states. They are a privately owned company with fewer than 100 employees.

They recently formed a special group called "Traveler Relations" that specifically focuses on the well-being of their travelers. They contact their nurses weekly to ensure that things are going well on each assignment. It's a level of personal care that no other travel nurse staffing firm provides to their knowledge.

They are both a member of the Joint Commission Certification program and a member of NATHO. They have a Clinical Nurse Liaison that is on duty 24/7/365.

They look to create long-term relationships with their travelers. Many of their travelers have been with Cirrus for several years. They have a very high rate of extensions and retention. Their biggest focus is not to find new travelers, but to retain those that they successfully work with and build relationships that last.

Their medical insurance is through United Healthcare with coverage from Day 1 of employment with Cirrus. They also provide vision and dental. Healthcare plans are same plans that internal employees have. And yes, they do offer a 401k with company match. Other benefits include: Sign On Bonus, Referral Bonus, Loyalty Bonus, Extension Bonus, Free CEUs, Housing, Dedicated support, Payroll specialists are assigned to answer all of your questions, Long term disability, Life insurance, and Supplemental Insurance Options are available. These include short-term disability, cancer insurance, hospital stay insurance, and accidental insurance. These do require a minimal employee contribution each pay period.

The biggest difference between Cirrus Medical Staffing and other companies is their outstanding benefits package, their Traveler Relations Dept., and their experienced RN recruitment staff's attention to detail are second to none. They want to create a long-term relationship with their travel nurses and their clients, not a "one and done". They pride themselves on the fact that many of their travelers have been with them for years and the very high rate of extensions they have annually. As a smaller firm, they have the ability to provide individual attention and focus to each RN.

Cirrus Medical Staffing has been in the Travel Nursing industry for over 11 years. Their longevity is indicative of their success in a very competitive healthcare field. In 2013 they were listed on Inc. Magazine's "5000 Fastest Growing Companies" in the US.

For more information contact Cirrus Medical Staffing at: 309 East Morehead Street, Suite 200, Charlotte, NC 28202. The can be reached by phone at: 800-299-8132, or visit their website: www.cirrusmedicalstaffing.com.

~*~

Core Medical Group

Core Medical Group staffs Registered Nurses (RN), Licensed Practical Nurses (LPN), Physical Therapists (RPT/MPT/DPT), Physical Therapist Assistants (PTA), Occupational Therapists (OTR), Occupational Therapist Assistants (COTA), Speech Language Pathologists (CCC-SLP), Surgical (Scrub) Technicians and Pharmacy Technicians nationwide, including the U.S. Virgin Islands, Hawaii, and Alaska.

They are a medium-sized company that has both time and resources to give travelers full, personalized attention and assist them with everything involved in the traveling process. This includes assisting the traveler with his/her application, housing, licensure assistance, and more. They are privately owned.

CoreMedical Group treats its nurses and allied health professionals like family members. Their recruiters consider it a common courtesy to give travelers their personal cell phone and home phone numbers, so nurses, etc., can reach their recruiters 24/7. They understand that their professionals work odd hours all across the country and they want them to know they can contact them any time for any reason. CoreMedical recruiters are focused on and dedicated to the best interests of the traveler. They also cherish the relationships they build with their travelers and enjoy being part of their lives. They also have a Clinical Nurse Liaison who is available 24/7.

They are Joint Commission Certified and recently passed a Joint

Commission audit with no requirements for improvement identified. They are also a proud member of NATHO. All of their recruiters provide second-to-none customer service to their travelers. They develop deep friendships with their travelers and are with them through good times and bad, always with a sympathetic ear and with a drive to ensure their travelers' happiness. If there is ever an issue or if a traveler has concerns about his or her recruiter, CoreMedical will automatically reassign a traveler to another recruiter that will be a better fit.

Core Medical Group's insurance is provided by Anthem Blue Cross Blue Shield. They also offer Delta Dental Insurance and VSP Vision Insurance. All of these benefits are effective Day 1 of employment. They provide travelers with a Matching 401K and will match $0.50 to the dollar with at least a 1% contribution with a max match at a 6% contribution. Other benefits include: Club CoreMed Annual Vacation Incentive—Travelers can earn points for an annual trip to the Caribbean each year just for working with them! Other benefits include: Weekly Pay With Direct Deposit, Referral Bonuses (earn cash or points toward their annual trip to the Caribbean), Travel Reimbursement, Licensure Assistance and Reimbursement, Tax Free Per Diem for lodging, meals and incidentals (must be traveling away from permanent residence and qualify per the permanent tax residence form), Free Private Housing or Complete Relocation Assistance for those receiving lodging per diem, Free Unlimited Online CEUs through CE Direct, Free Medical Testing and Screening for any medical services required for a traveler's assignment, Free 50K Life Insurance, Healthcare Reimbursement Account (HRA), Veterinary Pet Insurance (VPI), Professional Liability, Workers Compensation, Employee Assistance Program, Short Term Disability (Voluntary), Additional Life and AD&D (Voluntary), Long Term Care Insurance (Voluntary), and a 529 College Savings Plan (Voluntary).

They don't lose contact with their travelers once they're on assignment. They are with them through every step of the process before, during, and after an assignment. Travelers can contact their recruiter 24/7 and also have a direct line to our Recruiting Manager 24/7. Core also offers industry-leading benefits, including an annual trip to the Caribbean for travelers who work with them. No other travel company offers this benefit. The trip is also an opportunity for their travelers and recruiters to meet and greet on an all-inclusive trip to the Caribbean. Lastly, they don't just place nurses and other traveling healthcare professionals, they build relationships and long-lasting friendships that they value and cherish.

CoreMedical Group just launched a new website that is more user and mobile-friendly, so traveling nurses and other healthcare professionals can easily search for jobs, create job alerts, share jobs with friends on social media and email, create a profile, and more! The site is accessible whether you're on your cell phone, tablet, or personal computer. Searching and applying to travel nursing jobs has never been easier. Also, be sure to follow CoreMedical Group on Facebook, Twitter, Pinterest, LinkedIn, Instagram, and Google+! (Their social media links are in the top right corner of their website).

For more information on CoreMedical group, you can visit them at: 2 Keewaydin Drive, Salem, NH 03079. You can phone them at: 800-995-2673 or visit their website at: www.coremedicalgroup.com.

~*~

Critical Nursing Solutions

Critical Nursing Solutions (CNS) is a medium sized company that offers full-time, part-time, local per-diem, travel nursing, and allied health positions. You name it, they do it! They not only have local Phoenix assignment, but they provide travel nurses to hospitals all over the United States. At this time they do not do international travel. The time from application to on-the-job depends on the applicant and how eager they are getting the required modules and paperwork finished.

At CNS you will never be treated like a number. They view it as a partnership. If the applicant isn't working and making money, then the company isn't making any money. Personal service is number to them, and they have someone available to nurses 24 hours a day, 7 days a week, 365 days a year. Their Clinical Nurse Liaison is also on call 24 hours a day.

Benefits include Health, Dental, and Insurance through Blue Cross and Nationwide Met Life insurance, a housing choice, a choice of shifts, liability insurance, travel assistance, and tuition reimbursement program. They go beyond the industry standards of the Joint Commission and NATHO. They also provide CEU allowances, travel allowances, direct deposit, pay card (CNSIPS), referral bonuses, completion bonuses, a 401K with company match, and 24 hour service to their travelers.

They ensure that the recruiter and nurse are a fit by asking questions during the interview process. They don't have time to deal with the crap and you don't either. They are real. They will go above and beyond for you as long as you open the door and walk though; although, they can't open the door or walk through for you. Have fun and let's get to business and make some money.

For more information on Critical Nurse Solutions, you can visit them at: 2200 E. Camelback Road, Suite 230, Phoenix, AZ 85016. You can also call them at: 888-267-1314, or visit their website at: www.criticalnursingsolutions.com.

~*~

Cross Country TravCorps

Cross Country TravCorps is one of the top providers of travel nurses (RN) and allied healthcare professionals (OT, ST, PT). They have assignments nationwide, as well as in the US Virgin Islands. Cross Country TravCorps in a medium sized, publicly traded company (CCRN).

The key to a great travel nursing career is having a great Recruiter. Recruiters at Cross Country TravCorps are the best in the business. They are always on your side as your main contact, a shoulder to lean on and at the core, your advocate. They also have developed a Clinical Nurse Liaison Department comprised entirely of tenured registered nurses with someone on call 24 hours a day. Cross Country TravCorps is Joint Commission certified and belongs to NATHO (National Association of Travel Healthcare Organizations).

Nurses choose to travel with Cross Country TravCorps because of their top of the line Recruiters. No matter how stressful situations may be, your Recruiter is always on your side. To make sure CCTC nurses are 100% comfortable. They also have a Clinical Liaisons Department to provide support by tenured registered nurses, available 24/7.

As a Cross Country employee, you are insured by Cigna. You will receive major medical, preventative diagnostic and basic dental coverage, and life insurance on all 8-week or more staffing assignments. The employer makes matching 401K contributions equal to 25%, up to 6% of compensation. In addition to great health insurance, there are many other perks to traveling with Cross Country. They have an entire team devoted to finding their nurses comfortable living arrangements as well as discounts on everything from car rentals to hotels, free continuing education, and more.

At Cross Country TravCorps, they understand that what they

do makes a difference. As a result, they have made a commitment to give back to their communities. They currently sponsor the non-profit charity, Project Perfect World (PPW). Up to four times a year, PPW sponsors medical teams to deliver care to children in need. In addition, they are always looking forward to participating in March of Dimes in support of delivering stronger, healthier babies. Cross Country has exclusive relationships with healthcare facilities all across the country. They work with 80% of the nation's top hospitals and 93% of the nation's Magnet hospitals.

For more information Cross Country TravCorps can be visited at: 6551 Park of Commerce Blvd., Boca Raton, FL 33487. They can be reach by phone at: 561-998-2232, or visited at their website: www.crosscountrytravcorps.com.

~*~

Dzeel Clinical Healthcare Staffing

Dzeel Clinical Healthcare Staffing places Registered Nurses, Radiology Techs, Ultrasound Techs, RRT/CRT's, Cath Lab Tech's, Monitor Tech's Rehab—PT, OT, SLP, PTA, COTA Mental Health—Sitters, Aides, and Advanced Practice Nurses into nationwide travel contracts, local contracts, as well as, perm, temp to perm and direct hire positions.

Dzeel is a medium sized company who matches each HealthCare Professional (HCP), regardless of their discipline or specialty, to a single recruiter who is responsible for that HCP. As they work together, the recruiter and HCP build a relationship based on mutual respect and familiarity, which fosters a sense of friendship. Friends are never numbers...friends are family. Dzeel does have a Clinical Nurse Liaison that is available 24/7/365, and they are JCAHO certified.

To ensure that Dzeel HCP's are happy with their recruiters, leadership listens! If either gives the sense of dislike or discontent, leadership moves the HCP to another recruiter. If either openly asks, they move them no questions asked.

Dzeel offers all of their active HCP's health, vision and dental insurance through the national Blue Cross/Blue Shield network of providers. Every Dzeel HCP is automatically enrolled as a participant in Dzeel's Free Will Retirement Incentive program. For every hour a HCP works, Dzeel Clinical pays the HCP $.50 to apply towards the retirement option of the HCP's choice and Dzeel takes care of the taxes!!

Other benefits include: CASH Referral Bonuses whether you work for them or not, Overtime and Holiday Pay in excess of 1.5, Travel Pay and Travel Lodging Pay, Education Reimbursements, Free Nationally Accepted CEU's to all HCP's, PTO per assignment, Sign On and Completion Bonuses, Parking Reimbursement, Company Provided Coverage for Workman's Comp and Liability, and LIVE Personnel 24/7

Dzeel in the Navajo language can be translated to mean "heartfelt strength," and that is exactly what you will find with them. They strive every day to serve their clients and staff with the ultimate in integrity and their demonstrated commitment to reliability. Dzeel Clinical was created to help meet the demands for high-quality healthcare professionals. Dzeel Clinical Healthcare (Clinical Staffing Inc.) is a woman owned HUB certified North Carolina based company. Dzeel Clinical is licensed by the State of North Carolina, Department of Health and Human Services, Division of Health Service Regulation to operate as a Nursing Pool Agency. As an established organization in North Carolina, their employee recruitment process is exceptional and their in-house procedures are proven. Dzeel is invested within their home state. In doing so they have become involved with the North Carolina Nurses Association, The North Carolina Psychiatric Association, and they have been formally invited by the board and accepted as members of North Carolina Business Committee for Education which focuses on education and economic growth across North Carolina. Dzeel is also the only staffing company involved with Healthcare Works Partnership which is a regional organization addressing workforce needs in healthcare.

Their passion is building strong relationships while becoming the most reliable and educated Team in the health care industry. Their management philosophy is focused on 3 key words: Reliability, Relationships and Education. They know that by focusing on these 3 words both internally and externally Dzeel is able to form the partnerships needed to provide the very best in patient care. Reliability for Dzeel Clinical is vital throughout their organization; from their internal team to their healthcare providers, being reliable is a critical piece of their partnership commitment. They employ professionals who are committed and dedicated in their specialty and also have a passion for patient care. Dzeel Clinical knows having a well-built relationship within an organization is essential to their success. What makes them unique among other supplemental staffing agencies is that they know each facility site is different and each manager will have their own procedures. Communication and making sure they follow the facility's requirements is priority number one for Dzeel Clinical. They connect their clients with appropriate Dzeel internal staff at the start of all relationships to ensure that communication flows smoothly 24/7 and any questions that arise can be answered quickly. In regards to their HCP's, Dzeel believes in open communication and encourages their HCP's to address any concerns or questions that may arise during their assignment. Their organization's emphasis on continuing education is one factor that clearly sets Dzeel Clinical Healthcare apart. They offer the practical and procedural courses to their healthcare providers in addition to giving attention to patient care within their training curriculum. Dzeel Clinical only submits skilled healthcare providers with an absolute minimum of one year of related experience to the assignment they are being presented for.

For more information you can contact Dzeel Clinical Healthcare Staff at 140 Commerce Parkway Suite 101, Garner, NC 27529. They can be contacted by phone at: 866-598-1523, or visited on the web at: www.dzeelclinical.com.

~*~

Expedient Mestaff

Expedient Medstaff offers nursing leadership, advance practice, nursing and allied travel opportunities. They are a Joint Commission certified small to mid-sized company that is RN owned and operated, which offers nationwide travel assignments. They also provide PRN positions throughout Michigan.

At Expedient, each nurse is assigned to a team to make sure each aspect of the travel assignment meets the traveler's expectations. For quality assurance, they perform routine "How are we doing for you" surveys to allow our travelers to provide feedback on what we can be doing to make their assignment the best it can be. Nurses are their clients, they know their travelers are in high demand. With every interaction, they strive to remind travelers they made the right choice when they chose Expedient.

Expedient offers ALFAC, nations plans with vision and dental, a 401K that is nurse vested, and they even have pet insurance! They also offer excellent pay, quality housing, housing stipends, travel reimbursement, license reimbursement, and they come with a travel tax guarantee! They guarantee that their pay and benefit packages are 100% compliant with the IRS rules and regulations.

Related to the fact that they know travel nurses do not like to spend time on travel nursing applications, they have streamlined their application process to take less than 3 minutes to apply.

For more information on Expedient Medstaff, visit them at: One Heritage Place, Suite 250, Southgate, MI 48195. They can be reached by phone at: 877-367-8770, or visited online at: www.expedientmedstaff.com.

~*~

Fastaff

Fastaff is a medium sized privately owned company that hires RNs in urgent and critical care that have one to two years of experience in their specialty. Their travelers can travel nationwide for exciting jobs.

Their nurses are the very best in the industry and they treat them that way. Their recruiters go above and beyond working with their nurses to help them get placed, prepared and have the best possible experience on assignment. They also have Clinical Nurse Liaisons that are available 24/7 to support our working nurses. They have been Joint Commission certified since 2005, and they are members of NATHO.

They have a pre-qualification team that works with each nurse to help place them on their first assignment and then matches them with a legacy recruiter that best matches their travel needs/profile.

Day one benefits include, United Healthcare medical and vision insurance, and Metlife dental insurance. They also have a 401k that is offered after 90 days and with a discretionary company match. Other benefits include a competitive holiday bonuses, loyalty bonus program, free travel and housing, nurse appreciation program, and more!

Fastaff has the industry's top pay and has recruiters that care with 24/7 working nurse support. Their nurses and recruiters help to care for each and every nurse. You're never alone on the road when you join the Fastaff family

The average tenure of their recruiters is 9 years and they've been in business for over 25 years. Because they specialize in Rapid Response nurse staffing for urgent and critical care, their nurses make the industry's top pay giving them more flexibility throughout the year or allowing them to take home top pay. Their top earning nurse made over $175,000 in 2013!

For more information on Fastaff Travel Nursing come by and see them at: 6399 S Fiddlers Green Circle, Ste. 100, Greenwood Village, CO 80111. You can also phone them at: 800-736-8773, or visit their website: www.fastaff.com.

~*~

FlexCare Medical Staffing

FlexCare Medical Staffing specializes in contracting Registered Nurses, who have at least one year of current RN experience, in acute care facilities throughout the nation. Typical contract lengths vary from 4–26 weeks. On most occasions their travelers extend for multiple assignments at the same hospital and many eventually turn their travel assignment into a fulltime position. They feel, if the nurse likes his/her assignment so much that they decide to extend and/or go on fulltime, that is further proof that they are matching RN's up to the right jobs and right facilities.

FlexCare Medical Staffing places RN's nationwide, including Hawaii and Alaska, and currently holds contracts with some of the largest hospital chains throughout the nation including HCA, Kaiser Permanente, Dignity Health (formerly Catholic Healthcare West),Tenet Healthcare, Texas Health, and Florida Hospitals.

FlexCare has the job availability of a large company with the service of a small company. Having never advertised, FlexCare has built a company primarily off of referrals from other current working FlexCare travel RNs. You will be treated as not just a name, but also as a colleague and a friend.

One of the key differences between FlexCare and most other travel nursing companies is the fact that your recruiter at FlexCare is your sole point of contact. Your recruiter is responsible for handling every detail of your assignment, whether that is payroll, insurance, travel, housing, etc. Your recruiter has a very intimate knowledge of every piece of your assignment and always has a vested interest making your travel assignment all it can possibly be. If there is ever an issue while on assignment, your recruiter will be there to provide you with the most efficient solution as quick as possible. There is never the need to get transferred between multiple departments within FlexCare, because your recruiter is your sole point of contact for all of these things.

Yes they do have a Clinical Nurse Liaison. Consistent with their "Single Point of Contact" philosophy, all phone calls will initially be trafficked through that particular nurse's Recruiter; however, if there is a need to involved their Clinical Nurse Liaison they always do. If something comes up after hours or on weekends, their Clinical Nurse Liaison is available by cell phone.

Flexcare has been Joint Commission Certified since 2008. Additionally, they have passed each unannounced on-site evaluation with zero deficiencies, which is testament of their quality commitment to our healthcare providers and their clients. They currently do not belong to NATHO.

Their Vice President of Recruitment is always available to talk with any nurse if there is ever any conflict between recruiter and nurse. At the tail end of each assignment their Vice President also sends out an Assignment Evaluation that includes a section to rate and comment on the Recruiters performance. If there is a need to reassign a nurse to a different recruiter, that can easily be done. The bulk of the business that comes into FlexCare is via referral—and referrals typically want to work with the specific recruiter they were referred to. They have had very few instances where a nurse did not like his/her recruiter.

Their benefits packages include Anthem Blue Cross Insurance. Included in their Insurance is Medical, Dental, Vision, and Life Insurance. They offer a 401K through Lincoln Financial with a company match.

FlexCare creates 100% customizable pay packages for their RN's. You as an RN tell them what you need provided in your pay package and they will create a pay package that best suits your needs, whether that includes housing, a rental car, travel reimbursement, licensure reimbursement, certification reimbursement, health insurance, etc.

FlexCare have relationships with RN's that have spanned years and even decades. They truly have friendships with their RN's, along with the hospitals they staff; they don't just do business over the phone. They take every opportunity to meet their RN's face to face, whether that is a FlexCare sponsored Meet and Greet, Travel Nurse Conventions, or just lunch! Additionally, their Account Managers make monthly visits to their key hospitals, meeting with hiring managers to strengthen their relationships and find ways to improve their processes.

FlexCare is not your run of the mill staffing agency. They are a group of dedicated Nurse Centric folks that enjoy and value the relationships they have fostered with nurses across the country. They realize there are a lot of choices in agencies these days and they take pride in the fact they approach the industry in a unique way. They are focused on the long-term success of their nurses, employees, and business, not short-term gains. This long-term focus emphasizes the importance of a company culture that values lasting relationships built on honesty and integrity.

For more information on Flexcare Medical Staffing you can see them at: 990 Reserve Drive #250, Roseville, CA 95678. They can be called at: 866-564-3589, or you can visit their website at: www.flexcarestaff.com.

~*~

Fortus Healthcare Resources

Fortus Healthcare Resources has opportunities in Dialysis, L&D, MedSurg, ICU, OR, OR Tech's PACU, PICU, NICU, Telemetry, CCU, and ER for travel contracts. Fortus is a medium sized company that covers all the United States, the Virgin Islands, and some International assignments. Every nurse is a member of the "Fortus Family" and absolutely treated as a name.

Not only do they pride themselves on being a 24/7 concierge for their nurses, they also have a Clinical Nurse Liaison that is available 24 hours a day. Although they are not currently Joint Commission certified, they are hoping to have that accomplished in 2014. They are still exploring NATHO.

Many of their nurses give referrals to the recruiters within their company that they have worked with and are happy with. However, if a nurse was not happy with an individual recruiter they would certainly rectify that. To date, that has not been necessary.

Their medical and dental insurance is through Excellus Blue Cross/ Blue Shield, which is available on the first day of employment. A nurse is eligible for 401K after 1 year and 1000 hours of service. They do a 100% match up to 3% and a 50% match from 3–5%.

Fortus is proud of their quality of the positions that they offer, and their team and family approach. Their nurses feel a part of something with their company. Each and every traveler is able to contact them 24/7 should they need anything while on the road.

They are happy to provide any nurse with testimonials from other nurses they work with. They have an exceptional retention rate because their team treats their nurses as family. Come try them out today!

For more information on Fortus Healthcare Resources, you can see them at: 181 Genesee Street, New York, NY 13501. They also can be reached at 888-387-3625, or visit their website: www.fortusgroup.com.

~*~

Freedom Healthcare Staffing

Freedom offers 4–13+ week assignments to RNs and Allied Travelers. They are a national company that is able to contract in all the United States, including Hawaii and Alaska. They are a small privately owned company where each traveler is given personal attention. Many decisions are based upon the individual traveler rather than a basic company policy. You are never alone in that they have a vice president of clinical services that has been a nurse for over 20 years of Critical Care experience. She has many years of experience within their industry working both as a marketer and liaison. Advocating for their nurses and patient care are always her priority.

They are both Joint Commission certified and belong to NATHO. If there is trouble between a nurse and recruiter, it is taken care of promptly. Any traveler is able to request a recruiter change at any time. Their agency always respects the travelers right to do so and immediately makes any change requested.

United Healthcare provides their medical and prescription coverage. Their insurance package also provides life, dental, and vision coverage. Currently, they do not provide a 401K. Other benefits include: Free Corporate Housing, Free First Day Health Benefits, $600 round trip in travel, Licensure Reimbursement, and a hands on approach.

Freedom works hard to provide the best customer service possible to each of their travelers. They are very strong advocates for their travelers and their patients. They take a personal approach and treat their nurses as individuals rather than just another number. They have a "No Drama" approach to providing their travelers with the best experience possible as they travel.

You can contract Freedom Healthcare Staffing at 3025 South Parker Road, Suite 800, Aurora, CO 80014. You also call them at: 866-463-0385 or visit their website: www.freedomhcs.com.

~*~

Fusion Medical Staffing

Fusion Medical Staffing places both nursing and allied healthcare travelers to include: RN, LPN, CNA, Surg Techs, OT, PT, COTA, PTA, SLP, and Lab staff nationwide. They are a small privately owned company who makes personal service a top priority by having their structure set up to where a nurse has one point of contact which is their Nurse Recruiter. All of their employees also have their direct numbers to their cell phones to help with anything that may occur. They also have a nurse liaison that is available for employees during business hours.

They are Joint Commission Certified. They do not belong to NATHO yet, but they are considering it. Their recruiters treat their nurses as number one by conducting extensive phone conversations and are willing to adjust things as necessary to make things work for all parties involved!

Their benefits include: Blue Cross Blue Shield for medical and Guardian for dental and vision, immediate contributions to a 401K with matching after one year of employment up to 5%. Their other benefits include: Top-notch customer service with a single point of contact, 401k that starts after 2,080 hours of service with a Match or 100% of 3% and 50% of 2% through Hartford, Private Housing or Housing per diem, Weekly Per diem for meals, Referral Bonus of $500, Licensure Reimbursement, Travel Reimbursement, On Going Education Reimbursement, $300 a calendar year, Direct Deposit, and Vacation Hours-40 hours received after 1,560 hours worked.

They are a smaller company for a reason and they don't want to become a larger company. They want to maintain their integrity and their commitment to keeping their travelers as their first priority! Only a smaller company can do that! They will grow by leaps and bounds in numbers but they will never let the traveler feel like a number because of it!

The benefits of working with Fusion Medical: 1)You won't be just another number. You will be a valued employee. 2) They will be competitive with their pay packages. 3) You will receive top-notch customer service from your nurse recruiter. 4) You will have a client manager that will be willing to put in the time to find you the job that you want.

For more information you can visit Fusion Medical Staffing a 11506 Nicholas St, Omaha, NE 68154, call them at 877-230-3885, or visit their website: www.fusionmedstaff.com.

~*~

Health Providers Choice

Health Providers Choice is a mid-sized privately owned company held corporation, which offers Registered Nurses (RNs) throughout the

United States and Canada, travel, local contract, and per-diem positions. All nurses working with Health Providers Choice are employees of Health Providers Choice(W-2). They are able to offer assignment terms of 4 weeks up to 26 weeks in length for travel and local RN's and flexible scheduling for casual/perdiem RN's. Health Providers Choice specializes in nurse placement however they also place certified scrub techs and a few allied health personnel. You can visit their website for a complete list of their current positions. They place all specialties. They have a national client base. They are able to offer assignment terms of 4 weeks up to 26 weeks in length for travel and local healthcare providers and flexible scheduling for casual/per-diem healthcare providers. HPC was nurse founded in 2001 and remains nurse owned and operated.

They pride themselves on living their mission and their values. They honor each person in their organization and because of their commitment there are no numbers, everyone is a very important professional in their organization. They take time to build mutually beneficial relationships with the nurses they partner with as well as their clients. As a nurse owned and operated organization, the value of their nurses is inherent in the HPC Culture. Health Providers Choice understands and appreciates the challenges and rewards of providing patient care and they strive to help with the challenge and consistently find ways to help make it as rewarding as possible. From the introduction of their organization throughout your employment you will receive a personal and high touch experience. It is through the relationships their recruiters have with the employees they serve that earned Health Providers Choice bragging rights in the travel nurse industry. Greater than 65% of all nurses working with Health Providers Choice refer at least one colleague.

During every phase of the employment process including credentials, placement, housing, travel, and professional advocacy, HPC is available 24 hours, 7 days a week, and 364 days a year. Health Providers Choice has a 24-hour on-call as well as a Chief Nursing Officer available around the clock for clinical issues that may arise and nurse/patient advocacy. Health Providers Choice is Joint Commission Certified since 2005 and has been a proud member of NATHO since its inception.

Health Providers Choice takes great care in the selection process of their recruitment team. All of their recruiters have long tenures in the healthcare industry working either as a nurse, an allied professional, or healthcare recruiter. They are well educated in the industry and the roles they are recruiting for which allows for great synergy early in the process. Also, all of HPC's recruiters are a testament to the corporate mission and value structure, which allows for a mutually respectful partnership between themselves and the nurses they serve. Strong relationships are essential for their success. Health Providers Choice highlights their recruitment team on their website and each recruiter has a personal information page to allow nurses to review the team and find the best fit. Nurses working for Health Providers Choice can choose to change recruiters at any time if they wish to experience a new relationship within their company.

Health Providers Choice has Blue Cross Blue Shield Medical/ Dental/Vision. They offer 4 low deductible, Cobra qualified plans, with first day coverage to choose from. They also offer 401K through Lincoln Financial. They have a profit sharing match plan after the participant is vested. (ERISA Plan)

Other benefits include:Short-Term Disability Plan, 13 weeks, Voluntary Long Term Disability, Life Insurance of 50K, Death and Dismemberment Insurance of 50K, Unlimited Free CEU's, Reimbursement for BLS/ACLS, Paid Pre-hire and yearly medicals, Licensure Reimbursement, Employee Assistance Program through BCBS, Furnished Housing for Traveler, Tax Benefit Plan (Federal Tax Perdiem) for qualified travelers, Vacation Accrual and Sick Pay Accrual Available, Awards, Completion Bonus's, Sign on Bonus's are available on some of the assignments, and a very competitive referral bonus plan

Health Providers Choice is nurse owned and operated. All decisions that are made within the company are made by nurses for nurses. The nurse founders of HPC are dedicated to the success of their colleagues. HPC uses full disclosure and open negotiation allowing for mutual decision making and collaborative contracting. They are proud to have high retention rates and employee satisfaction scores that are 68% higher than the national average.

At Health Provider Choice their mission is to exceed the service and quality expectations of their customers, the community, the professionals they employ and themselves. They are true to this mission and are always excited to have another industry professional join them in successfully executing it.

For more information, you can visit them at 691 N. Squirrel

Rd, Suite 105, Auburn Hills, Michigan 48038 or on the web at www.hpcnursing.com. You can also call them at 888-299-9800.

~*~

Healthcare Starz

Healthcare Starz provides nationwide travel nursing assignment along with permanent jobs for registered nurses. They cover all of the United States, including Alaska and Hawaii.

Healthcare Starz is a small to mid-size and has that special "Family Like Atmosphere." You can definitely be expect to be treated with the utmost respect and dignity as you are their client as much as the hospital is their client. Every nurse they work with is special in his/her own way and they treat everyone as an individual and don't generalize or lump you into a large group that makes you feel like you're nothing more than a number. The only number you will feel like when you work with their agency is the Number 1, because you are so important to them and the success of their company.

The only service they know how to give is personal. You have access to them whenever you need them and you can always count on having any phone call message or email you send to them returned the same day. No exceptions. You are the lifeblood of their company and without you, they have no company. Therefore, personalized service is the only service you will get. Their Clinical Nurse Liaison is available 24 hours a day along with their executive on call at the company for any emergencies you may have and if you call, you can expect to be treated with class, dignity, and empathy for whatever problem you may be having. They train their recruiters to recruit from the perspective that they are dealing with a member of their family and that each nurses needs to be treated like they are one of the recruiters adored family members.

Although they are not currently JCAHO Certified, they do follow all JCAHO compliance processes along with the specific requirements of their clients. They are always praised by their clients for the attention to detail that they exhibit when it comes to giving them the compliance documentation they need. They are investigating becoming a member of NATHO.

They provide the best and most generous matching 401K in the travel industry. They match dollar for dollar up to the first 3% of a traveler's contribution and then 50% of the next 2% of the traveler's contribution. So, if the travelers contribute just 5% of their pay, then Healthcare Starz will match them 4% and they will have a total of 9% contribution. This gives the traveler an 80% return on their money before factoring in any stock market returns which is unheard of in the healthcare staffing industry. For this reason alone, they have many travelers who choose to work with them because no other company helps them build up their retirement nest egg faster then Healthcare Starz. They also provide United Healthcare PPO for their travelers and offer dental and vision as well.

They provide all their travelers with wonderful benefits and the Best Retirement Plan in the industry, guaranteed. When you work with Healthcare Starz you get the Healthcare Starz Benefits Advantage Which Is:

Health Insurance Including $20,000 Life Insurance—You can participate in their POS/PPO with United Healthcare. Healthcare Starz Contribution: 50% of the Employee Only premium. Eligibility: 1st of the Month following 30 days of employment You also have the option of getting your own plan or continuing with COBRA Coverage from your current employer for up to 18 months and they will reimburse you up to $500 of the monthly premium. COBRA is a way for people to continue with the Health insurance plans of their former employer until such time as they enroll in a new plan of their own with their new employer, in this case (Healthcare Starz, Inc.) 401K Retirement Plan—Healthcare Starz has an industry leading 401K plan with Transamerica Financial Services. There are multiple investment choices to satisfy your own risk tolerance and there are no fees to participate other than your annual account maintenance fee of $50. Company Match: This plan will match your elective contributions dollar for dollar up to the first 3% of your salary and then 50% of each dollar you contribute up to the next 2% of your salary. So, if you put in 5% of your pay to the plan, you will get a match of 4% from the company.

Short and Long Term Disability: Can be purchased for a nominal fee from their payroll company as a Supplemental Benefit. Dental Insurance: Can be purchased for a nominal fee from their payroll company as a Supplemental Benefit.

CEU Reimbursement: You can earn up to $200 for every 13 week assignment you complete with the company to put towards your required CEU courses. All you have to do is submit a receipt for the course you registered for and they will reimburse the money on your paycheck.

Licensure Reimbursement: Healthcare Starz reimburses it's contract therapists up to $150 for cost of renewing their current state license or for getting a new license in a state where he/she takes a travel assignment with the company.

Travel Reimbursment: Healthcare Starz Reimburses up to $600 for travel assignments that are greater than 50 miles from a healthcare professional's permanent residence with half of the tax free reimbursement (Up to $300) being provided on the healthcare professional's first paycheck and half on the last paycheck of his/her assignment. They even pay weekly with an online log in to see pay history of up to 1 year of paychecks and deductions.

Tax Advantage Program: Under certain situations, a contract therapist is able to receive part of their hourly compensation as Tax Free Per Diems. a. Healthcare Starz's Tax Advantage Program lets you use the IRS regulations to maximize your take-home pay. Here's how: As a healthcare traveler you probably maintain a primary residence and earn your wages by working away from your home. As such, some of your expenses may be duplicated between your primary residence and where your work assignment is located. To address this issue, the Internal Revenue Service (IRS) allows certain tax breaks for healthcare travelers that meet the IRS guidelines. The IRS recognizes that some occupations require duplicate expenses, so they created a table of rates that estimates the average food and housing costs for each U.S. city. These rates are called "per diem" or daily reimbursement rates for two categories of expenses: (1) Housing and (2) Meals and Incidentals. Healthcare Starz combines these daily per diem rates into its compensation plans for travelers to maximize their Take Home Pay. The net result of the Tax Advantage Program is that you get to keep more of the money in your paycheck rather than paying the government more in taxes...Sounds Great Right? This program usually amounts to the healthcare traveler taking home hundred more dollars per week in his/her paycheck!

Eligibility for the Tax Advantage Program.To qualify for the Tax Advantage Program, traveling healthcare professionals must meet some guidelines as set forth by the IRS:

1. You must have a permanent residence where you reside and pay taxes. If you constantly travel and have no permanent residence, you likely will not qualify for this program.

2. Your permanent residence must be different from your travel assignment location. The commute to/from your permanent residence to your travel assignment must be more than 50 miles each way for you to qualify for the tax advantage program.
3. Your assignment must be less than one year. You may have multiple travel assignments and extensions of assignments, but each original assignment must be less than a year. All expense reimbursements for assignments that are longer than one year are fully taxable.

Questions regarding your specific situation should be directed to your personal tax advisor.

They are more than just another Travel Company because they treat people differently than all the other companies do. The owners of the company have been in the Healthcare Staffing business for the past 12 years and had a very successful travel nursing company called Abetta-Care that they sold in 2007. Abetta-Care was designed and built under the premise that all of their caregivers are human beings first and each traveler should be treated with dignity, respect, and with the utmost honesty and integrity. Since they started Healthcare Starz over 3 years ago, they have brought those same time-tested principles to this company and as such, their reputation is excellent. They train all of there employees to do the right thing by people whenever there is an issue to be solved and they teach everyone to treat every caregiver they come in contact with as if they were a member of their own family.

Just try them out for one assignment. They guarantee that once you work with them and experience the special way they treat you, you will never want to go back to working with one of the other companies that does not value you or the contribution you make to improving patients' lives each and every day.

For more information on Healthcare Starz, you can find them at: 5717 South Dixie Highway, Suite #334 Miami, FL 33167. You can call them at: 888-777-4920, or visit them on the web at: www.healthcarestarz.com.

~*~

HealthChoice Staffing

HealthChoice Staffing is a small company that places RNs and LPNs in nationwide and local assignments. The staff at HealthChoice

Staffing will speak with each nurse, potential candidate, or any customer without having them pre-screened. They work with the nurse to set their ideal job and pay package. There is nothing set or standard about what they offer their nurses. It is all customizable to meet the needs of the nurse while at the same time ensuring they are taking care of their clients. They are readily accessible 24 hours a day/7 days a week. They have several RNs who serve as a clinical nurse liaison for our company on staff with one being available at all times. They also have a recruiter available 24/7 to address any concerns or emergencies.

They are currently working towards their TJC certification. They have actually met with Executive Director and Assistant Director of TJC for Healthcare Staffing. The Assistant Director has visited their office and provided resources to make sure that they are on track for their review. It is their goal for every nurse to speak not only with their recruiter during the hiring process but also the Account Manager who is an RN. There is a process and evaluation during the conversation to make sure the nurse is satisfied with not just the recruiter but with their company as a whole.

They offer health, vision, and dental insurance with one of the leading nationwide insurance providers BC/BS. HealthChoice Staffing contributes to the cost of the insurance in order to make sure that they are also offering a plan that is affordable while still offering top tier coverage. Other benefits include Top pay, private housing, pet friendly housing, family friendly housing, life along with AD&D insurance. They also include travel reimbursements, round-trip airfare, rental car stipends, pay extension bonuses, loyalty bonuses, referral bonuses, vacation bonuses, holiday bonuses, license reimbursement, continuing education, and weekly direct deposits.

HealthChoice Staffing, LLC (HCS) is a travel nurse staffing agency owned and operated by nurses and a board certified physician. Having over 10 years of experience within the industry, HCS was established to offer nurses a choice in working with an agency that is truly a partner-not just another recruitment firm or staffing agency. Every time you call them, you speak directly with experienced recruiters and staff whose number one goal is to help you with your choices! When you work with HealthChoice Staffing, you are working with professionals who not only understand the dynamics of the travel nurse-staffing environment, but they have been in your shoes. They feel that they offer something different—an attitude and outcome that is focused solely on you!

You can visit Health Choice Staffing at 2008 Stonegate Trail, Suite #100, Birmingham, AL 35242. You can phone them at: 855-427-4100, or visit their website at: www.healthchoicestaffing.com.

~*~

IPI Travel

IPI (aka Innovative Placements) specializes in RN's and Rehab, Nurse Practitioners, and Pharmacist. They have nationwide assignments, and they are available in most cities.

IPI is a privately owned and operated mid-western company, they are medium in size but huge in heart and customer service. They are a direct reflection of many years of hard work and dedication. IPI treats each traveler as a unique individual. Customizing each travel assignment, asking the question, "What are you looking for in an assignment?" Their staff is always available to answer questions; their goal is to makes each traveler feel welcome and valued from the first hello.

IPI has a phone number that their nurses can call in the middle of the night and weekends. They realize that they are your lifeline and once they receive your page they try to contact the nurses as soon as possible. A Clinical Nurse Liaison is also available as needed.

IPI is Joint Commission Certified with 100% compliance with all re-certifications. Thanks to their wonderful staff and travelers! They do not currently belong to NATHO.

Personalities are key and not everyone clicks. They have an open door teamwork policy. If the traveler isn't clicking with the staffing specialist, they are more than welcome to give the president a call, and she will take care of it promptly. If you found the right recruiter, give IPI a call and they will find the right fit!

Medical insurance coverage is provided by Cigna; Dental and Vision are provided through United Healthcare. IPI also offers additional supplemental insurance through Colonial. IPI matches 50 cents on the dollar up to 50% of the employees' compensation on the 401K. The vestment schedule is 33% year 1, 66% year 2 and 100% year three. IPI's has paid profit share to qualified employees in 2011 and 2012. Other benefits include: travel pay, paid vacation, allocation for "life happens" with missed shifts during an assignment, personal service, extras during the assignment, leer jets, 5 star condos on the beach…(just kidding :)

From the president: On many occasions I have been asked the question "Why should I choose IPI Travel" I don't have to think twice when I answer this question; IPI is a direct reflection of many years of hard work and dedication. We treat each traveler as a unique individual. Customizing each travel assignment, asking the question "what are you looking for in an assignment" These are the principles IPI Travel has maintained since 1999. To this day we demand continued excellence from all of IPI's internal staff as well as our travelers. Our goal is for each of our customers to have a feeling of "Wow" when interacting with the IPI team. IPI achieves the "Wow" factor with each placement by on-time delivery of completely detailed contracts, special thanks before and during the assignment, detailed housing packages, free CE's and a knowledgeable staff to help with all traveling details! I believe in holding staff and travelers accountable and I expect wonderful things from all of them. Success in in the team and IPI wouldn't be successful without our great travel professionals, account managers, staffing specialist and support staff. In addition to all the services IPI offers we also continue to develop client relationships throughout the United States, giving our travelers a huge network of resources and the flexibility for unlimited travel assignment choices. Each assignment is custom-designed around the traveler. IPI Travel understands healthcare professionals are in great demand; this is why we are committed to making your travel assignment rewarding and hassle-free. I will personally guarantee your assignment will be everything we promised. For questions regarding IPI Travel or comments please feel free to call.

IPI's values their travelers, and work every day to improve their processes and service. Just doing isn't good enough, being the best is what they strive for.

For more information you can visit them at: Innovative Placements (IPI Travel), 14701 Cumberland Road, Suite 140, Noblesville, IN 46060. They can be called at: 800-322-9796, or you can visit them on the web at: www.ipitravel.com.

~*~

Medical Solutions

Medical Solutions offer opportunities for RNs ranging from staff RN to case management to nursing management. They also offer opportunities for LPN and allied health careers such as OT, ST, and PT. Their jobs are located all over the 50 states.

They are the third largest travel nurse staffing company in the nation. They have approximately 200 full-time internal employees between their four locations (Omaha, San Diego, Cincinnati, and Tupelo). They are currently privately held.

Their company culture is all about treating people well and celebrating their individual talents and successes. This spirit extends through their Career Consultants (their name for "Recruiters") to their Travelers, who they also consider a part of their team. Ultimately this positive attitude extends into the hospital, which makes for great patient care and happy nurses. They don't just staff nurses; they help them build their careers. But they also care deeply for them as individuals. Their Career Consultants work to be both professional and personal with their Travelers, and their work is not done when a nurse is placed. Their Career Consultants check in to make sure all is going well and are there throughout an assignment to provide any support a Traveler may need. And because they have such extraordinary Travelers, they also love to tell their stories on their blog.

At this time, Medical Solutions has four internal RNs who act as Clinical Nurse Liaisons. They have a 24-hour on call emergency line, which can easily connect to one of them 24 hours a day, 7 days a week. Quality assurance is also provided through being Joint Commission certified and a NATHO member. Medical Solutions was one of the first Joint Commission-certified companies, and their President, Craig Meier, sits on the NATHO board.

Initially, their Career Consultants spend a lot of time getting to know the person up front during the qualifying process. They ask a lot of questions to make sure it is going to be a good match personality-wise as well as a fit for what the Traveler is looking for in a company. They also have managers who call their Travelers within the first 1–2 weeks of their assignments to check in and ask for feedback on how the recruiter is doing, and they do the NPS surveys to gauge customer satisfaction and identify any areas of improvement. Overall, they work hard to encourage an open forum so that travelers feel comfortable addressing any concerns they have with Career Consultants, but if they are still not entirely comfortable addressing the issues directly with their Career Consultant, they will always have other means to do so.

Medical Solutions offers day one United Healthcare coverage, and in 2013 they drastically lowered insurance costs for their Travelers! With a larger contribution from Medical Solutions, they now offer basic, single policy medical plans starting at just $10 per week. They offer day one dental benefits through Guardian. For vision they offer

Vision Access or Vision VSP. Vision Access benefits come free with paid dental plan enrollment.

The benefits with Medical Solutions are never-ending! They are a pet-friendly company and they offer loyalty and referral bonuses, 24-hour customer care, an RN to BSN program, license and certificate reimbursement, their Go Rewards program (which gives Travelers access to all kinds of discounts on phone service, scrubs, rental cars, pet supplies, and more), paid private housing, and more. They also award one Traveler of the Month and one Rising Star of the Month (the latter a first-time Traveler with them) in order to reward their Travelers for excellent service based upon hospital evaluations. They sponsor a lot of really cool contests with great prizes throughout the year! They also offer day one 401k through Nationwide. They offer a traditional 401k as well as a Roth plan. Company match is 50% of the first 3% elected.

Their amazing people and quality of customer service is really what sets them apart. They came up with 9 core values that they live and work by, which really explain what's important to them and what sets them apart. They are: (1) Remain flexible and embrace change. (2) Show passion for work and have fun doing it. (3) Challenge yourself and strive for excellence. (4) Create a positive experience with everyone you encounter. (5) Treat people like you want to be treated. (6) Be an expert at your job. (7) Be proactive not reactive. (8) Focus on the solution, not the problem. (9) Use open and honest communication to build trust.

More interesting facts about Medical Solutions! (1) They have a lot of fun online. Check out their Facebook page, the Medical Solutions blog on their site, and Travel Nursing Blogs. (2) They think Travel Nurses are so special that in 2013 they created and celebrated the first-ever Travel Nurses Day, October 11, 2013. (3) Give them a call! If you like fun people and an agency that focuses on its Travelers' satisfaction and not the numbers, then traveling with Medical Solutions is for you.

For more information, you can visit Medical Solutions at: 9101 Western Ave, Suite 101, Omaha, NE 68114. You can also call them at: 866-333-3548, or visit their website: www.medicalsolutions.com.

~*~

Medical Staffing Network (MSN)

Medical Staffing Network offers travel nurses excellent career opportunities at hundreds of exciting destinations across the U.S. Their 13-week contracts are flexible enough to work with your lifestyle and find the right balance of work and play wherever you choose to be. They have client partners all across the United States (even Alaska and Hawaii!), so chances are they have an assignment where you want to be. At this time MSN focuses its travel nursing assignments on the U.S. only. MSN has over 55,000 healthcare professionals in their network, more than 60 local offices, two travel offices, and over 600 corporate employees who work hard every day to ensure that their nurses and other healthcare professionals receive the personalized service they deserve.

Their professional recruiters and staffing coordinators are trained to provide unparalleled customer service. They're available to assist their travelers 24/7/365 with whatever they may need. Their Clinical Liaison at this time is Marisa Zaharoff, MSN, RN, Medical Staffing Network's Senior Vice Present of Performance Outcomes and Chairperson of our Clinical Quality Council. She is available 24/7. MSN received Joint Commission Health Care Staffing Services Certification in 2005 and has been re-certified each two-year renewal period since. MSN is also a member of NATHO.

Recruiters are trained, experienced professionals who are committed to making sure the hiring process is as smooth and seamless as possible. They are matched with nurses based on geography, so they have a familiarity with the particular job market. Should issues of "fit" arise, they would be addressed by the recruiter's supervisor to the nurse's satisfaction.

MSN offers healthcare professionals medical insurance through Blue Cross Blue Shield. Dental coverage is provided by Delta Dental, and vision coverage/discounts are provided by VSP. They do provide a 401k with some company match, which is decided by the management team every December.

Medical Staffing Network offers a competitive benefits package that includes: free individual medical insurance and dental coverage, free short-term disability coverage, free workers compensation coverage, free private housing or subsidy, licensure reimbursement, and free continuing education. They also offer matching 401(k), bonuses, online access to pay info, discount savings programs, and more.

Medical Staffing Network is the only healthcare staffing firm you'll want to work with for your entire career. As a top-ranked provider of healthcare professionals, MSN has the flexible travel (and local) opportunities you want, and the pay and benefits you deserve. They respect you and your career, so they only present opportunities that are right for you. They offer a variety of practice settings at top healthcare facilities across the United States. With MSN you get the opportunities and support that come with an established national leader in the industry, and the personalized service you'd expect from a smaller local agency. Finally, we have received Joint Commission Health Care Staffing Services Certification every renewal period since it began in 2005, which means you'd be working with a company that passes the rigorous certification process that ensures only the highest levels of patient care.

For more information, you can contact them at: 901 Yamato Road, Suite 110, Boca Raton, FL 33431. You can call them at: 800-676-8326, or check out their website: www.msnhealth.com.

~*~

Medical Staffing Solutions, Inc. (MSSI)

Medical Staffing Solutions Inc. (MSSI) is a Joint Commission Certified staffing company that has career opportunities for Registered Nurses, Speech Therapists, and Physical Therapist nationwide. They are a medium sized company who doesn't outsource anything! All recruiting, credentialing and payroll is done by their employees in their office. They are big enough to serve their employees, but small enough to take care of their employees on a personal basis. Their recruiters work not only as a recruiter, but as a career coach as well. They ask questions and listen to their nurses needs to determine the best fit for their nurses and therapists.

MSSI offers health insurance as well as vision and dental. They also pay for life insurance, AD&D, and short term disability. At this time they do not have a 401K program.

Most agencies advertise that they are the best or largest or something similar to that. They understand that it truly is a partnership between the agency and the employees, so they do everything that is in their control to grow that partnership resulting in both the agency and the employee being very satisfied. They don't advertise that they are the biggest or best. They are all about providing the traveling nurse or traveling therapist an opportunity to work with an agency that they can truly rely on to be honest and hardworking on their behalf.

For more information on MSSI, check them out at: 35 West Newton Street, Rice Lake, Wisconsin 54868. You can call them at: 877-217-9825, or visit them online at: www.medicalstaffingsolutionsinc.com.

~*~

Nationwide Nurses

Nationwide Nurses is a Joint Commission certified company that provides nationwide opportunities for the following disciplines: RN, LPN, Surgical Tech, Cath Lab Tech, PT, OT, SLP, RT, and CRTs. These opportunities include short and long term travel assignments. They are a smaller company that offers great personalized service to each and every employee. Your recruiter is available to you 24/7 to help you handle anything that may come up during the course of employment/assignment. They have a clinical nurse liaison that is available 24/7.

They strive to give the very best to their nurses. If ever there were a conflict with a nurse and their recruiter, they would transition the nurse to a new recruiter that would better suit their personality needs.

Nationwide Nurses offers a health benefit package tailored to meet your individual needs. They provide you a dedicated representative to assist you in customizing a health plan for you individually or for your family. Nationwide provides competitive financial support, regardless of the duration of your travel assignment. Your benefits continue without interruption, as long as there is no more than a 30 day break in assignment annually. You are eligible day one for insurance coverage and support.

They also offer an IRA savings plan for all associates. Your retirement plan is a high priority to Nationwide, so they offer a company match of 50% up to 3% of your total annual contribution, upon completion of your anniversary hire date. Your individual contributions are fully vested day one and are always are under your full control, regardless of the duration of your assignment. You are supported with a certified financial planner to provide expert advice on how to build a quality portfolio, diversified to meet your long-term investment goals.

Nationwide Nurses also have high hourly wages, free private housing or a generous stipend, weekly pay through direct deposit, lucrative completion bonuses along with referral and loyalty bonuses. Other benefits include: travel pay up front, rental car stipends, overtime opportunities, personal crisis assistance, licenses paid in full, health insurance stipends, along with other great incentives and perks.

The personalized service that their nurses receive gives them peace of mind is what makes their company different than other companies! Their recruiters truly go above and beyond to ensure that things go off without a hitch for their nurses. And in the event that something doesn't go as planned, your personal recruiter is available to you 24/7 to help get things back on track. Most of their travelers have been with them for years! They continue to travel with Nationwide because of how well they are respected and treated! Ultimately, Nationwide offers great pay, great assignments, and their recruiters are the cream of the crop in service!!

For more information you can visit Nationwide Nurses at: 9435 E. 51st Street, Suite A, Tulsa, OK 74145. You can call them at: 866-836-8773, or visit their website: www.nationwidenurses.com.

~*~

Nursing Options

Nursing options staffs Registered Nurses, Licensed Practical Nurses, Occupational Therapists, Physical Therapists, Physical Therapy Assistants, Patient Care Techs, Respiratory Therapist, and Surgical Techs all over the United States.

They are a smaller company that believes in personal service and open communication. They not only have a recruiter on call 24 hours a day, but also a Clinical Liaison Nurse is available 24 hours a day. If there is a problem anytime with a recruiter, a nurse may most definitely request a different recruiter! At this time, they are not Joint Commission or NATHO certified. They have been working with nurses since 2002.

For more information on Nursing Options, you can visit them at: 4505 Seaway Circle, Fort Collins, CO 80527. You can phone them at: 877-687-7350, or visit them online at: www.nursingoptions.com.

~*~

OneStaff Medical

OneStaff Medical is a medium sized company that places RNs as well as Allied Health modalities. They staff nurses and allied workers nationwide.

To assure personal service, they hire only experienced recruiters that focus on customer services instead of just sales. Their Clinical Nurse Liaison is only available during normal business hours. They are

Joint Commission certified, and do regular evaluations with RN's to ensure the fit is still good for all parties.

OneStaff's medical insurance is through Blue Cross/Blue Shield with dental and vision provided through Met Life. At this time they have a 4% dollar for dollar match in our 401K. Company match is after 1 year of service. Another great benefit is the paid private apartments.

They make a difference related to their experience. They consist of experienced recruiters that started with other firms. Their average recruiter has been in the industry at least 5 years.

You can visit OneStaff Medical at: 10801 Blondo Street, Omaha, NE 68164. You can contact them by phone at: 877-783-1483, or visit them online at: www.onestaffmedical.com.

~*~

Onward Healthcare

Onward Healthcare is a medium sized company headquartered in Wilton, CT with local staffing offices in Albuquerque, NM, Deerfield Beach, FL, Elkhorn, NE, Livingston, NJ, Melville, NY, Mount Laurel, NJ, and Solana Beach, CA. They provide travel nursing, physical therapy, occupational therapy, speech language pathology, advanced practice, and locum tenen positions across the country.

They are a Joint Commission certified company that has a 24 hr. a day Clinical Nurse Liaison who strives to provide amazing customer service. They cater to all individual nurse or therapists traveling needs. To make sure the recruiter is a good fit for the traveler, there is a pre-screening process that takes place.

Onward provides full medical insurance through Cigna as well as vision and dental insurance along with a 401K with a 3% company match. Other benefits include: a competitive base pay, generous bonus options, weekly pay through direct deposit, CEU reimbursement, along with compliance document reimbursements.

Onward Healthcare was founded with the mission of providing the highest quality nursing and allied professionals to healthcare facilities by utilizing advanced technological recruitment systems and providing unparalleled customer service. They recognize the challenges in today's health care staffing industry. New choices, new opportunities and new standards, brought on by high-tech medicine, rigid industry accreditation and rapidly escalating costs, present a challenging and engaging operating environment while creating a greater demand for experienced healthcare professionals. This environment demands leadership and Onward Healthcare is uniquely positioned and willing to help both healthcare facilities and healthcare professionals make the right choices for the times ahead. Their experienced team of senior managers and recruiters possess a vast knowledge of the industry and prides themselves on one-on-one personal service, which in turn translates into top-level satisfaction ratings from our clients and travelers. "Onward and Upward!"—It's not just their slogan; it's their way of thinking. They are pushing the boundaries of what a health care staffing company can offer both its clients and its candidates.

You can visit Onward Healthcare at: 64 Danbury Road, Wilton, CT 06897. They can be reached by phone at: 800-278-0332, or visit them online at: www.onwardhealthcare.com.

~*~

PPR Travel Nursing

PPR is a medium sized company that places RNs nationwide. Their top priority is customer service. Their recruiters are trained to answer many questions regarding other departments and keep their recruiter to nurse ratio manageable. This enables their recruiters to give 100% service to each nurse. They are Joint Commission certified and belong to NATHO. They are very fortunate to have Dr. Ruth Stiehl, Vice President, Clinical Quality on their staff. Dr. Stiehl is available during business hours. Recruiters and nurses typically know right away if it will be a good match for the two of them. If a nurse ever feels that she would prefer another recruiter in the company, she is able to reach out to the Recruitment Manager to discuss working with another recruiter.

PPR offers three plans through Aetna for their health insurance, dental is through Guardian, and Comp Benefits provides vision coverage. Their 401k is with Nationwide, the nurse is eligible at 6 months of employment and she/he is immediately vested at that time. PPR matches fifty cent on the dollar up to 6%. Other benefits include: life insurance, short and long term disability, professional insurance, online shopping store, and $1000 referral bonuses for any specialty.

PPR always does the right thing for the nurses. Their motto has never changed, "We Put You First." Their recruiters have a long tenure with PPR and their knowledge in the business ensures that they are strong nurse advocates.

For more information you can visit PPR Travel Nursing at: 333 First Street North, Suite 200, Jacksonville Beach, FL 32250. You can visit with them by phone at: 866-581-5038, or visit them online at: www.pprtravelnursing.com.

~*~

PRCS

PRCS is a mid-sized staffing firm, which equates to more competitive pay packages for their travelers. They offer RN, RT, and rehab assignments nationally, including Hawaii and the USVI.

Being a mid-size firm owned and operated by previous healthcare travelers, PRCS prides itself in caring for and knowing their travelers. Many of their travelers have been with them for years, some near a decade. Their travelers are a direct reflection of their firm and its quality. Their phones are answered 24/7, and they have a clinical liaison that is available. They have been a Joint Commission certified company since May 2010.

Nurses are paired with a nurse recruiter dedicated to their clinical specialty. They also account for gender and personality preferences when assigning recruiters.

PRCS has outstanding united health, dental and vision benefit packages offered to travelers, with custom package options. They choose to offer more money to nurses as opposed to putting money to 401k. This allows the nurse to allot additional money to his/her already established 401k or IRA accounts. Other benefits include: referral bonuses, license and certification reimbursements, and round-trip travel reimbursement.

What makes PRCS different? (1)They have been in business since 1981 (long standing), (2) They are Joint Commission certified with quality standards, (3) PRCS is owned and operated by previous healthcare clinicians which familiar with clinical settings and travel staffing. They understand the environment nurses work in, and the challenges they face caring for patients in a high stress environment, (4) They are a mid-size and can offer the most competitive pay packages, and (5) PRCS knows and cares for their travelers. As a result, their business has been established largely by referrals from happy employees.

Their motto at PRCS is "Work hard, Play Hard." They are committed to working hard for their travelers and playing hard to have some fun with them!

For more information on PRCS, you can visit them at 3801 N. 24th Street, Phoenix, AZ 85016. They can be reached by phone at: 888-508-2111, or visit them online at: www.prcshealthcare.com.

~*~

Premier Healthcare Professionals

PHP has numerous openings for RN's LPN's, OT's, ST's, and PT's throughout the 50 States. They offer Nationwide assignments through PHP and its subsidiary Bridge Staffing. They can also offer International assignments (when available) through their company owned offices in England, Australia, and South Africa. They have evolved from once being a publicly traded organization. It is now privately owned by its management team and should be classified as a medium-sized business.

The level of care and support provided to their healthcare professionals is their major focus. Most of PHP's staff have worked for the company for over 12 years, and they believe that they have built up a vast experience on how their healthcare professionals should expect to be treated. They are continually amazed by the 'horror' stories they hear about from professionals wanting to switch from other staffing companies. Each of their professionals is assigned to a personal recruiter who is tasked with understanding their professionals' needs and identifying the most suitable assignments. Their recruiters are continually assessed for how many professionals continue to re-contract with them at the end of each assignment.

PHP is Joint Commission Certified and a member of NATHO. As a company they strive to provide the best possible service to their clients and professionals alike. Certification by the Joint Commission and membership of NATHO is an integral part of this process. They also have a full-time RN on staff that has responsibility for being a Clinical Nurse Liaison. She is available 24/7.

They understand that their healthcare professionals are human and each have personal targets and personalities. Their healthcare professionals are each assigned to a personal recruiter who is trained to both recognize and adapt to each of their clinical colleagues being different and having varying requirements. The management of PHP review and discuss all communication with their professionals that is stored on their company's database. Management also makes itself readily available to all healthcare professionals should any issues arise. They work quickly to resolve any such matters and could always assign a professional to a new recruiter.

PHP is recognized for its industry leading pay and benefits packages. Apart from providing first day, free health coverage with Aetna, they also provide dental, life, long and short-term disability if required. Their comprehensive benefits package includes the option of a company match 401k plan if required. Apart from all of the insurance options above, they offer free housing, housing allowance, contribution to utilities, sign-on bonuses, relocation, referral bonuses, CEU, and many, many more financial incentives. There is of course also the benefit of working for one of the longest serving and most awarded staffing companies in the world!

They truly believe that are business is special and so do all of the professionals that continue to trust in us through multiple assignments over several years. The facts are that they know what they are doing... they have been doing the same thing for 25 years. Their staff are some of the most experienced in the industry. On average each of them has been employed by PHP for over 10 years. They place in all 50 States in the USA and internationally. On top of all of this they have won numerous awards within the industry for their pay and service standards. Not many staffing companies can boast all of this.

Apart from all of the outstanding service standards that you can expect, PHP will never be beaten on a genuine pay or benefits package. They recognize that healthcare professionals have a choice when it comes to staffing companies. They simply have to offer the best packages in order to grow and flourish.

You can visit Premier Healthcare Professionals at: 2450 Atlanta Highway, Suite 601, Cumming, Georgia 30040. You can speak to them on the phone at: 866-296-3247, or visit them online at: www.travelphp.com.

~*~

Prime Time Healthcare

Prime Time Healthcare is a medium privately owned company that staffs LPNS, CNAs, RNs, DONs, MTs, MLTs, OTs, PTs, RTs, STs, Surgical Techs, Rad Techs, Administrators, CEOs, Pharmacy, Physicians, NPs...

basically all nursing and allied with a few exceptions! They have staff in all 50 states currently, and are exploring the international contracting business.

Prime Time Healthcare consistently follows up weekly, and you also are provided with the recruiter's cell phone number. Prime Time Healthcare and their recruiters will send gifts throughout the year to nurses to show their constant appreciation. They also send appraisals to the nurse to find out how you are doing. Prime Time Healthcare Management will send out appraisals on the recruiter to the nurse. Also management occasionally calls to ensure everything is going good. They also have a Clinical Liaison Nurse who is on call 24 hours a day.

Prime Time Healthcare is starting the process to become Joint Commission certified for 2014. They currently do not belong to NATHO, but will look into it after Joint Commission accreditation.

They currently offer the affordable care act exchange and reimburse for insurance, dental, and vision. At this time they do not offer a 401K. Other benefits offered include per diem rates, car rentals, flights, shuttles, weekly direct deposit, flexible housing and amenities, reimbursement for licensing/certifications, drug testing, and immunizations. Their employees get all those benefits, plus a competitive pay!

They make a difference related to their industry knowledge, true competitive pay, referral bonuses, and additional bonuses for contests throughout the year along with special gifts for the holidays throughout the year. They provide top-notch nursing services in their emergency line and the fact that each nurse how their recruiters cell phone number. They will meet or beat any pay package out there at the same facility! And they Care!

For more information on Prime Time Healthcare visit them at: 8212 South 109th Street, La Vista, NE 68128. You can also get in touch with them by phone at: 402-933-6700. They can be found online at: www.primetimehealthcare.com.

~*~

qShift Travel Nursing

qShift Travel Nurses is a division of Cascade Healthcare Services, LLC, that provides travel nursing and allied health jobs nationwide for RNs, PTs, OTs, SLPs, OR Techs, LPNs, and CNAs.

They are a small to medium company that is very involved with every step of the process from beginning to end and during contract, as well. They value the clinicians who work for them and want to make sure they are taken care of and happy overall. They have a Clinical Nurse Liaison that is available 24 hours a day. They have been Joint Commission Certified since 2008 and they recently decided not to renew our subscription with NATHO because they did not see the benefit. They make a difference related to pre-screening all the health care professionals to make sure they are matching them with the best recruiter.

They provide Blue Cross and Blue Shield along with a health package with Medical, Vision and Life Insurance and Dental is separate. They provide a nurse only 401K at this time. Other benefits include license reimbursement, loyalty bonuses, completion bonuses, and CEU reimbursements.

They have internal employees and nurses who have worked for them over 10 years. They take pride in their work, and they advocate for their clinicians. They are honest and upfront with what they provide regarding what they offer as a company and the contracts they have available.

For more information on qShift Travel Nurses visit them at: 9925 Federal Drive, Suite 150, Colorado Springs, CO 80921. They can be reached by phone at: 800-733-6877, or visit them online at: www.qshift.com.

~*~

Randstad Healthcare

Randstad Healthcare places healthcare professionals from all nursing specialties (RN and LPN) as well as Surgical Technologists, Advanced Practice Providers, and all allied health professionals ranging from Radiation Therapists to Cardiac Cath Lab Technicians and other Technicians, Sonographrs, Phlebotomists, Perfusionsist, Pharmacists, Medical Coders, and much, much more.

Randstad Healthcare is a medium sized company in the travel nursing space. However, they are a part of Randstad, the second largest staffing company in the world and publicly traded on the NYSE Euronext Amsterdam. They offer travel, local contract and permanent positions nationwide across all 50 states, from Maine to California.

Randstad Healthcare places high priority on each and every one of their travelers. Their size allows them to assign candidates to specific recruiter's where a true relationship and bond is formed. The recruiter knows every in and out of that nurse's job requirements, as well as his or her personality traits, and will work with that nurse throughout the duration of their career with Randstad Healthcare. Their recruiter's become intimately involved in their travelers lives, often checking in on them just to ask about a new pet, sick relative or recent vacation with a childhood friend! They also have their support divisions reach out to their nurses throughout their assignment with us. For example, their payroll department will reach out to their nurses after receiving their first paycheck to make sure they understand it and everything is correct. Additionally, their housing department will reach out after a nurse moves in to a new apartment to make sure everything is running smoothly and find out if there is anything they can do to make the new living quarters feel a little bit more like home. Furthermore, their management team is also intimately involved in their placement process and wants to receive feedback from their travelers. Their President, Cynthia Kinnas, is highly visible and always has an open door policy, attending conferences to speak with travelers and providing her personal email address to attendees—and when you email Cynthia, you are guaranteed to get a response back from her, and not from an assistant or automatic reply!

Melissa Knybel, RN, BSN, is their Clinical Nurse Liaison and Vice President of Operations, and is available 24 hours a day, 7 days a week via their emergency line or on email. Melissa has over 10 years of clinical experience herself, and understands how important it is to be able to seek advice, and have an agency representative speak up on your behalf, when situations arise while on assignment.

Randstad Healthcare is Joint Commission certified and also a founding and current member of NATHO. Cynthia Kinnas, their President is the 2013 President of NATHO, and Melissa Knybel, Vice President of Operations is a member of the Joint Commission Advisory Board for Health Care Staffing Services, and sits on the Clinical Executive Committee of NATHO. They are actively involved in all industry associations representing the travel and staffing industries.

They understand how important "fit" is in ensuring a positive traveler experience. Some of their recruiters focus on specific types of professionals or specialties in order to ensure optimal match between the candidate, recruiter, and assignment. They believe that by having niche recruiters, they will become more intimately knowledgeable about the healthcare professional disciplines they support and be able to more effectively communicate. Furthermore, their travel recruiters focus

100% on travel and do not work local contract or perm jobs at the same time. While they rely on their recruiters to know when a relationship is not the right fit and reassign to a recruiter that would be a better match, they will also survey their candidates on a frequent basis to ensure their recruiter, and in that matter all Randstad departments, are delivering the level of service that is expected. If personalities do not match or service is not being delivered to the level they expect, candidates will be contacted by a senior level manager and reassigned based on their feedback and the recruiter relationship that would best fit their needs moving forward.

Randstad Healthcare travelers are offered the same insurance that their internal employees receive. There are numerous medical plans to choose from, all provided through Cigna and available for employees and spouses/dependents/domestic partners. They also offer MetLife Dental insurance and EyeMed Vision insurance.

At Randstad Healthcare, they believe giving a healthcare professional the opportunity to save for their future is very important and they want to make sure they have the financial stability to enjoy life in their retirement years! As such, they make the process very easy for their travelers by automatically enrolling them in their 401K plan—but providing an option to easily opt-out for those that are not in a position to contribute immediately. All travelers who participate will also receive a company match based on their level of contribution.

Besides medical related benefits and 401K, Randstad Healthcare also offers travelers free furnished housing or stipend, Life and AD&D coverage, optional Disability Insurance, FREE Liability and Workers' Compensation Insurance, paid drug screens, flexible spending accounts, and more! They also provide a discount program that allows their travelers to receive a discount at merchants such as Dell, Red Envelope, AT&T, Verizon, 1-800-Flowers, Cherry Moon Farms, Extended Stay, Avis and Budget Car Rental, and more! Their candidates are also eligible to enroll in an exclusive, member's only discount program called Working Advantage that provides discounts on tickets, travel and shopping.

Randstad Healthcare has been in business over 25 years and we've worked hard to build a reputation based on trust, honesty and loyalty. Are they perfect, of course not! But when they do make a mistake they will own up to it and work hard to resolve the issue with as little impact as possible to their travelers and to patient care. It's this reputation that has resulted in many of their travelers choosing to work with them for the duration of their travel career, and referring their friends and family to us as well. They take pride in the fact that employees across their company —rom their recruiter's to their referencing team, all the way up to their President—know the names of many of their travelers and have also developed a personal connection with them. They are in the "people business" and that is the treatment you can expect when working with Randstad: as a person with unique and individual needs!

At Randstad Healthcare, they work hard to know their candidates. They also work hard to know their clients. They have a deep understanding of both their candidate's and client's requirements, and are able to align needs, cultures, and work styles to ensure the best match is made. With over 25 years of experience, their industry knowledge takes their Travelers to where they want to be in their travel nursing career, whether learning new skills at large teaching hospitals or mentoring the next generation in a local community hospital. They are so committed to helping their Travelers be successful that they mentor their career development from the moment they join their talent network to the moment they walk through their clients' doors— working hand-in-hand at every step of the process to gain a deeper understanding of their needs, capabilities, and career goals. As a result of their perfect match, over 70 percent of their candidates have been asked to extend their assignments. But more than that, 100 percent of them are hired for the positions that truly match their skills and aspirations.

For more information, you can contact them at: Randstad Healthcare, 150 Presidential Way, 3rd Floor, Woburn, MA 01801. You can phone them at: 800-919-9100, or visit them online at: www.randstadhealthcare.com.

~*~

RN Network

RN Network (RNn) offers 4 to 26 week assignments for RNs, LPNs, Sterile Processors, and ST. They provide nurses in all 50 states as needed. They are a privately held mid-size company. They truly believe this offers the best of both worlds to their clients. They have the backing of a large organization but can operate like a boutique.

Their nurses have one main point of contact, but a full internal team supporting them. They are committed to providing excellent customer service every step of the way. Their recruiters check in with their travelers weekly while on assignment, assuring that they feel a connection with their recruiter, and not like a number. They also conduct monthly net promoter surveys to help them continually improve their service and focus on areas that are most important to travelers.

RNn has a Clinical Nurse Manager on staff, and they have 24/7 emergency support. They are Joint Commission certified and an active member of NATHO. Their President is on the Board of Directors, and their company was one of the founding members.

RNn recruiters spend a lot of time qualifying a traveler during the initial phone call. Their objective is to find out what is most important to the traveler not only in an assignment, but also in an agency and in a recruiter. Their recruiters treat every relationship like a partnership. If during the initial process or assignment the recruiter and traveler do not seem to be a good fit for each other, their leaders will get involved to determine the best next steps, which may include switching to a recruiter that would be a better fit.

They offer excellent medical plans that use the Aetna physician network. They also offer dental and vision insurance. All benefits begin day one of the assignment. They also offer a family and domestic partner coverage. They also offer day one 401K with a company match. Other benefits include: paid Life and AD&D insurance, as well as optional short-term disability, accident insurance and critical illness insurance. In addition, they have a benefits team committed to providing a variety of unique benefits that travelers will not find with any other agency. Another amazing benefit is their telephone physician benefit. Nurses can reach a physician 24/7 365 days via this free benefit and receive care and even prescriptions via the telephone.

RN Network is part of CHG Healthcare, they are proud to be ranked #3 on Fortune Magazine's "100 Best Companies to work for in 2013". Their company has great tenure throughout every department, and very little turnover, which allows them to build better relationships with their travelers. They are a company that is built around the idea of "putting people first." They go above and beyond for both their travelers and client facilities to assure that they are providing the best possible service. They are a turn-key establishment; travelers get more personal service and quicker response time for any issues of concerns that may arise. But, the number one thing that makes them more than "just another" travel company is our people, and their passion for what we do.

They start at yes. Their packages are customized and they always seek out of the box solutions to meet our clients/provider's needs. Every provider and situation is different...and they treat them as such.

For more information on RN Network, you can visit them at: 2000 NW Corporate Blvd., Boca Raton, FL 33431. You can contact them by phone at: 800-866-0407, or visit them online at: www.rnnetwork.com.

~*~

RTG Medical

RTG Medical has opportunities for nurses, allied health, and therapists nation wide. They are a medium sized company with a goal for their recruiters to develop personal relationships with each of their nurses. Their nurses work with the same recruiter, regardless of what location they travel to.

They are Joint Commission certified company that provides a clinical liaison for their travelers 24 hours a day. They interview each nurse thoroughly to find out specifics about that nurse and what they are looking for in a recruiter. They also give their nurses a choice as to which recruiter they would like to work with. If they do not feel like they are a good fit with their initial recruiter they can be transferred to another recruiter that better fits their personality and needs.

They are self-insured and managed by Mid-American Benefits They also offer Dental & Life Insurance and a VSP through MetLife. Their 401k includes a match of up to 4% and you can participate from Day 1. Other benefits include: Reimbursement for Certifications, Licensure, and some CEU's required for assignment, weekly direct deposit, travel reimbursement, and a rental car upon request.

They are different from other companies because "People Are Their Only Asset," and they provide their service accordingly.

You can contact RTG Medical at: 1005 East 23rd St, Suite 200, Fremont, NE 68022. They can be reached by phone at: 866-784-2329. They can be found online at: www.rtgmedical.com.

~*~

Sagent Healthstaff

Sagent Healthstaff place all healthcare professionals throughout nursing as well as allied health in all 50 states. They operate on the notion that they are company with "Local Touch/National Reach." They are a privately held company and have the feel, customer service, and comfort level obtained by working with a small company but the ability and contracts to continually offer their healthcare professionals a wide range of options for various assignments.

They have been in business for 12+ years and believe that outstanding customer service to their healthcare professionals are number one and not to be undervalued. Their recruiters are limited to the number of healthcare providers they can have on assignment for this reason. They want everyone in the office to always be aware of who is, was, and will be working for Sagent. Quality assurance is also provided by a Clinical Nurse Liaison, and she is available during business hours but can be reached in an emergency type of situation. They are in the process for Joint Commission Certification and membership to NATHO. They do adhere to all the standards that they require.

Sagent Healthstaff evaluate in their system several things. They look at how long a recruiter and a nurse have been in discussion; how often these discussions take place, have they taken an assignment with them during this time; if not, why not? Have there been offers? A lot of times the healthcare professionals don't feel comfortable asking for a new recruiter so the manager will step in and make a call to that healthcare professional and see who might be a good fit. They encourage their recruiters to stay on top of this as well as they are here to service the healthcare provider's.

They offer three different types of Aetna PPO plans depending on needs and wants of the individual or family. They also offer a comprehensive dental plan. Vision is a part of the Aetna plan as well. They offer all these effective day one. Their 401K is through Great West and at this time there is no matching. You can start contributing from day one. Other benefits include: Day One Health and Dental Insurance, Weekly Pay, Direct Deposit, 401K plan starting on day one, Travel Reimbursement, License Reimbursement, Higher Pay Rates, and Outstanding Customer Service

Sagent is a privately held national travel healthcare staffing company. They have been in business over 12 years. With very little overhead and not having to answer to shareholders, etc. they have the ability to work on smaller profit margins, which allows them to give more to their healthcare professionals. They offer all the same benefits as the larger companies in the industry but they offer better compensation packages. Their healthcare providers truly are a name and friend here at Sagent and they do everything they can to make your assignments exceed your expectations.

Give Sagent a shot and you won't want to travel with another company again. They will shoot to #1 on your list.

For more information on Sagent Healthstaff, visit them at 36 Washington St. Ste 170, Wellesley, MA 02481. You may also contact them by phone at: 781-419-0709, or visit them online at: www.sagenths.com.

~*~

TaleMed

TaleMed offers travel assignments for RN's, Allied Health, and Physical Therapy professionals. These assignments range from 8 weeks, 13 weeks to 26 weeks, a large percentage of their Healthcare Professionals extend with TaleMed for 3 or more assignments. They also have Healthcare professionals that have been with them for over 3 years. 91 % of their employees work three assignments or more with TaleMed. They offer assignments in all 50 states and Puerto Rico; you can choose a rural location or a large metropolis.

They are a medium sized company located in Cincinnati, Ohio with a satellite office in Irvine, California. Their staff takes pride in finding the best assignment for you. Each individual looks for different opportunities. It is their job to find them for you and make sure you are taken care of.

TaleMed treats their Healthcare Professionals as people instead of numbers. They understand what it takes to be a Healthcare Professional. The level of education, patience, flexibility, and sacrifice to do your job day in and day out, and above all, the appreciation of this incredible service is how TaleMed goes about always treating their Healthcare Professionals as people and not numbers. There is no employee ID number which a Healthcare Professionals must give when they call in and they will never reach a voice automated system. They merely call in, state their name, and are transferred to the appropriate person. They have a clinical nurse liaison available for all their employees and are Joint Commission Certified. They have been TJC certified since 2007!

From TaleMed's initial phone conversation with the Healthcare professional a relationship is built. Their Healthcare professionals don't work FOR TaleMed they work WITH TaleMed. It is a team effort to find your first and next assignment. They ask basic personality questions so that you as an employee can learn more about us.

Their benefits include: medical insurance thru United Healthcare, Dental Insurance thru Guardian and optional Vision thru Davis Vision. TaleMed pays the premium for all healthcare professionals. Any healthcare professional can add on coverage for a spouse or dependents this portion is just payroll deducted. They also offer a Safe Harbor 401K, that is nurse only. They will match 100% of elective contributions up to 4%. Other benefits TaleMed offers are full Professional Liability Coverage for the healthcare professional while on assignment. Other additional benefits are 100% paid housing, travel bonuses, mileage reimbursement, and many other personal benefits to assist you in your travel experience as you care for those in need.

What makes TaleMed more than just another travel company is their personal touch. TaleMed personal touch is the Staffing Specialist knowing your name, listening to what you are looking for in an assignment and where you want to go next, being able to get a hold of your Staffing Specialist when you need them. Having jobs located all across the country, and having sales staff contact hospitals where you want to go. If an incident may occur during their assignment (whether it is with the hospital, housing, or travel i.e. Car breaks down, Airfare is delayed, etc.) TaleMed is there for you all the way.

Talemed would like for you to know that it is very important for them to let healthcare professionals know that they are here for all of you. They know going to a new place having to get all of your compliance documents and sometimes a new certifications, or RN license is time consuming and can be stressful. If you every have any questions or just need to talk during these processes TaleMed is here for you.

You can visit TaleMed at: 6279 Tri-Ridge Blvd, Suite 110, Loveland, OH 45140. You can phone them at: 800-494-0087, or visit them online at: www.talemed.com.

~*~

The Right Solutions

The Right Solutions is a medium sized company with large company rates and boutique style customer care service. They have successfully staffed healthcare professionals since their conception in 1990. They specialize in staffing RNs, LPNs, and Allied Health professionals. Assignments range from 4 to 13 weeks and sometimes longer. Travelers often have the option to extend a great assignment they love or move on to their next adventure.

The Right Solutions offers travel assignments thorough out the United States, The District of Columbia and the Virgin Islands. They also offer assignments in a variety of settings including hospitals, clinics, schools and correctional facilities nationwide in the state, public, and private sectors. The Right Solutions' mission is to Comfort and Restore Lives across the Nation; from large teaching hospitals to remote clinics and everything in between.

The Right Solutions' motto is "You're a Nurse not a number," and they make sure they practice what they preach. From the first point of contact with their receptionist, to their recruiters, and thorough out their whole network; they serve each traveler that joins The Right Solutions team. The bottom line—they know the sacrifices you make to give quality care to so many and feel that it is their duty and their privilege to take care of you.

They provide clinical liaisons who are available 24 hours a day, 7 days a week. They also provide additional after hour support staff on call for any issue or question their healthcare professionals may have.

The Right Solutions was one of the first supplemental nurse staffing agencies to go through The Joint Commission Accreditation process in 2005 and receive The Joint Commission certification. They have scored 100% on their last five separate Joint Commission Audits. The Right Solutions is also a member of NATHO.

With over 85 years combined healthcare recruitment experience, their recruiting team is versed in connecting with and finding the best assignment for their travelers. With an aligned focus on treating their travelers as a Nurse and not a Number, they as a company foster an open and honest relationship between recruiter and traveler. If at any time a traveler or recruiter does not feel the relationship is a fit, a new recruiter is assigned to help best serve the traveler.

The Right Solutions provides Transamerica medical insurance, as well as dental, vision and professional liability. Insurance is also available for dependents and can be deducted from payroll if a nurse so chooses. Other benefits include an IRA to all their HCP's with a 50% company match. The IRA is fully vested from day 1; you keep your investment in addition to any matching the company has provided. If you decide to leave, the IRA goes with you.

The Right Solutions was one of the first in the industry to offer a tiered loyalty bonus program which offers increasing hourly differentials, cash bonuses and new scrubs as a traveler works more contracts. Reaching the highest level of their loyalty program can result in a traveler earning over $6,000 additional per year! They also offer sign on and completion bonuses along with license reimbursements at the beginning of an assignment.

Their Founder, Diana Wright knew that comforting and restoring lives was something not only for her patients, but also for nurses in the Northwest Arkansas area. She began The Right Solutions by working shifts herself. Diana would return home from working a 12-hour shift in the ICU to call nurses to fill the hospitals unfilled shifts. When there was no one to fill the shifts, Diana returned to the hospital to work the shift and care for patients. As the pool of nurses grew, Diana worked less on the floor and was able to transition from an Arkansas per diem agency to a nationwide travel company. She saw the transition to a travel company as an opportunity for her fellow nurses to enhance their lives financially, to broaden and hone their skills, and to comfort and restore lives across the Nation. They are one of the few companies that can deliver customer service with a Nurse's touch.

The Right Solutions' focus on customer service and taking care of their travelers requires a whole team of staffing professionals. Every member of their in-house team treats each individual as a unique person and walks hand in hand through every step of the process. Whether you are a veteran traveler or looking for your first assignment, assistance is only a phone call away. When you join The Right Solutions, you truly are joining a family.

To find out more about their recruiters check these profiles out: 311 W. Henri DeTonti Blvd, Tonitown, AR 72770. They can be reached by phone at: 888-987-8233, or online at: www.therightsolutions.com.

~*~

Travel Nurse across America

At Travel Nurse across America (TNAA), they specialize in 8 to 26 week travel assignments for registered nurses. The typical assignment is 13 weeks. They focus on exceeding expectations and take pride in the fact that they provide highly personalized service and accommodate each nurse's unique needs and career plans. They place a high value on individual attention, respect, and a genuine commitment to every nurse we work with. Their entire staff builds positive, long-lasting connections with the travel nurses they serve.

Travel Nurse across America is a medium-sized company who places nurses all over the United States, but do not currently offer international assignments. Being a medium sized company allows them access to a wide array of clients while, at the same time, helps them stay nimble and able to respond quickly to changes in the marketplace. Because they are not a huge organization, their recruiters are able to spend time getting to know the nurses they work with, thereby providing highly personalized service. They have representatives on call 24/7/365 so that you can reach someone who has the authority to address any issues that might arise while you are on assignment. After-hours calls are answered by a live person so that you receive immediate attention. Typically the on-board process takes between two and four weeks, based on both the hospital and nurses' needs, desires, and readiness. If a traveler is truly ready to go, and the hospital is ready to receive, they can take a nurse from acceptance of application to their first day on the job in less than two weeks.

They offer an extremely competitive benefit package, including:

- Your Way Is Paid. They pay all costs associated with getting the licenses and certifications you need for the travel assignment you've accepted. They also arrange and pay for any physical examinations and immunizations you may need to start working.
- Guaranteed pay. If you've contracted to work 36 or 40 hours each week and the hospital census drops to the point that you're not needed for a day, don't worry. If your paycheck is going to be less than normal due to low census, they'll make up the difference.
- Tax-Advantage. They'll help you understand whether you qualify for our tax-advantage program and, if you do, leverage the use of it.
- Travel Money. They reimburse for up to $1,000 in expenses for you to get to your assignment. How you choose to travel is up to you. If you're working close to home and don't need travel expense money they roll what they would have reimbursed into a higher hourly pay rate.
- Housing. They offer several housing options to fit our nurse's individual needs. You can chose from high-quality, furnished, private, company provided housing with 100% of the utilities paid. A housing subsidy or, you can opt for our Housing Assistance Program (HAP). HAP pays our nurses like a housing

subsidy but their housing specialist does all the work of finding housing, utilities, furniture, etc. for them. They do the work and you reap the benefits!

- Free Continuing Education. When you travel with us, you have access to more than 400 CE courses online through CE Direct. There is no limit on the number of courses you can take.
- Insurance. Their travelers are covered from day 1! They offer a low-deductible PPO plan through United Healthcare that covers doctor visits, wellness exams, diagnostic tests, prescription medications, and hospitalization. TNAA pays 100% of their traveler's premium and spouse and/or children can be added at a low cost. Their comprehensive insurance package also offers dental insurance through Delta Dental and liability. Their insurance are as good as you'll find anywhere in the industry.
- Multiple Bonus Opportunities. They offer all of the usual sign on, completion, extension, and referral bonus plans, but their unique extra shift bonus is the one that nurses seem to love the most. If a hospital offers you extra shifts and you accept, you get a bonus in additional to the usual extra pay you earn.
- Loyalty Bonus program. This unique program allows you to earn points for every hour you work and redeem those points for cash anytime you're on assignment with them. There is no limit to the number of points you can earn and you can use them for anything—home improvements, holiday shopping, to build up your rainy day fund, to tap into when you miss work due to illness, or to give yourself a paid vacation.
- Referral Bonus. Their Referral Bonus plan is different from other firms. When you refer a colleague who works with them for at least eight weeks, you get $500—half up front and half when they complete their assignment.
- Assignment Benefits Summary. For each assignment you're considering with Travel Nurse across America you'll receive a one-page document that spells out your hourly rate, applicable taxes, benefits, and your net take home pay, both weekly and for the length of the assignment.
- JobWatch. This one-of-a-kind program notifies you immediately by email or text message when a job you've been waiting for becomes available.

They consistently hear from our nurses that their obvious focus on personal attention is the single most important reason for their enduring loyalty to TNAA. They don't take that loyalty for granted and they're always looking for new and better ways to make their nurses feel like they are part of their family. They have both a Clinical Nurse Liaison and a Director of Nursing who are available 24/7.

Travel Nurse across America is Joint Commission Certified and have been awarded a Gold Seal of Approval. Meeting high quality standards and adhering to the most stringent clinical and ethical criteria in the industry is very important to them. They have been a member of NATHO since its inception.

They screen and hire their internal recruiters based on their experience and ability to understand what nurses want and need. It almost never happens, but if a travel nurse ever feels that a recruiter is not a good match for them they will happily assign them to someone else within the firm.

Their travelers are covered from day 1 with a quality PPO! They offer a low-deductible plan through United Healthcare that covers doctor visits, wellness exams, diagnostic tests, prescription medications, and hospitalization. TNAA pays 100% of their traveler's premium and spouse and/or children can be added at a low cost. Their comprehensive insurance package also offers dental insurance through Delta Dental and liability. Their insurance are as good as you'll find anywhere in the industry.

They don't offer a 401K at this time. Instead, they have several unique bonus programs that nurses can participate in to boost their income and contribute all or part of that bonus money to their own personal retirement plan.

Call them to talk about what you want from your travel nursing career. They will listen and you will be happy you made the connection – they promise.

For more information you can visit them at: Travel Nurse across America, 5020 Northshore Dr., Suite 2, North Little Rock, AR 72118. They can be reached by phone at: 800-240-2526, or you can visit them online at: www.nurse.tv.

~*~

Trinity Healthcare Staffing Group

Trinity Healthcare Staffing Group offers travel assignments to various specialties of healthcare professionals that typically range in duration from 8 to 13 weeks. Longer or shorter assignments can be negotiated. Also, a traveler typically has the option of renewing the assignment or rolling into a new assignment. Per Diem shifts are also available. Travel assignments are offered nationwide, including Alaska and Hawaii. There are a variety of settings to include teaching hospitals, rural facilities, LTC, clinics, and rehab facilities. Assignments are chosen based on skills, specialties, certifications, and experience.

Trinity Healthcare Staffing Group is a medium sized company that offers large company rates and benefits. Once the lead or referral is made and a recruiter is assigned and makes contact with a nurse, the process is initiated to create that relationship. They never refer to their nurses as numbers but always by name. As the nurse goes through the application, credentialing and submittal processes, the nurse will become familiar with many of the internal staff apart from the recruiter as well (Placement Specialist, QA, Payroll, Housing, CNO, etc.). Each contact makes the nurse feel welcome and assists with helping in the placement process. The recruiter provides the nurse with his or her contact phone number and email address so that the nurse may have 24/7 access. There is also after hour support staff on call in case the nurse has questions or issues. They also have a Clinical Nurse Liaison who is also available 24 hours a day, 7 days a week. Trinity has been Joint Commission certified since 2006, and is a member of NATHO.

Trinity Healthcare Staffing Group helps a nurse to get his/her travel career headed in a positive direction by matching not only with the right job order but also with the right recruiter. Connecting the professional with an employment opportunity that will give them a chance to utilize his/her specific skills and training to serve patients in a variety of different types of medical facilities is the job of the recruiter. It is also the role of the recruiter to create and build a relationship with the professional. Their goal is to help find the ideal position to meet the individual needs of each traveler. They take care of all of the ground work for securing a position, even locating housing if needed, so that the professional can focus on providing an exceptional level of care. Although rarely occurring, there are times when a switch in recruiter and/or nurse is requested and this is handled without any negativity among staff.

Trinity provides Blue Cross insurance, as well as vision, dental, life and professional liability. Benefits for dependents are also available and can be payroll deducted. Trinity also has a great 401K retirement plan. Other benefits include full reimbursement for licensure fees once the assignment is started. Trinity also will reimburse for cost of continuing education that is specific to your clinical specialty for current travelers with prior approval. Free CEUs are also offered. Travel reimbursement is available and depends on the package selected, and is completely tax-free. Trinity also offers free housing so you pay nothing for your housing or furniture.

What's different about Trinity? Everything! Trinity Healthcare is owned and operated by a former traveling nurse, and their internal staff consists of nurses and other professionals who have been there, done that. The Recruiter and/or support staff are always available, day or night, 24/7 ensuring the Traveler never gets left stranded away from home without support. Trinity offers some of the highest compensation plans in the industry. Most importantly, they operate according to their core mission and values, meaning "We'll do what we say we'll do." They have many longstanding relationships with clients, vendors, and employees to prove their commitment to being one of the best staffing companies in the industry.

Trinity was started by a traveling nurse who struggled with the inconsistencies and disorganization that defined the profession. Often showing up to bewildered looks instead of secured housing. Paychecks that rarely landed in on time, and when they did, routinely were inaccurate. It is because of these experiences that make Trinity very difference from other travel companies. "We do what we say we'll do." Bottom-line. No questions asked. How simple is that? You will not find another company that will give you the support, security and respect that Trinity provides each and every travel nurse.

For more information on Trinity Healthcare Staffing Group, you can visit them at: 1834 Sally Hill Farms Blvd, Florence, SC 29501. They can be reached by phone at: 877-417-9507, or visit them online at: www.trinityhsg.com.

~*~

TotalMed Staffing

TotalMed Staffing Travel Division specializes in 4 to 26 week travel assignments for Registered Nurses, Dialysis Technicians, Surgical

Technologists and Surgical Assistants all over the United States. On average, the typical travel assignment for a healthcare professional is 13 weeks in length. TotalMed feels there is no substitute for honest, caring relationships. Patients know it. You know it. That is why TotalMed Staffing strives to engage in genuine relationships. Your professional goals in healthcare drive them to find the right healthcare staffing solution for you. Their dedicated experts in your specific field take time to get to know you, your experience, your aspirations and your personality. They take pride in providing an individually personalized service and finding the right solution that meets your requirements for pay, benefits, employer support, or whatever else you may need. No matter what the employment opportunity, from local staffing to travel staffing, they match the right people with the nation's top healthcare organizations.

TotalMed Staffing is a medium-sized, minority-owned and privately owned healthcare staffing agency that offers flexible staffing solutions such as: per diem, local contract, travel nursing, contract-to-hire, and direct placement. In addition, they have recruitment experts in allied health, scientific, insurance, and healthcare financial services. Being that TotalMed Staffing is a medium sized company it allows their recruiters to spend quality time getting to know their nurses they work with and also allows the one on one interaction between the nurse and their recruiter.

TotalMed Staffing has a Clinical Nurse Liaison available 24/7 to both clients and healthcare professionals. They also have an after-hours person that is available 24/7 so both a client and healthcare professional can reach someone at any time if any issues would arise or if the healthcare professional would just need to vent. They are a Joint Commission Certified company and have been awarded a Gold Seal of Approval. TotalMed Staffing's core values are both in quality and integrity, so they are constantly measuring ways to improve our already high quality standards through clinical screening. TotalMed Staffing is also a member of NATHO (National Association of Travel Healthcare Organizations). As a quality assurance measure they conduct an exit interview with the healthcare professional that asks an array of questions; some of them pertaining to the assignment itself and the experience they had at the facility, how their experience was working with TotalMed and the on-boarding process, how are benefits were if they enrolled in them and overall how their experience was with their recruiter.

TotalMed is proud to offer a full variety of benefits for full time employees. Their health insurance is through United Health Care Group and to ensure they can accommodate the individual needs of their employees, they offer two plans and also staff a Benefits Coordinator that contacts each individual who enrolls in the program and walks them through their options. Their health insurance also offers "day one" eligibility which they have found is crucial for traveling healthcare professionals that work multiple assignments throughout the year. They believe this extra effort sets us apart from other agencies as it offers an olive branch for employees in trying to decipher the insurance world and what best fits their situation. In addition to health insurance, they also offer dental, vision, and supplemental plans such as cancer, accident, disability and additional life options. Because they also offer a Flexible Spending Plan, employees can choose to defer dollars pre-tax to cover reimbursable medical and dependent care expenses. All employees who enroll in benefits also receive a $10,000 company paid life insurance plan as well as short-term disability coverage.

Their 401(k) plan is through Lincoln Financial and offers both traditional and Roth options. TotalMed contributes $.50 on the dollar up to 6% of dollars deferred. All employees who meet the requirements of age 21 and one hour of service are eligible so again, day one eligibility sets them apart from other employers. In addition to the above, they also offer a free Employee Assistance Program. They believe as employers they must look out for the well-being of their employees and when that well-being is compromised, it is their duty to offer options that may contribute to a solution.

TotalMed prides themselves on genuine relationships and currently walks in their travelers to each assignment if it is at a new client or local to Wisconsin, Illinois or Minnesota which not only helps them get acclimated to the facility and unit but also helps us educate the traveler of the environment they are going to be working at. They understand a relationship starts with listening. Contact TotalMed Staffing today. A professional healthcare staffing recruiter is ready to talk about your employment needs.

For more information on TotalMed Staffing you can visit them at: 10 East College Ave., Suite 300, Appleton, WI 54911. You can contact them at: 866-288-8001, or visit them online at: www.totalmedstaffing.com.

~*~

Trustaff

Trustaff offers RN, LPN, OT, COTA, PT, PTA, ST, and Healthcare IT travel opportunities nationwide, with contracts ranging from 4 weeks to one year, as well as permanent positions and per diem/PRN shifts. They are a medium sized company that offers contracts in all 50 states as well as the Virgin Island. They are a privately owned company that operates out of Cincinnati, Ohio, with multiple satellite offices across the country.

Trustaff treats each traveler as an individual. Every nurse is matched with a dedicated recruiter who takes the time to listen and learn the details of their traveler's needs, long-term goals, and personal preferences. Their recruiters use these criteria to seek out positions that specifically meet or exceed the traveler's requirements. Once a nurse has accepted a job, they maintain contact, provide support, and develop a personal, longstanding relationship that continues throughout the assignment and years into the future.

They have a dedicated department of Nurse Advocates, who provide personal support for each of our travelers. Immediate assistance is available 24 hours a day, 7 days a week via our support line, which is routed directly to a live member of our team. As a Joint Commission certified staffing company, they have perfect scores on each of our biannual audits. Trustaff is a member NATHO and is committed to abiding by and furthering ethical business practices in the travel industry.

Trustaff recruiters are experienced professionals who are versatile and comfortable working with a wide range of personalities. Since so much of their business is built on relationships, they believe it is critical that recruiter and traveler have open lines of communication built on trust. In the rare event that a nurse is not 100% satisfied with their recruiter, they will happily match them to a recruiter here at Trustaff who will be a better fit.

Trustaff offers a variety of insurance options to choose from, including day-one insurance coverage through Assurant Health or the ability to select a benefits plan through United Healthcare. Programs cover medical, dental, and vision for each nurse, as well as additional family members or dependents. Benefits continue uninterrupted so long as there is not a break between assignments longer than 28 days.

All Trustaff travelers are eligible to make contributions to a 401(k) savings account upon acceptance of their first assignment. After completion of one year of employment and at least 1,000 hours of service, Trustaff will match 401k contributions at 50% up to the first 4% of compensation. Their 401k plan is managed by UBS.

In addition to their excellent compensation, benefits packages, and personal service, Trustaff offers all employees paid time off, weekly direct deposit pay, holiday pay, guaranteed hours, licensure reimbursement, continued education services, a fully staffed housing department at their disposal, and loyalty, extension, referral, and sign-on bonuses.

The personal relationships they develop with their nurses year after year truly set Trustaff apart. They make it their business to be #1 in customer service, and their recruiters make that happen by genuinely caring about each nurse they place. They want their travelers to have more than just a job; they want them to have a great experience. Trustaff makes their best effort to go above and beyond to make sure each traveler's needs are being met, which means being available when they need them and listening carefully to their feedback. When you're out in an unfamiliar location, away from family and friends, it makes a big difference to have someone on your side who knows the ins and outs of the business. They know they're doing their jobs right when their nurses are happy, and their recruiters and their support teamwork very hard to make that happen.

For more information on Trustaff, you can visit them at: 4270 Glendale-Milford Road, Cincinnati, OH 45242. You can call them at: 877-880-0346, or visit them online at: www.trustafftravel.com.

~*~

Worldwide Travel Staffing

Worldwide Travel Staffing offers career opportunities for all medical specialties, but specializes in psychiatric nursing and correctional nursing. They offer assignments in all 50 states, the U.S. Virgin Islands and Guam. They also offer international engagements in 13 countries. They are a small business that is privately owned.

Worldwide Travel Staffing (Worldwide) places a strong emphasis on customer service. Worldwide provides all nurses with quality service in a manner that is courteous, responsive, accessible and seamless. Worldwide pledges to serve their nurses with patience, understanding, and good will, without regard to their own convenience. A Worldwide representative will be available 24 hours a day, seven days a week to answer any questions or address any concerns that may arise. Nurses are never directed to an automated system. All communications will be with a representative from their company. Worldwide's recruiters are constantly in contact with their nurses. Nurses are encouraged to call their recruiters with any questions or concerns. Worldwide's C.E.O. is also available by phone or email to speak with their nurses. Their compensation packages are personalized to fit the nurses' needs. Their recruiters also assist their nurses in finding housing for their travel assignments.

Worldwide Travel Staffing has a Masters prepared Clinical Director on their staff. The Clinical Director is available 24 hours a day by phone or email. They are Joint Commission certified, but does not belong to NATHO.

When a nurse shows interest in Worldwide Travel Staffing, they connect him/her to a recruiter that is an appropriate fit for the nurse's specialty, skill set and geographic preference. If at any time, a nurse is unhappy with his/her recruiter, he/she will immediately be directed a new recruiter.

Worldwide Travel Staffing offers some of the best medical coverage in the travel nurse industry. Platinum Plan BlueCross and BlueShield are offered on a nurse's very first assignment. Eyeglass, Dental and Prescription plans are also standard benefits. They have partnered with Paychex and RBC Wealth Management to establish a 401(k) plan. Company matching in Worldwide's 401(k) plan with immediate vesting is available upon enrollment. Their nurses can contribute a portion of their income to the plan on a pre-tax basis. Worldwide matches up to 6% of the employee's contribution.

Another benefit that Worldwide Travel Staffing (Worldwide) nurses enjoy is a generous daily lodging and relocation per diem allocation. Worldwide also issues round trip travel reimbursements on most assignments. Worldwide's bonus programs are tailored to suit employees individually. Their completion bonuses are the highest in the industry. Worldwide's nurses are immediately enrolled in their Loyalty Rewards program. As their nurses' employment continues with Worldwide, they accumulate clearly defined bonus points upon the successful completion of each consecutive 13-week assignment. Once earned, their nurses' points can be converted immediately to a cash bonus. Worldwide has a terrific Referral Bonus Program. If you know any R.N.s who may be interested in their assignments, please be aware of their generous referral bonuses. Upon successful completion of the first 13-week assignment, you will receive $1,000. In addition, if your referral completes a second 13-week assignment, you will then receive an additional $1,000 bonus. You do not need to be an active employee of Worldwide to qualify for the referral bonus.

Worldwide has helped healthcare professionals find their dream assignments since 1993. Worldwide is an R.N. owned and operated travel nursing company. The partners are experienced professionals that understand the nuances of travel nursing. They are committed to providing their clinical staff with pleasant and memorable engagements. Their unique distinction in international penetration sets Worldwide apart from every other travel nursing company. Worldwide offers positions in 13 international locations. Some of their uncommon U.S. assignment locations include the U.S.V.I., Guam and Saipan. New Zealand, Australia and Bermuda are among the most popular international requests. Worldwide recognizes that maintaining quality patient care requires continued education. All employees are encouraged to advance their education and certifications by attending in-service programs and continuing education courses. Worldwide compensates full time employees for attendance at both mandatory and non-mandatory in-service programs.

The New York State Department of Economic Development, Division of Minority and Women's Business Development has granted Worldwide Women Owned Business Enterprise status (certificate no. 07619-2006).

For more information on Worldwide Travel Staffing you can visit them at: 2829 Sheridan Drive, Tonawanda, NY 14150. You can contact them by phone at: 866-633-3700, or you can visit them online at: www.worldwidetravelstaffing.com.

~*~

Valley Healthcare Systems

Valley Healthcare Systems is a medium sized company that provides RNs to all 50 states. They survey all of their travelers throughout their assignment (week 2 and week 9) so that they know what they are doing well and where they need to improve to better support the nurse on their assignment. They also provide a concierge, available 24 hours per day, 7 days per week. A Clinical Nurse Liaison is available 24 hours a day. They are Joint Commission certified and are members of NATHO.

They provide medical insurance through Essential StaffCare (Division of Blue Shield). Coverage for the nurse is free, and vision and dental can be added for $7 per week. Valley offers a Simple IRA. Matching depends on company year-end profitability. Other benefits include free continuing education units.

Valley Healthcare System's mission is to provide an easy and pleasant experience for the traveler. Every traveler receives a welcome kit complete with "hoodie" and scrubs, and a welcome letter that includes the CEO's mobile phone number that they can use for any issue—and it will be addressed immediately. They are all wholly committed to the traveler in providing quality clinical care and also do everything in our power to remove any of the burdensome tasks that would otherwise make their assignment unpleasant.

Valley will do whatever it takes to make the travel assignment easy and enjoyable. They do not want a traveler to work one assignment—they want a relationship that leads to years of assignments.

You can visit Valley Healthcare Systems at: 1401 El Camino Ave, Suite 510, Sacramento, CA 95815. You can phone them at: 916-669-0508, or you can check them out online at: www.vhcsystems.com.

~*~

Voyage Healthcare

Voyage Healthcare has opportunities for RNs PTs, OTs, SLPs, Diagnostic Imaging, Surgical Techs, Respiratory Therapists, and occasionally medical device opportunities in all 50 states.

Their minimum time for a traveler is 5 days, as they must complete background screening which includes drug screening for all employees. Their application process is very easy as every piece of it is online and accessible through their website. They are a medium sized company but they always know the names of all of their travelers. They receive many referrals based on their approach.

They strive to make all of their employees feel they are a member of the Voyage family. They have a 24-hour hot lines that pages their staff 24/7/365.

They offer fully paid medical; fully matched 401k with zero vesting period; weekly pay; fully online application and testing; excellent referral bonuses; dental, health and life insurance; personalized assignment agreements to meet the needs of the individual. They have an excellent insurance policy to cover all of their travelers. They are happy to discuss it if anyone is concerned or wants more information.

They focus on the individual. There is no stone that they will leave unturned to achieve what their travelers have asked of them. They hire new individuals every day who are frustrated and feel as though their current company does not value them. They value every employee.

Voyage is a great company. The difference is immediately noticeable from every staff member in their offices. Give them a call, you will see.

You can visit Voyage Healthcare at: 1525 International Pkwy, Suite 1011, Heathrow, FL 32746. You can phone them at: 800-798-6035, or visit them online at: www.voyagehealth.com.